The Marshall Cavendish
ILLUSTRATED ENCYCLOPEDIA OF
PLANTS
AND
EARTH SCIENCES

The Marshall Cavendish
ILLUSTRATED ENCYCLOPEDIA OF
PLANTS
AND
EARTH SCIENCES

VOLUME FOUR

EDITOR-IN-CHIEF
Professor David M. Moore

SPECIALIST SUBJECT EDITORS
Professor V. H. Heywood
Botany
Professor A. Hallam
Earth Sciences
Dr S. R. Chant
Botany

ADVISORY EDITORS
Professor W. T. Stearn
Flowering Plants
Dr I. B. K. Richardson
Flowering Plants
Dr Peter Raven
Plant Ecology
Professor Lincoln Constance
Special Consultant

EDITORIAL DIRECTOR
Dr Graham Bateman

Marshall Cavendish
New York · London · Sydney

CONTENTS

Reference Edition Published 1988

Published by:
Marshall Cavendish Corporation
147 West Merrick Road
Freeport N.Y. 11520

AN EQUINOX BOOK

Planned and produced by:
Equinox (Oxford) Ltd
Littlegate House
St Ebbe's Street
Oxford OX1 1SQ
England

Copyright © Equinox (Oxford) Ltd 1988

Library of Congress Cataloging-in-Publication Data
The Encyclopedia of plants and earth sciences.
  Bibliography: p.
  Includes index.
  1. Botany—Dictionaries. 2. Botany, Economic—Dictionaries.
3. Crops—Dictionaries. 4. Angiosperms-Dictionaries. 5. Earth
sciences—Dictionaries. 6. Ecology—Dictionaries. I. Marshall
Cavendish Corporation.
QK7.E53 1988   580'.3'21   87-23927

ISBN 0-86307-901-6 (Set)
ISBN 0-86307-905-9 (Vol 4)

Previous page
Plants belonging to the family Leguminosae (see p.500).

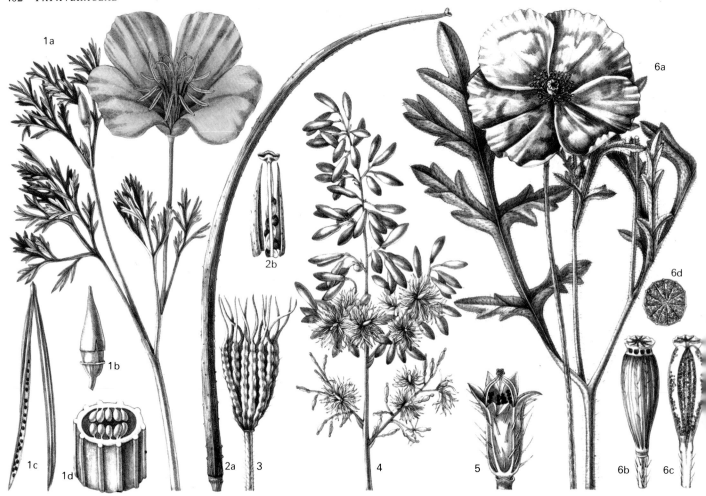

Papaveraceae. 1 *Eschscholzia californica* (a) leafy shoot and flower with four petals (×1); (b) flower bud with calyx forming cap (×1½); (c) fruit—a capsule dehiscing by two valves (×1); (d) cross section of fruit (×7). 2 *Glaucium flavum* (a) capsule (×⅔); (b) tip of opened capsule showing seeds and apical valve (×1½). 3 *Platystemon californicus* fruit—a group of follicles (×1½). 4 *Macleaya cordata* inflorescence (×⅔). 5 *Argemone mexicana* dehisced spiny capsule with seeds exposed (×⅔). 6 *Papaver dubium* (a) shoot with dissected leaves and solitary flowers (×⅔); (b) capsule dehiscing by apical pores (×1½); (c) vertical section of a capsule (×1½); (d) cross section of capsule (×1½).

PAPAVERALES

PAPAVERACEAE
Poppies

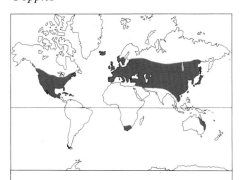

Number of genera: 26
Number of species: about 250
Distribution: temperate.
Economic uses: opium and many species cultivated as ornamentals (poppies).

The Papaveraceae is a family of mainly herbaceous annuals or perennials but with some shrubs, all of which produce latex.

Distribution. The family is mainly native to the north temperate zone.

Diagnostic features. The leaves are alternate, without stipules, entire but often lobed or deeply dissected. The stems, leaves and other parts of the plant contain a well-developed system of secretory canals which produce yellow, milky or watery latex. The flowers are large and conspicuous, either solitary or arranged in cymose or racemose inflorescences. They are regular, bisexual and hypogynous, possessing two free sepals which fall off before the flower opens. There are usually two whorls, each of two free showy petals (absent in *Macleaya*) which are often crumpled in the bud. There are usually several whorls of numerous stamens. The filaments are sometimes petaloid while the anthers have two locules and dehisce longitudinally. The gynoecium consists of two to numerous fused carpels (separate except at the base in *Platystemon*). The ovary is superior and contains usually a single locule with intruding parietal placentas, the number being equal to the number of carpels and each bearing numerous ovules. The stigmas are equal in number to the carpels and are opposite to or alternate with the placentas. The fruit is a capsule, opening by valves or pores (follicular in *Platystemon*) and containing seeds with a small embryo and copious mealy or oily endosperm.

Classification. *Papaver* is the largest genus, containing about 100 species. *Meconopsis* (40 species, North America), *Glaucium* (25 species, Europe and Asia) and *Argemone* (10 species, America) have flowers similar to those of *Papaver*, although the leaves of some *Argemone* species are prickly. The flowers of the 10 species of *Eschscholzia* are very variable, while the 60 species of the American genus *Platystemon* are distinctive in that the numerous carpels are united only at the base. The genera *Bocconia* (10 Asian and tropical American species) and *Macleaya* (two east Asian species) are of interest as they possess apetalous flowers which are aggregated into compound racemes. *Sanguinaria* is represented by one North American species. The genus *Pteridophyllum* has flowers with only four stamens, and with *Hypecoum* (Fumariaceae) is sometimes regarded as constituting a separate family (Hypecoaceae) or is given separate family status as Pteridophyllaceae.

The Papaveraceae is sometimes placed

Fumariaceae. 1 *Corydalis lutea* (a) shoot with much divided leaves and irregular flowers in a racemose infloresence ($\times\frac{2}{3}$); (b) half flower showing spurred petal and elongate ovary. ($\times$4); (c) vertical section of fruit ($\times$2). 2 *Pteridophyllum racemosum* (a) habit showing fern-like leaves ($\times\frac{2}{3}$); (b) flower—the simplest form in this family ($\times$2); (c) vertical section of ovary ($\times$4). 3 *Fumaria muralis* (a) flowering shoot ($\times\frac{2}{3}$); (b) half flower with spurred petal and stamens in two bundles ($\times$3); (c) vertical section of bladder-like fruit ($\times$6). 4 *Dicentra spectabilis* (a) leaf and inflorescence ($\times$1); (b) flower dissected to show varied form of petals and stamens arranged in two bundles ($\times$2).

with the Cruciferae, Capparidaceae and Resedaceae in an order Rhoeadales. Here it is placed with the irregularly-flowered Fumariaceae into an order Papaverales.

Economic uses. Economically the most important species in this family is *Papaver somniferum* (opium poppy) which yields opium. The seeds do not contain opium and are used in baking. They also yield an important drying oil. Likewise the seeds of *Glaucium flavum* and *Argemone mexicana* yield oils which are important in the manufacture of soaps. Many species are cultivated as garden ornamental plants, for example *Dendromecon rigida* (Californian bushy poppy). *Eschscholzia californica* (Californian poppy), *Papaver alpinum* (alpine poppy), *P. nudicaule* (Iceland poppy), *P. orientalis* (oriental poppy) and *Macleaya cordata* (plume poppy). S.R.C.

FUMARIACEAE
Dicentras and Fumitory

The Fumariaceae is a family of annual and perennial herbs, whose best-known genera are *Fumaria* (fumitory), *Corydalis* and *Dicentra*.

Distribution. The Fumariaceae occur

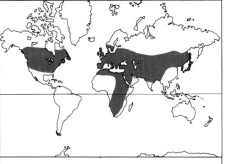

Number of genera: 16
Number of species: about 400
Distribution: mainly temperate.
Economic uses: limited use as garden ornamentals (*Corydalis* and *Dicentra*).

throughout north temperate regions. Only a few are found south of the Equator – a few species of *Corydalis* on mountains in East Africa, and the small genera *Phacocapnos*, *Cysticapnos*, *Trigonocapnos* and *Discocapnos* in southern Africa.

Diagnostic features. Perennials often have swollen, corm-like stocks. Many species of *Corydalis* have only one developed cotyledon, even though the family clearly

belongs to the dicotyledons when all other characters are considered. A few species are climbers or scramblers with tendril-like leaf axes. All contain alkaloids, though in smaller amounts than the Papaveraceae. The leaves are usually alternate, without stipules, and frequently pinnately or palmately compound. The inflorescence is usually racemose. The flowers are of complex and unusual structure, whose derivation from the simpler papaveraceous type is, however, demonstrated by some of the smaller genera. In the simplest case (*Pteridophyllum*) there are two small sepals, four stamens and an ovary of two united carpels; the two inner petals are slightly larger than the outer two, and a small amount of nectar is secreted at the base of the filaments. A more complex situation is found in *Hypecoum*, in which the two inner petals are prominently three-lobed, with the middle lobe stalked and with an expanded, cup-like apex; the apexes of the middle lobes wrap around the anthers and form a chamber into which the pollen falls. Here again there are four stamens, with nectar secreted at the filament bases. In *Dicentra* there is further elaboration – all four petals are variably fused, particularly towards the apex; the outer petals are spurred at the base, and the apexes of the inner petals are fused around the anthers. The stamens are arranged in two bundles opposite the inner petals; each bundle has a single filament which divides into three parts at the apex; the central division of each bears a complete anther, while the lateral divisions each bear half an anther. This complex structure appears to have evolved from the four-staminate condition by the splitting of the stamens opposite the outer petals. The base of each compound filament is prolonged into the petal spur, and secretes nectar there. In the other genera only one of the outer petals is spurred, producing a very unusual irregular flower; all have similar staminal arrangements to *Dicentra*, and all have a bicarpellate ovary, which is usually many-ovuled, though with one ovule in *Fumaria* and related genera. The fruit is usually a capsule, sometimes swollen and bladder-like; more rarely it is indehiscent, either a one-seeded nutlet, or many-seeded and breaking up into one-seeded indehiscent segments. *Ceratocapnos heterocarpa* has dimorphic fruits. The seed has a small embryo and fleshy endosperm.

Classification. The Fumariaceae can be divided into two distinct subfamilies: HYPECOIDEAE (containing the genera *Pteridophyllum* and *Hypecoum*) and FUMARIOIDEAE, which contains the rest of the genera, distributed in two tribes. The largest genus is *Corydalis* (about 320 species); *Fumaria* has about 50 species; all the other genera are small. Many authorities include the family in the Papaveraceae.

Economic uses. The family is of little economic importance. A few species of *Corydalis* and *Dicentra* (Dutchman's breeches, bleeding heart) are grown as garden ornamentals. Some species of *Fumaria* are agricultural weeds, such as *Fumaria officinalis* (fumitory).

J.C.

SARRACENIALES

SARRACENIACEAE
Pitcher Plants

The Sarraceniaceae is a small family containing three genera, all of which are carnivorous pitcher plants.

Distribution. They are found on the Atlantic coast of North America (*Sarracenia*), in California (*Darlingtonia*) and tropical South America (*Heliamphora*). All of the species

Number of genera: 3
Number of species: 17
Distribution: marshy habitats of Atlantic and Pacific coasts of N America, and north S America.
Economic uses: limited use as ornamentals.

are perennial herbs adapted to live in marshy habitats that are devoid of available nutrients.

Diagnostic features. The leaves are highly modified organs produced in rosettes arising directly from perennating rhizomes. All or some of the leaves are represented by long, narrow pitchers forming gracefully curved funnels covered by a lid. The insect prey is lured to the mouth of the leaf pitcher by several means: the release of strong-smelling

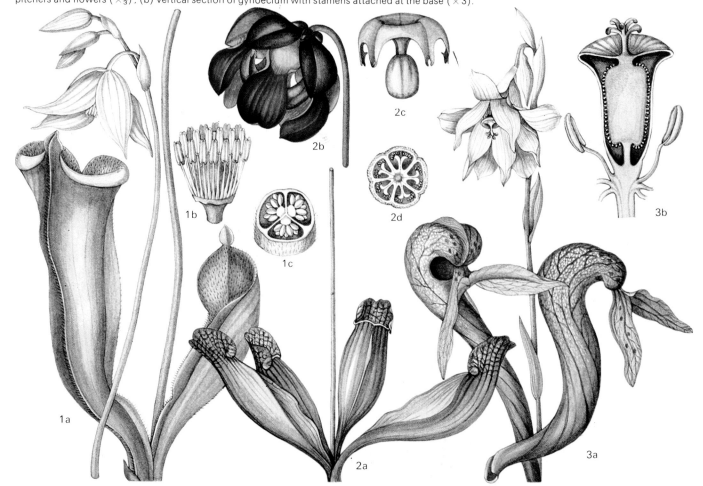

Sarraceniaceae. 1 *Heliamphora nutans* (a) pitchers (leaves) and flowers on leafless stalks (×⅔); (b) stamens, ovary and style (×2); (c) section of trilocular ovary with ovules on axile placentas (×3). 2 *Sarracenia purpurea* (a) pitchers and flower stalk (×2), (b) flower with green sepals and reddish petals (×1), (c) style and stigma (×1), (d) cross section of ovary with ovules on inrolled carpel walls (×2). 3 *Darlingtonia californica* (a) pitchers and flowers (×⅔); (b) vertical section of gynoecium with stamens attached at the base (×3).

odors, the secretion of nectar from glands at the top and a short distance inside the pitcher, the exhibition of attractive colors (usually as reddish stripes on the pitcher) and bright, window-like perforations (fenestrations) around the necks of the pitchers. Once inside, the insects slip farther down on a "slide zone," then over a series of downwardly projecting hairs and finally into a pool of water in which they eventually drown. The prey is digested by excreted acids and enzymes.

The nodding flowers are borne on leafless stems (scapes) arising from the center of the rosettes; each consists of four, five or six free or overlapping sepals, five simple white or colored petals, many short stamens and an ovary with three to five locules, each locule containing numerous ovules on axile placentas. The fruits are capsules filled with many small seeds.

Classification. The 10 species of *Sarracenia* possess solitary flowers; the styles have umbrella-shaped apexes and the pitchers have oval-shaped lids. The monotypic *Darlingtonia* also has solitary flowers but has a style with a five-lobed apex and a recurved pitcher with a fish-shaped appendage; the six species of *Heliamphora* have racemose inflorescences, blunt-ended styles and pitchers with minute, appended lids.

In their insectivorous habit the Sarraceniaceae are allied to two other families, the Nepenthaceae and the Droseraceae; and all three used to be placed together in a single order, Sarraceniales. They are now generally placed in three different orders, the Sarraceniales, Aristolochiales and Rosales.

Economic uses. *Darlingtonia californica* and several species and hybrids of *Sarracenia* are cultivated as ornamentals both for indoor and outdoor culture. C.J.H.

HAMAMELIDAE

TROCHODENDRALES

TROCHODENDRACEAE

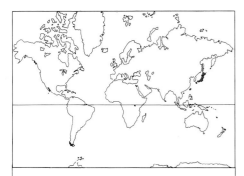

Number of genera: 1
Number of species: 1
Distribution: Japan, Taiwan, Ryu Kyu Islands.
Economic uses: birdlime.

The Trochodendraceae is a very small family of Asian forest trees containing a single genus *Trochodendron*.

Distribution. The only member of the family, *Trochodendron aralioides*, is native to Japan, Taiwan and the Ryu Kyu Islands, growing at altitudes of up to 10,000ft (3,000m).

Diagnostic features. The tree grows to form trunks 16ft (5m) in diameter and has alternate, pseudo-whorled leaves which are evergreen, leathery and without stipules. They have long petioles and are diamond-shaped, with scalloped edges and a glossy surface. The regular or slightly irregular green flowers are bisexual and occur in terminal racemose cymes; they lack sepals and petals. There are many stamens in three or four whorls surrounding a superior ovary consisting of six to numerous slightly fused carpels with free stigmas. Each carpel contains one to several pendulous ovules. The fruit develops into a ring of coalescent, several-seeded follicles, the seeds having an oily endosperm and tiny embryo.

Classification. The genus *Euptelea* is frequently placed within this family, although it is sometimes segregated into a family, Eupteleaceae, differing from *Trochodendron* in having carpels free and stipitate and fruits with wings. More debatable is the inclusion of *Tetracentron*, which is also sometimes regarded as constituting a separate family, Tetracentraceae.

The family is probably related to the Winteraceae and Illiciaceae. The wood does not contain vessels, a "primitive" feature it shares with the Winteraceae and other allied families.

Economic uses. Birdlime is made locally from the aromatic bark of *T. aralioides*. B.M.

HAMAMELIDALES

CERCIDIPHYLLACEAE

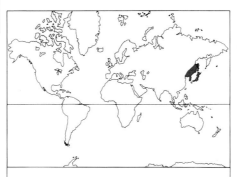

Number of genera: 1
Number of species: 1
Distribution: China and Japan.
Economic uses: limited use of wood and as an ornamental.

The Cercidiphyllaceae is a very small family of Asian trees represented by a single genus, *Cercidiphyllum*.

Distribution. The family is native to China and Japan.

Diagnostic features. *Cercidiphyllum japonicum*, the only species in the genus, bears two kinds of simple deciduous leaves: those on short shoots (spurs) are palmately veined and alternate, while those on the long shoots are pinnately veined and usually opposite. Stipules are fused to the petiole.

The flowers are unisexual and without petals; male and female are borne on separate plants. The male flowers are axillary, solitary or borne in close clusters. They have four small sepals (or bracts) and 15–20 stamens, with slender, long filaments on a conical receptacle. The female flowers are in clusters of two to six, each subtended by a bract, and consisting of only a single carpel, containing many ovules attached in two rows to a parietal placenta in its single locule. The style is thread-like and terminates in two stigmatic ridges. The fruit is a follicle, splitting down the ventral suture to release the many compressed, winged seeds. The seed contains copious endosperm, surrounding the embryo.

Classification. The combination of unusual features of this plant, including the dimorphic leaves, short and long shoots, apetalous, unisexual flowers and the nature of the carpels, is not found in other dicotyledonous families. The fossil evidence indicates that this genus may be a primitive relict. Although it has been linked with both the Ranunculaceae and the Magnoliaceae there is no sound evidence that it is closely related to these or to other dicotyledonous families.

Economic uses. The tree is valuable for its light, soft, fine-grained wood, which is used for cabinet-making and interior work in houses. It is in limited cultivation as an ornamental. S.R.C.

PLATANACEAE
Plane and Buttonwood Trees
The Platanaceae is a small family of large, attractive trees with scaling bark which are widely cultivated in urban areas particularly the London plane (*Platanus hybrida* (*P. acerifolia*, *P. hispanica*)).

Distribution. Apart from *P. orientalis* (Balkan peninsula and Himalayas) and *P. kerrii* (Indochina), all species are North American.

Diagnostic features. The leaves are simple,

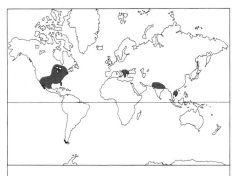

Number of genera: 1
Number of species: 10
Distribution: chiefly N America
Economic uses: ornamental town trees and wood is used for veneers.

palmately three- to nine-lobed (elliptic to oblong, unlobed, with pinnate, not palmate, veins in *P. kerrii*). The long petiole is swollen at the base to form a hood to the axillary bud. The stipules are large, embracing the stem, soon falling. All vegetative parts, the calyx, ovary and fruit bear stellate hairs. The flowers are unisexual and borne on the same tree, in one to several crowded globose heads on separate long peduncles. There are three to eight small, free, hairy sepals, and as many larger spathulate petals. The male flowers have three to eight subsessile stamens, the connectives fusing above to form a conspicuous peltate scale. Three or four staminodes are sometimes present in male and female flowers (catkins). The female flowers have six to nine (sometimes three) free, superior carpels with tapering styles whose stigmatic surface is on the inner side. The ovules are one (rarely two) per carpel, pendulous. The fruit is a globose head of top-shaped caryopses or achenes, the styles persistent and surrounded by a pappus-like ring of long bristly hairs. The single seed has little or no endosperm and is wind-dispersed.

Classification. The family is perhaps related to the Hamamelidaceae.

Economic uses. The planes (in America known also as sycamore and buttonwood trees) are widely grown for ornament. The hard, fine-textured wood is used for veneer and other purposes. F.B.H.

HAMAMELIDACEAE
Witch Hazels and Sweet Gums

The Hamamelidaceae is a medium-sized family of trees and shrubs including the witch hazel of pharmacy (*Hamamelis virginiana*), the gum- and timber-producing sweet gums (*Liquidambar*) and other ornamental species.

Distribution. The family shows a very discontinuous distribution in the temperate and subtropical regions of both hemispheres.

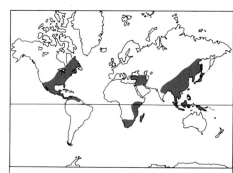

Number of genera: 23
Number of species: about 100
Distribution: very discontinuous, in subtropical and temperate zones.
Economic uses: timber, fragrant gum (storax) used in perfumery, witch hazel lotion and ornamentals.

Hamamelidaceae. 1 *Hamamelis mollis* (a) leaf ($\times\frac{2}{3}$); (b) shoot with flowers ($\times\frac{2}{3}$); (c) flower with four hairy sepals, four linear petals, four stamens and bilobed stigma ($\times 3$); (d) vertical section of ovary ($\times 9$); (e) fruit—a woody capsule ($\times 2$). 2 *Fothergilla major* (a) leafy shoot and inflorescence ($\times\frac{2}{3}$); (b) bicarpellate gynoecium ($\times 3$); (c) dehisced fruit ($\times 2$). 3 *Rhodoleia championii* (a) shoot with many-flowered capitula surrounded by numerous bracts giving appearance of single flower ($\times\frac{2}{3}$); (b) five gynoecia on capitulum ($\times 1$); (c) cross section of ovary ($\times 2$); (d) ripe fruits ($\times 1$).

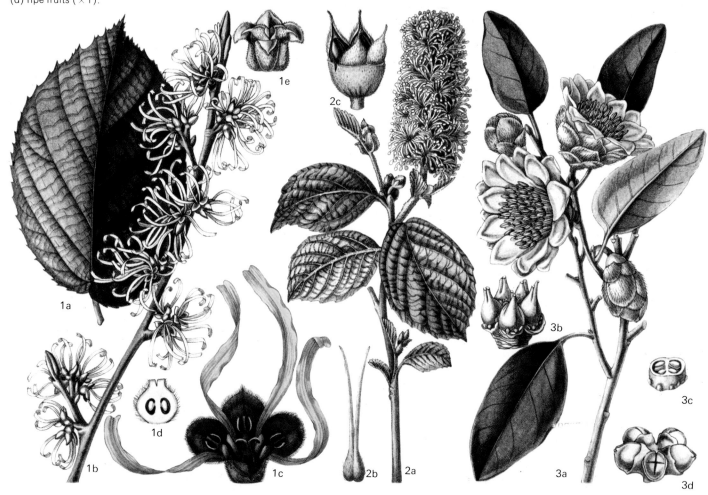

Diagnostic features. The Hamamelidaceae are trees and shrubs with generally alternate, simple or palmate leaves with stipules. Stellate hairs are sometimes present. The flowers vary considerably in the different genera, and can be bisexual or unisexual, with different sexes on the same plant (monoecious), or on separate plants (dioecious); they are often in a spike or head, sometimes subtended by colored bracts. The calyx consists of four or five united sepals, the corolla of four or five distinct petals (absent in *Liquidambar*, *Fothergilla* and *Altingia*). The stamens vary from two to 14 in number and the ovary from hypogynous to perigynous and epigynous. The ovary has two locules and two styles; each locule contains one or more ovules. The fruit exocarp is woody and the endocarp somewhat horny. The seeds are straight and with endosperm.

Classification. The family is usually divided into five subfamilies (with chief genera):

DISANTHOIDEAE. Flowers separate in two-flowered heads, petals long and narrow, and up to six ovules in each locule: *Disanthus* (endemic to Japan).

HAMAMELIDOIDEAE. Bisexual and female flowers clearly separate from each other (male flowers in the male inflorescence sometimes not so) and one or two ovules in each loculus: *Hamamelis* (eastern Asia and North America), *Trichocladus* (tropical East and eastern South Africa, the only African genus), *Diocoryphe* (endemic to Madagascar), *Corylopsis* (the largest genus, Himalayas to eastern Asia), *Parrotia* (endemic to Iran).

RHODOLEIOIDEAE. Flowers bisexual and borne in a five- to ten-flowered capitulum, surrounded by numerous bracts so as to resemble a single flower: *Rhodoleia* (northern Burma and southern China; Malaysia and Sumatra).

EXBUCKLANDIOIDEAE. Plants polygamomonoecious with uni- and bisexual flowers in capitula; petals in the bisexual flowers are narrow and two to five in number and there are 10–14 stamens; the leaves are palmately nerved from the base; the stipules are broad and closely folded face to face, enclosing the young shoot: *Exbucklandia* (eastern and southeastern Asia).

LIQUIDAMBAROIDEAE. Plants dioecious, although female flowers often have staminodes; the male inflorescence is a terminal raceme of globose stamen clusters, with no perianth; the female inflorescence is a globose head, with a perianth of numerous scales; the ovary has two locules, with the stigmas elongate: *Altingia* (Assam to Southeast Asia, Java, Sumatra), *Liquidambar* (eastern Asia, western Asia and North America).

The genus *Myrothamnus* (tropical Africa and Madagascar), an isolated relict group of undershrubs, is sometimes placed in the Hamamelidaceae, but usually in a segregate family, Myrothamnaceae, in which the plants differ in being always dioecious and having opposite leaves; the flowers have no sepals or petals, the anther filaments are fused and the three or four carpels contain many ovules. Some authorities view the Hamamelidaceae as being intermediate between the Rosales and Amentiferae (an assemblage of catkin-bearers); others have held the view that they are nearly allied to the Saxifragaceae and the small family Cunoniaceae. Current data tends to indicate that the ancestral forms of the Hamamelidaceae gave rise to the Casuarinaceae, Fagales and Urticales.

Economic uses. *Liquidambar styraciflua* (the American sweet gum or red gum) gives a useful heavy close-grained heartwood for furniture making and a white sapwood. A fragrant gum (storax) used in perfumery, as an expectorant, inhalant and as a fumigant in treatment of skin diseases is derived from *L. styraciflua* and *L. orientalis* (western Asia). *Liquidambar* species, the largest in the family, are frequently grown for their ornamental autumnal foliage. *Altingia excelsa* (rasamala) yields a heavy timber, and a fragrant gum used in perfumery. *Hamamelis* (witch hazel) provides several species and varieties of ornamental shrubs. *Hamamelis virginiana* yields the widely used astringent and soothing lotion for cuts and bruises. Water diviners favor witch hazel twigs for their dowsers. *Corylopsis*, *Fothergilla*, *Loropetalum* and *Parrotia* are shrubs also cultivated for ornament. S.L.J.

EUCOMMIALES

EUCOMMIACEAE

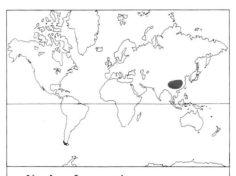

Number of genera: 1
Number of species: 1
Distribution: China
Economic uses: limited medicinal use and as rubber source.

The Eucommiaceae comprises a single species of small trees, *Eucommia ulmoides*.

Distribution. The tree is native to China, but has yet to be collected in the wild.

Diagnostic features. The trees grow to about 30ft (9m) tall with deciduous leaves which are simple, serrate and without stipules. The flowers are unisexual, and male and female are borne on different plants; they lack any perianth. The males are arranged in loose-stalked clusters consisting of the subtending bracts and about 10 elongated anthers which open by slits. The female flowers are solitary in the axils of bracts on the lower parts of the shoot, and comprise a flattened, superior, bicarpellate ovary with two divergent stigmas arising from a notch at the apex. There are two apical, pendulous ovules in the ovary, which matures into a one-seeded samara (like an elm fruit), the wings of which are chaffy and tough but still notched at the apex. The seed hangs from inside the apex of the fruit chamber. The embryo is straight and endosperm plentiful.

Latex is present in all the younger parts of the plant, but not in the wood. When snapped and pulled apart gently a series of fine threads can be drawn out, and this affords a useful means of identification.

Classification. The species, although lacking a perianth, is thought to be related to the Ulmaceae.

Economic uses. The bark is locally known as "tu-chung" or "tsze-lien" and is well established in the Chinese pharmacopoeia as a tonic and for arthritis. The tree also produces an inferior rubber which it has not been economic to exploit. B.M.

LEITNERIALES

LEITNERIACEAE
Florida Corkwood

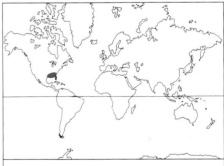

Number of genera: 1
Number of species: 1
Distribution: SE N America.
Economic uses: light wood used as floats for fishing nets.

The Leitneriaceae consists of a single deciduous shrub species, *Leitneria floridana*, the Florida corkwood.

Distribution. *Leitneria* is native to swampy areas in the southeastern part of the United States of America.

Diagnostic features. The leaves are alternate, simple, entire, somewhat leathery, with long petioles and no stipules. The unisexual flowers are borne in catkin-like spikes which appear before the leaves. Male and female are on separate plants. Each male flower is subtended by a bract. It has no perianth, and consists only of three to 12 stamens with free filaments and a rudimentary, sterile ovary. Each female flower is subtended by a bract and possesses a "perianth" of two to six distinct bract-like scales. The ovary is superior and has a single locule containing one ovule attached near the apex. There is a single style, constricted at the base and bearing a single stigma. The fruit is a leathery, rather flattened drupe subtended by the persistent bract. The seed contains a large straight embryo surrounded by thin fleshy endosperm.

Classification. The extreme reduction in floral structure suggests that this is an advanced family. However, no close affinities are evident with any other family except possibly the Myricaceae.

Economic uses. *Leitneria* is not economically important but the close-grained, soft wood is less dense than cork and is used for floats for fishing nets, hence the common name "corkwood."   S.R.C.

MYRICALES

MYRICACEAE

The Myricaceae is a small family of aromatic trees or shrubs.

Distribution. The family is more or less cosmopolitan except for some warm tem-

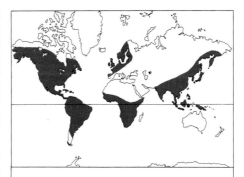

Number of genera: 2
Number of species: about 35
Distribution: almost cosmopolitan.
Economic uses: fruits boiled to produce wax.

perate parts of the Old World, and Australia.

Diagnostic features. The leaves are alternate, simple or pinnatifid, with or without stipules. The flowers are unisexual and borne on axillary catkin-like spikes, male and female on the same plant. The male flowers usually have two bracteoles, and a disk at the base of the stamens which are usually four, but sometimes two or up to 10 in number. The filaments may be joined at the base. The

female flowers have two to four bracteoles, and no disk; the ovary is superior, comprising two fused carpels which form a single locule with one erect ovule; the style has two short stigmatic branches. The fruit is a small, rough, often waxy drupe with a hard endocarp, and the seed has no endosperm and a straight embryo.

Classification. All species of *Myrica* conform to this general pattern. The only other genus, the monotypic *Canacomyrica* from New Caledonia, differs considerably in floral structure: bisexual flowers replace the female flowers of *Myrica*, and they have six stamens which are fused below into a ring surrounding the ovary. Also surrounding the ovary is a six-lobed disk which enlarges in fruit to enclose the ovary completely. *Canacomyrica* also has a certain amount of endosperm in the seeds, and this (along with other, morphological differences) makes for some doubt about its affinities with this otherwise homogeneous family.

The family is thought to be related to the Betulaceae, but is sufficiently distinctive to stand in an order of its own; some authorities relate it to the Juglandaceae.

Economic uses. The fruits of some species of *Myrica* are boiled to produce wax. I.B.K.R.

Myricaceae. 1 *Myrica gale* (a) shoot with leaves and catkin-like male and female inflorescences (×⅔); (b) female flower (×10); (c) fruit (×5); (d) cross section of fruit (×5); (e) male flower (×5). 2 *Canacomyrica monticola* (a) leafy shoot (×⅔); (b) half fruit surrounded by enlarged disk (×10). 3 *Myrica asplenifolia* (a) flowering shoot (×⅔); (b) male catkin (×⅔); (c) half female flower (×2). 4 *M. nagi* (a) shoot with fruits (×⅔); (b) female flower (×4); (c) ovary and styles (×4); (d) male flower (×4); (e) fruit cut away to reveal hard endocarp (×⅔).

FAGALES

BETULACEAE
Birches, Alders, Hazels and Hornbeams

The Betulaceae is a family of trees and shrubs which includes the birches (*Betula*), alders (*Alnus*), hornbeams (*Carpinus*) and hazels (*Corylus*).

Distribution. The family belongs predominantly to the north temperate regions, though also occurring on tropical mountains, the Andes of South America and in Argentina. (See also p. 884.)

Diagnostic features. The leaves are simple, alternate, deciduous and with stipules. All species have separate male and female flowers which are borne on the same plant, either singly or in cymose groups of three, adhering to their bracts. The groups of male flowers are aggregated into characteristic pendulous cylindrical catkins. The groups of female flowers are borne on a stiff axis, often held erect. The perianth, when present, is of a variable number of scale-like segments. There are two to 12 stamens with two-celled anthers in each male flower, but no traces of vestigial carpels. The female flower, completely lacking vestigial stamens, has a single

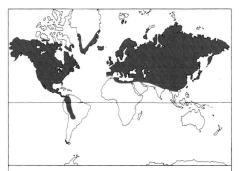

Number of genera: 6
Number of species: about 170
Distribution: N temperate, some species on tropical mountains and in S America.
Economic uses: timber, filberts from *Corylus* species and ornamental trees.

inferior ovary of two fused carpels. Pollination is by wind in early spring. The fruit is a single-seeded nut which is often winged for wind-dispersal, maturing in late summer or autumn. The seeds have no endosperm and a straight embryo.

Classification. The family has two subfamilies:

BETULOIDEAE. The male flowers are borne in three-flowered groups and have a perianth. The female flowers lack a perianth. The single tribe, BETULEAE, has two genera, *Betula* (about 50 species) and *Alnus* (about 30 species).

CORYLOIDEAE. The male flowers are solitary, the inflorescence therefore a simple spike; perianth absent. Female flowers possess a perianth. The tribe CORYLEAE (male flowers with an average of up to two stamens per flower) has two genera, *Corylus* (about 15 species), and *Ostryopsis* (about two species). The tribe CARPINEAE (male flowers with an average of six stamens per flower) has two genera, *Carpinus* (about 30 species) and *Ostrya* (about 10 species).

The Betulaceae is generally thought to belong with the Fagaceae to the order Fagales, but each family is often placed in its own order. Some workers now go further and split up the Betulaceae, recognizing each of the three tribes as a family in its own right: Betulaceae, Corylaceae and Carpinaceae.

The absence of fossil evidence makes it necessary to determine the evolutionary origin of the family on information from extant forms. On this evidence it is considered to be relatively advanced, with its very small unisexual flowers borne in com-

Betulaceae. 1 *Betula pendula* (a) habit showing typical drooping shoots; (b) leafy shoot with serrate, alternate entire leaves and immature male inflorescences (catkins) ($\times\frac{2}{3}$); (c) pendulous mature male catkins ($\times\frac{2}{3}$); (d) leaves and fruiting catkins ($\times\frac{2}{3}$). 2 Barks of various birch trees (a) *B. pendula*, (b) *B. humilis*; (c) *Betula* sp ($\times\frac{2}{3}$). 3 *Alnus glutinosa* (a) habit; (b) male catkins ($\times\frac{2}{3}$); (c) shoot with (from base) old fruiting cones, immature cones and young male catkins ($\times\frac{2}{3}$).

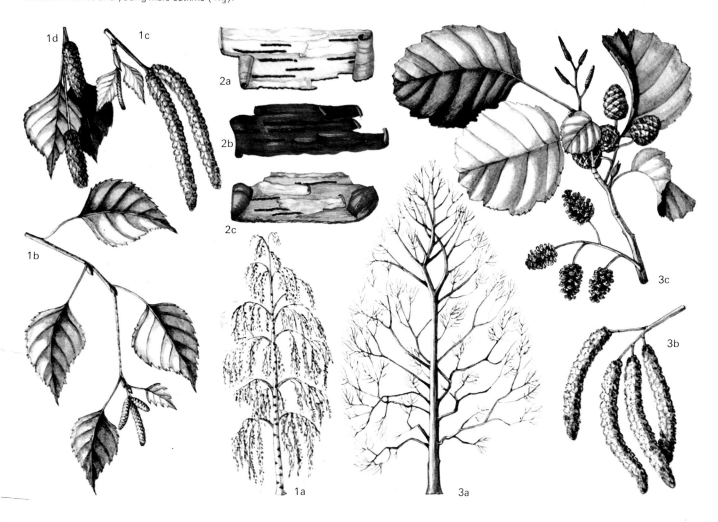

plex inflorescences with inferior ovaries, lack of nectar and scent, and wind pollination. These features together with further evidence from wood anatomy suggest that the Betulaceae is a derived family.

Economic uses. The birches provide valuable hardwood timbers. *Betula lutea* and *B. lenta* are important in North America for providing wood for furniture, doors, floors etc, and *B. papyrifera* is used for plywood, boxes, and in turnery. The bark of the latter is also used by the native Indians for making canoes and fancy goods. Branchlets of *Betula* species are used to make the besom brushes used by gardeners. *Alnus rubra* also provides a valuable timber which is a good imitation of mahogany. Both genera provide high-grade charcoal. *Ostrya* has extremely hard wood used for making mallets. Hazelnuts, cobnuts or filberts are produced by species of *Corylus*. Birches, hazels and hornbeams are cultivated as ornamentals.   S.L.J.

FAGACEAE
Beeches, Oaks and Sweet Chestnuts

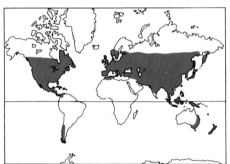

Number of genera: 8
Number of species: about 1,000
Distribution: temperate and tropical forests often as dominants in the former.
Economic uses: hardwood timber (*Quercus*, *Fagus*, *Nothofagus*), edible fruits (*Castanea*) and ornamentals.

The Fagaceae is an important temperate to tropical family of hardwood trees and, more rarely, shrubs, which embraces the beeches, oaks, and sweet chestnuts.

Distribution. The Fagaceae are prominent and frequently dominant members of the broad-leaved forests which cover, or used to cover, vast areas at middle latitudes in the Northern and, to a much less extent, Southern Hemisphere. In the extensive deciduous and mixed forests of North America and Eurasia beeches (*Fagus*), oaks (*Quercus*) and chestnuts (*Castanea*) figure prominently, while the comparable forests along the southern Andes are dominated by the southern beeches (*Nothofagus*). Evergreen oaks are important members of the forests around the Gulf of Mexico and in southern China and southern Japan, while the "black birch" forests of southern New Zealand are dominated by evergreen southern beeches. In Southeast Asia the

structure of the mixed mountain forest is largely determined by evergreen members of the family, particularly oaks and southern beeches. In total, therefore, the Fagaceae family produces a colossal biomass, possibly exceeded only by the conifers. The Fagaceae have a long fossil record suggesting an origin by at least the middle Cretaceous period, about 90 million years ago. (See p. 838.)

Diagnostic features. The Fagaceae are deciduous or evergreen trees, rarely shrubs, with alternate (rarely whorled) simple, entire to pinnately lobed leaves, and usually deciduous stipules.

The flowers are unisexual and usually arranged in catkins or small spikes (in *Nothofagus* the male flowers may be single) that may comprise only flowers of one sex, as in oaks, or may have female flowers at the base of otherwise male inflorescences, a more ancestral condition found, for example, in chestnuts (*Castanea*). The perianth is bract-like, with four to seven lobes. Male flowers have as many or twice as many stamens as perianth segments, but occasionally have up to 40. The filaments are free, with or without a rudimentary style. Female flowers are in groups of one to three, each group being surrounded by a basal involucre. The ovary is inferior, with three or six styles and locules, and two ovules in each locule. The fruits are single-seeded nuts, in groups of one to three, surrounded or enclosed by an often hardened "cupule"; the seeds lack endosperm.

The pollen and other features, such as a strongly scented inflorescence, suggest that insect pollination is the ancestral condition in the Fagaceae, and this is retained in most members except *Fagus*, *Nothofagus* and the temperate species of oak.

The familiar acorn "cup" of the oak is one example of the great variety of forms shown by the cupule, surrounding one or more fruits, which is a unique feature of the family and the origin of which has caused much controversy. Only with the discovery in 1961 of the remarkable genus *Trigonobalanus*, restricted to north Borneo, the Celebes, north Thailand, Malaya and Sarawak, has it been possible to suggest firmly that the cupule is derived from a three-lobed extension of the pedicel below each flower, which has been variously fused around single flowers, or groups of flowers. It is possible that the cupule gives a link with the pteridosperm ancestors of the flowering plants (angiosperms). The tremendous diversity of scales and spines on the cupules appears to be derived from branched spines.

The fruits of the Fagaceae have a slow and restricted capacity for dispersal and their germination power decreases rapidly with age. These features, together with the great antiquity of the family, have been responsible for its importance in discussions concerning the migration of plants brought about by continental drift in earlier geological epochs, notably evidence from *Nothofagus*.

Classification. The Fagaceae is divided into three subfamilies:

FAGOIDEAE. Inflorescence a one- to many-flowered axillary cluster; contains *Fagus* (male inflorescences long-stalked, many-flowered; styles long) and *Nothofagus* (male inflorescences sessile or short-stalked, one-to three-flowered; styles short).

QUERCOIDEAE. Catkin-like inflorescences, flowers usually with six stamens and more or less basifixed anthers 0.02–0.04in long; contains *Quercus* (female flowers borne singly in the inflorescence; fruit round in transverse section, cupule not lobed) and *Trigonobalanus* (female flowers in clusters of three, sometimes up to seven; fruit three-angled; cupule lobed).

CASTANEOIDEAE. Catkin-like inflorescences, flowers usually with 12 stamens and dorsifixed anthers about 0.01in long; contains *Chrysolepis* (cupule divided into free valves), *Castanea* (cupule valves joined when young; styles six or more; leaves deciduous), *Castanopsis* (cupule valves joined when young; styles three; leaves evergreen) and *Lithocarpus* (cupule without valves).

The family is most closely related to the Betulaceae (birches, hazels and hornbeams).

Economic uses. The Fagaceae family is the source of some of the most important hardwood timbers of the world, the most notable being oak (particularly the North American white oaks), beech, chestnut and, to a lesser extent, southern beech. This, together with clearance for agriculture, has resulted in the destruction of large areas dominated by the family. Although their timber is of good quality, the tropical members of *Castanopsis* and *Lithocarpus* have as yet been little exploited. Taken as a whole the timber of these genera exhibits a very wide range of properties and there is a correspondingly wide range of uses, from floorboards and furniture to whisky barrels and, formerly, sailing ships. Commercial cork is derived from the bark of the Mediterranean cork oak (*Quercus suber*), and in southeast Europe and Asia Minor the galls on certain oaks are a source of tannin. Many species of chestnut, but principally the sweet chestnut, *Castanea sativa* of southern Europe, are grown for their large edible nuts, from which are made, for example, purees, stuffings, stews and the famous French delicacy *marrons glacés*. The nuts ("beech-

Fagaceae. 1 *Quercus ilex* leafy shoot with male flowers clustered in pendulous catkins and female flowers at the bases ($\times \frac{2}{3}$). 2 *Fagus orientalis* leafy shoot with slender-stalked globose heads of male flowers ($\times \frac{2}{3}$). 3 *Trigonobalanus veticillata* fruits ($\times 2$). 4 *Quercus robur* leafy shoot showing fruits (nuts) surrounded at base of the familiar cup or cupule ($\times \frac{2}{3}$). 5 *Castanea sativa* young fruit with closed spiny cupule forming at the base of remains of the male catkin ($\times \frac{2}{3}$). 6 *Quercus robur* leafless tree. 7 *Fagus sylvatica* leafless tree. 8 *Nothofagus procera* dehisced four-valved cupule ($\times 2$).

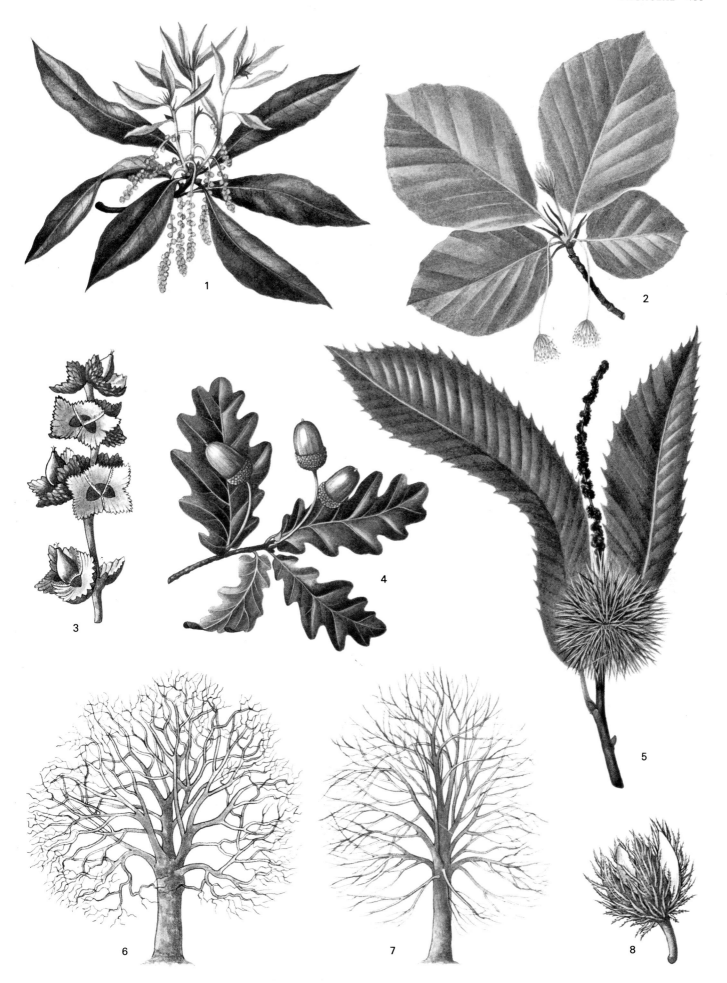

mast") of beech are rich (46%) in oil and in many regions constitute an important food for pigs, as do the fruits (acorns) of oaks.

Because of their form and, in many deciduous species, their rich autumn coloring, many Fagaceae, particularly oaks, chestnuts, beech and, to some extent, southern beech, are grown for ornament in parks and larger gardens. The only American species of *Castanopsis* (*C. crysophylla*) and *Lithocarpus* (*L. densiflorus*) are sometimes grown for ornament in warmer regions.   D.M.M.

BALANOPACEAE

The Balanopaceae (sometimes called Balanopsidaceae) is an isolated family containing a single genus (*Balanops*) of trees and shrubs which are restricted to Queensland in northeastern Australia, New Caledonia and Fiji. The leaves are alternate or pseudo-verticillate (appearing whorled) and without stipules. Male and female flowers occur on separate plants. The male flowers are arranged in catkins and the females are solitary. The males are each subtended by one scale and have two to 12 (usually five or six) stamens, while the females have many scales

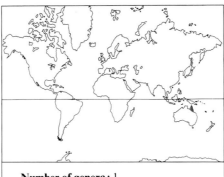

Number of genera: 1
Number of species: 12
Distribution: SW Pacific.
Economic uses: none.

and two to three carpels. The fruit is an acorn-like drupe with one or two seeds.

The family is an isolated one, perhaps distantly related to the beeches (Fagaceae). The flowers are so simple as to suggest to some workers that the family may be a very ancient one, representing a stage of "pre-floral" evolution. On the other hand, the flowers may be simplified and, therefore, highly developed. There are no reported economic uses for the family.   D.J.M.

CASUARINALES

CASUARINACEAE
She Oak and River Oak

The Casuarinaceae is a distinctive family of trees and shrubs adapted to dry habitats, comprising one genus, *Casuarina*.

Distribution. The family is distributed in northeast Australia, Malaysia, New Caledonia, Fiji and the Mascarene Islands.

Diagnostic features. The Casuarinaceae are mostly tall trees with a characteristic weeping habit caused by their jointed branches with short internodes. The leaves are very peculiar in structure, appearing as whorls of reduced, many-toothed sheaths surrounding the articulations of the jointed stems. The flowers too, are highly reduced, and usually unisexual, with the males and females borne on different parts of the same plant. The male flowers are borne in simple or branched terminal spikes growing towards the tops of the trees, and the whole inflorescence is attached by short green branchlets. The individual flowers tend to be aggregated into groups along the spike giving the appearance of a cup with several stamens protruding out of it. In fact, each flower has only one stamen

Casuarinaceae. 1 *Casuarina suberosa* (a) portion of much-jointed stem with clusters of female flowers on side branches (×⅔); (b) female inflorescence (×3); (c) female flower comprising bract, ovary, short style and bilobed stigma (×9); (d) cluster of cone-like fruits (×⅔); (e) vertical section of seed with persistent woody bracteole behind (×10); (f) tip of shoot bearing male inflorescences (×⅔); (g) cluster of male flowers in inflorescence (×6); (h) male flower comprising a single stamen (×12). 2 *Casuarina* sp portion of ribbed photosynthetic stem with whorl of reduced leaves (×12). 3 *Casuarina sumatrana* habit.

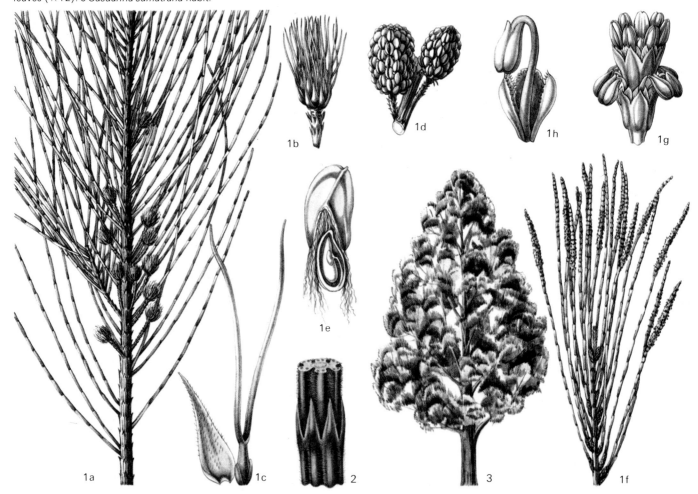

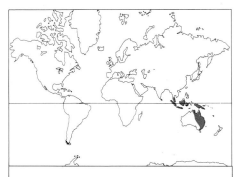

Number of genera: 1
Number of species: about 65
Distribution: SE Asia and SW Pacific
Economic uses: hardwood used for furniture-making.

and a perianth of two small lobes each subtended by two more small, leaf-like scales or bracteoles. The females tend to grow on side branches lower down the tree, and are borne in dense, spherical or oval-shaped heads. Each flower is naked, growing out of a leaf-like bract axil, and consists of a tiny ovary of two fused carpels, the posterior locule empty, the anterior locule containing

two ovules. The style is short and divided into two long stigma branches. During development the styles hang out well beyond the bracts to catch wind-borne pollen grains, and after fertilization the ovary develops into a single-seeded samaroid nut. The fruits are enclosed in hard bracteoles which later open to release them, with the result that mature inflorescences resemble pine cones. The seeds have a straight embryo and no endosperm.

Casuarinas are well adapted to very dry habitats in regions of high temperature and low rainfall and are thus remarkably xeromorphic. Besides the obvious reductions to the leaves, already mentioned, there are distinctive modifications to the branches themselves. They are quite slender and more or less circular in outline, but deeply grooved. The green photosynthetic tissue and the respiratory stomata are confined to the grooves, as a protection against low humidity and strong light. The ridges themselves are heavily armored with sclerenchyma so that the branches do not wilt in periods of drought.

Classification. At first sight the casuarinas appear to be quite distinct and independent

from all other flowering plant families. The question whether they are a primitive or an advanced family has divided the opinion of taxonomists. Earlier workers tended to think that with their reduced leaves and small, wind-pollinated flowers they were the oldest group of flowering plants and probably related to the gymnosperms (notably the pine family and the genus *Ephedra*). Modern biologists, however, are inclined to the opinion that the family is quite derived and that its peculiar features are the result of extreme specializations in isolated conditions, which have affected all the vegetative and floral parts of the plants. In many of the important morphological features the Casuarinaceae are similar to other petal-less flowering trees of the Hamamelidaceae, and it is now believed that both families have a common ancestry.

Economic uses. The wood from several species is extremely hard and valued for furniture manufacture. Red beefwood, *Casuarina equisetifolia*, is the most widespread cultivated species. Other valuable timbers include the Australian native she oak, *C. stricta*, and the cultivated *C. cunninghamiana* (river oak). C.J.H.

CARYOPHYLLIDAE

CARYOPHYLLALES

CACTACEAE
The Cactus Family
The Cactaceae is a large family of perennial, xerophytic trees, shrubs or shrublets of distinctive appearance, all more or less succulent and (excepting *Pereskia*) leafless or nearly so. Many species are valued as ornamentals.

Distribution. Cacti are mainly plants of semideserts of the warmer parts of North, Central and South America, and are doubtfully native or early naturalized in Africa, Madagascar and Sri Lanka (*Rhipsalis*); *Opuntia* is naturalized in Australia, South Africa, the Mediterranean and elsewhere. The characteristic habitats of cacti experience erratic rainfalls with long drought periods in between, but night dews may be heavy. (See p. 848.)

Diagnostic features. Most cacti have spines, and the spines, branches and flowers arise from special sunken cushions or areoles which may be regarded as condensed lateral branches; these are either set singly on tubercles or serially along raised ribs. Tufts of short barbed hairs (glochids) may also be present in the areoles. Photosynthesis is undertaken by the young green shoots, but with age these become corky and in the arborescent species develop into a hard, woody, unarmed trunk as in conventional trees. The vascular system forms a hollow cylindrical reticulated skeleton and lacks

Number of genera: 87
Number of species: over 2,000
Distribution: semi-desert regions of North, Central and South America.
Economic uses: some garden and house ornamentals with local uses for fruits.

true vessels. The roots are typically superficial and in the larger species widely spreading and adapted for rapid absorption near the soil surface.

The flowers are solitary and sessile (*Pereskia* excepted), bisexual (with rare exceptions) and regular to oblique-limbed. Color range is from red and purple through various shades of orange and yellow to white; blue is lacking. The stamens, petals, sepals and bracts are numerous and spirally arranged, the last three in transitional series without sharp boundaries between them. The ovary is inferior, and consists of two to numerous carpels, forming one locule with numerous ovules on parietal placentas. It is borne on an areole and is commonly covered in hair,

bristles or spines. The style is simple. In *Opuntia* the detached "fruit" (pseudocarp) grows roots and shoots, which form a new plant. The fruit is a berry, which is typically juicy, but may be dry and leathery, splitting open to release the seeds in various ways. The seeds have a straight to curved embryo and little or no endosperm.

Classification. The Cactaceae is of especial interest to botanists for its combination of a primitive, unspecialized flower with highly advanced vegetative organs; to the ecologist for its survival under adverse conditions and drought; and to the evolutionist for its parallel life-forms to other unrelated xerophytes, eg *Stapelia*, *Euphorbia* and *Pachypodium*. To the taxonomist it presents great problems, being apparently still in a state of active evolution, and resisting the standard herbarium procedure based on dried specimens. Under pressure from collectors and commercial growers large numbers of "genera" and "species" have been created, more nearly equivalent to subgenera and subspecies or varieties in other plant families. It is here considered to contain 87 genera, while others recognize over 300. There are three subfamilies:

PERESKIOIDEAE. Leaves present, glochids absent, seeds black and without an aril; genera *Maihuenia* and *Pereskia*.

OPUNTIOIDEAE. Leaves and glochids present, seeds covered by pale, bony aril or winged; five genera *Opuntia*, *Pereskiopsis*, *Pterocactus*, *Quiabentia* and *Tacinga*.

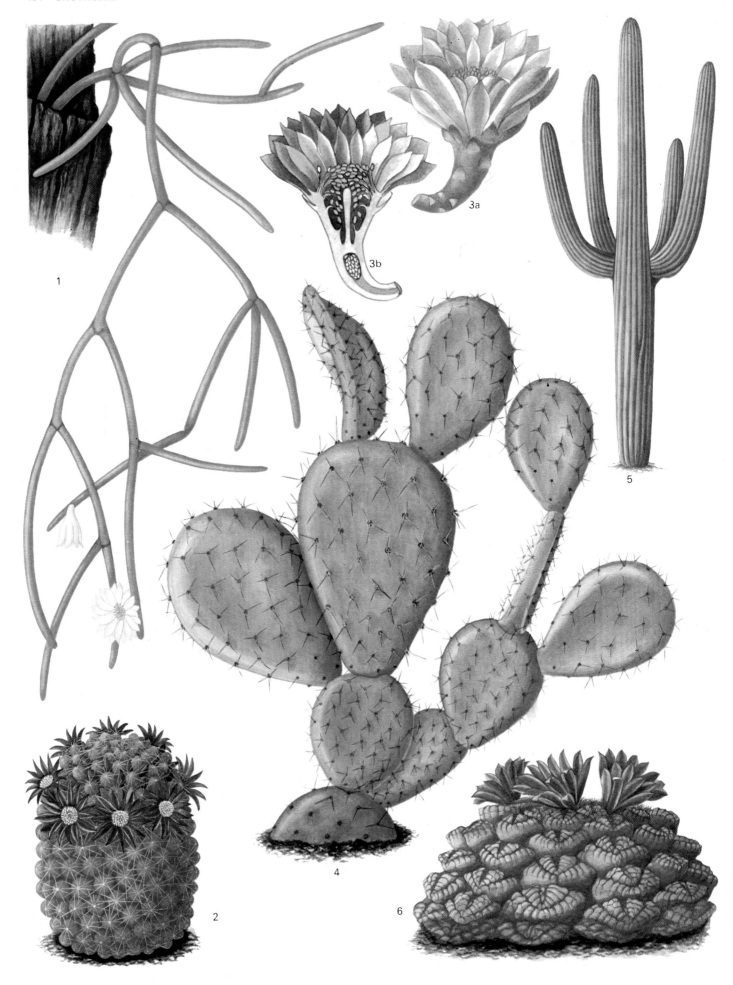

CACTOIDEAE. Leaves absent or very minute, glochids absent, seeds black or brown, not enveloped by a bony aril; 80 genera in two tribes: CEREEAE, plants predominantly columnar with usually few-ribbed jointed stems, or, if dwarf, flowering from the old areoles, 40 genera including *Cereus, Carnegiea, Echinocereus* and *Echinopsis*; CACTEAE, plants mainly dwarf with usually many ribbed non-jointed stems, flowering from the new areoles, 40 genera including *Rhipsalis, Schlumbergera, Notocactus, Echinocactus, Mammillaria, Lophophora, Ferocactus.*

The Cactaceae has no close relatives and for long it defeated efforts to fit it into existing systems of classification. It is now considered to be most closely related to the Phytolaccaceae, Portulacaceae and Aizoaceae with which it shares embryological and phytochemical peculiarities.

Economic uses. Apart from their wide appeal to specialist growers and collectors of the unusual, cacti have few uses. The fleshy fruits of many are collected locally and eaten raw or made into jams or syrups. Some are used for hedging, while those with woody skeletons are used for rustic furniture and trinkets. Opuntias (prickly pears) are grown commercially in parts of Mexico and California for their large juicy fruits.

Probably all the 87 genera are represented in cultivation, collectors being undeterred by difficulties of growing them. The most popular genera among collectors are those that remain dwarf and combine attractive spine colors and rib formations with freedom of flowering: eg *Rebutia, Lobivia, Echinopsis, Mammillaria, Notocactus, Parodia, Neoporteria. Astrophytum* is valued for its very prominent ribs and cottony white tufts, and *Leuchtenbergia* for its extraordinarily long tubercles. More for connoisseurs are the curiously squat, tuberculate, slow-growing species of *Ariocarpus, Pelecyphora* and *Strombocactus. Melocactus*, the "Turk's cap cactus", one of the first cacti to reach Europe, is unique for the large, furry inflorescence terminating the short, stumpy axis.

Even more widely grown are the epi-

Cactaceae. 1 *Rhipsalis megalantha* an epiphytic cactus with many-jointed, spineless stems that are often produced in whorls (×⅔). 2 *Mammillaria zeilmanniana* a dwarf cactus with a solitary stem of spirally arranged tubercles tipped with spine-bearing areoles; flowers arise from the base of the tubercles (×⅔). 3 *Gymnocalycium mihanovichii* (a) entire flower showing the gradual transitional series from bracts to sepals and petals (×2); (b) vertical section of flower showing inferior ovary and numerous stamens (×2). 4 *Opuntia engelmannii* showing the characteristic disklike, many jointed stem bearing numerous glochids—fine readily detached spines (×⅔). 5 *Carnegiea gigantea* showing the characteristic much-branched candelabra habit and ribbed stems (×1/72). 6 *Ariocarpus fissuratus* a dwarf cactus with a many-ribbed, non-jointed stem bearing flowers on new areoles (×⅔).

phytes, so dissimilar in habit and requirements to the foregoing that many a cottage gardener cherishing a 'Christmas cactus' or 'Ackermannii' fails to associate it with cacti at all. The large-flowered epicacti are products of a long line of intergeneric crossings paralleled only in the orchids. These are the only group of cacti where hybridization has been pursued on a grand scale, and the only group grown primarily for flowers. But for the shortness of the flowering season (May to June) and the uninspiring sameness of the green, flat or three-winged stems, these epicacti could become more popular.

The columnar cacti of the tribe Cereeae mostly need to be quite tall before flowering, and are less suitable for small glasshouses.

The name "cactus" is commonly misapplied to a wide range of spiny or fleshy plants quite unrelated to the Cactaceae.

G.D.R.

AIZOACEAE
The Mesembryanthemum Family

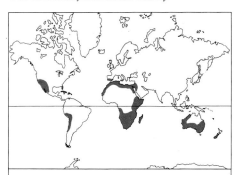

Number of genera: 143
Number of species: about 2,300
Distribution: pantropical, but centered in S Africa.
Economic uses: many greenhouse and garden ornamentals (eg *Mesembryanthemum, Lampranthus*) and ornamental curiosity (living stones).

This is a large family of succulent plants with usually showy, daisy-like flowers, often forming brilliant sheets of color when growing in the mass. It contains many popular garden plants. The Aizoaceae is most familiar through the members of the subfamily Ruschioideae (broadly identifiable with *Mesembryanthemum*), which are showy-flowered, highly succulent, tender xerophytes of often curious habit and growth form.

Distribution. The family is centered in South Africa, but there are a few pantropical weeds extending to the West Indies, southwestern North America, Florida, South America and Australia.

Diagnostic features. The Aizoaceae are annual or perennial herbs or small shrubs, usually more or less succulent, with alternate or opposite, mostly simple, entire leaves with or without stipules. The flowers are solitary or in cymes, and regular, with their parts in whorls, and usually bisexual. The sepals are

four to eight in number (usually five) and are imbricate or rarely valvate, more or less united below. The petals are numerous and of staminodial origin; occasionally they are absent. The stamens are perigynous, usually numerous, sometimes with connate filaments. The ovary is superior or inferior, with one up to 20 (usually five) stigmas and locules and usually numerous ovules. The fruit is a dry capsule, rarely a berry or nut. The seed has a large curved embryo surrounding a mealy endosperm.

Many of the features of the Aizoaceae are the result of adaptations to extremely dry climates (xeromorphy) and typical members are able to survive long periods of extreme insolation and drought, eg in the desert regions of South Africa. The leaves are more or less succulent, and in addition some plants have succulent roots or caudices. Often the plant is reduced to a single annual pair of opposite leaves, which may be so condensed as to approach a sphere, with minimal surface in relation to volume, enabling the plant to resist desiccation.

The internal tissues also show modifications. Large, watery cells rich in sugars called pentosans are characteristic of succulents. In *Muiria* these cells may be 1mm in diameter and can retain their moisture for weeks when separated and exposed to dry air. The possession of two different leaf forms (heterophylly) is common (*Mitrophyllum, Monilaria*), the leaf pair formed at the start of the dormant season being more united and compact than that formed when in full growth, and acting as a protective sheath to the stem apex. Other genera are partly subterranean, with only the clear 'window' in each leaf tip exposed above soil. A type of optical system exists whereby a layer of apical tissue rich in calcium oxalate crystals acts as a filter to intense sunlight before it reaches the thin chlorophyllous layer below (*Fenestraria, Frithia, Ophthalmophyllum*).

Other so-called mimicry plants show a striking similarity to their background rocks and are difficult to detect when not in flower. These are the pebble plants or living stones (*Lithops*); each species is associated with one particular type of rock formation and occurs nowhere else. *Titanopsis*, with a white incrustation to the leaves, is confined to quartz outcrops. It is suggested that this is a rare case of protective coloration in plants akin to that found in the animal kingdom.

The phenomenon of crassulacean acid metabolism occurs in members of the Aizoaceae, having evolved independently in a number of different families of succulent plants.

The mostly showy, many-petalled, diurnal flowers have a superficial resemblance to the flower heads of the Compositae. They are insect-pollinated and most require full sun before they will expand. Several have set hours for opening and closing. *Carpobrotus*

1a

1b

2

3

4

5

6

7

8

9a

9b

9c

produces an edible berry, the hottentot fig, but the remainder form dry, dehiscent capsules operated by a hygroscopic mechanism which expands the valves in response to moistening, closing them again on drying out. In desert conditions this ensures germination during the brief rainy periods.

Conicosia and certain related genera have three different methods of seed dispersal. The capsule first opens hygroscopically and some seeds are washed out by the impact of raindrops. It remains open when dry and the remaining loose seeds are shaken out as from a pepper-pot over a longer period. Finally the whole fruit breaks up into segments which are dispersed by the wind, each wing-like lamella containing up to two seeds trapped in two pocket-like folds. These rank among the most specialized of all angiosperm fruit structures.

Classification. The Aizoaceae is divided into five subfamilies, four of which are based on the large *Mesembryanthemum* complex. What Linnaeus treated as a single large genus *Mesembryanthemum* is nowadays split up on the basis of fruit structure into 125 genera, and accounts for some 2,000 of the species of the family. Some authors treat the *Mesembryanthemum* complex as a separate family Mesembryanthemaceae, whereby the Aizoaceae is restricted to a small group of rather insignificant and small-flowered weedy genera.

The Aizoaceae belongs to the Caryophyllales and shares with most families therein the possession of betalains in place of anthocyanin as a floral pigment. Its affinities lie with the Phytolaccaceae.

Economic uses. Shrubby members of the Ruschioideae (*Lampranthus, Oscularia, Drosanthemum, Erepsia*, etc) are half-hardy and grown for summer bedding especially in southern Europe where they flower profusely. Only one species, *Ruschia uncinata*, verges on complete hardiness, although *Carpobrotus* survives most winters in coastal areas and is much planted (and naturalized) as a sandbinder. Hybrids of the annual *Dorotheanthus* enjoy great popularity, and

Aizoaceae. 1 *Lampranthus* sp (a) shoot with opposite succulent leaves and terminal, solitary flowers (×⅔); (b) half flower with free sepals, several series of petals, numerous stamens and gynoecium with separate styles and numerous ovules (×2). 2 *Sesuvium portulacastrum* jointed, succulent stem with opposite leaves and tubular flowers (×⅔). 3 *Pleiospilos bolusii* a plant comprising two large succulent leaves with flowers produced between (×⅔). 4 *Ruschia uncinata* flowering shoot (×⅔). 5 *Lithops pseudotruncatella* and 6 *L. lesliei* pebble-like plants (living stones) of two succulent leaves with flowers arising from the fissure (×⅔). 7 *Oscularia deltoides* flowering shoot (×⅔). 8 *Faucaria tigrina* with a dense rosette of spiny leaves (×⅔). 9 *Mesembryanthemum crystallinum* (a) the ice plants, so-called for the glistening papillae that cover the whole plant (×⅔); (b) dehiscing capsule (×2); (c) capsule from above (×1⅓).

have supplanted the original ice plant *Mesembryanthemum crystallinum*, which has glossy papillae-like water droplets covering the foliage, in popularity in gardens.

G.D.R.

CARYOPHYLLACEAE
The Carnation Family

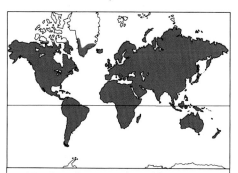

Number of genera: about 80
Number of species: about 2,000
Distribution: temperate regions, centered in the Mediterranean area.
Economic uses: many popular garden ornamentals, notably pinks and carnations; others are widespread weeds.

The Caryophyllaceae is a large family of mainly temperate herbaceous plants, of somewhat doubtful relationships. It includes the popular carnations and pinks, and some well-known wild flowers and weeds such as campions and chickweed.

Distribution. The family is found in all temperate parts of the world and sparingly on mountains in the tropics; several species of *Stellaria* (chickweed) and *Cerastium* (mouse-ear chickweed) have become almost cosmopolitan weeds. The center of distribution is, however, in the Mediterranean region and adjoining parts of Europe and Asia. Representation in the temperate Southern Hemisphere is small in terms of genera and species. All the larger genera (*Silene, Dianthus, Arenaria*, etc) are found in the Northern Hemisphere, with a strong concentration in the Mediterranean region.

Diagnostic features. In spite of its large size, the Caryophyllaceae is a relatively uniform and easily recognized family. Plants are usually herbaceous, either annual or perennial and dying back to the crown. A few species are somewhat shrubby with persistent woody stocks. The leaves are almost invariably opposite; the stem nodes are swollen, and the bases of each leaf pair often join around them to form a perfoliate base. The leaves themselves are always simple and entire. Stipules are usually absent; when present (as in the subfamily Paronychioideae) they are usually scarious.

The inflorescences are of cymose construction, although varied in detail; the most complex is the dichasial panicle, in which each of the two bracteoles of the terminal flower subtends an inflorescence branch itself bearing a terminal flower and two

bracteoles, which repeats the structure. Suppression of individual flowers can lead to raceme-like monochasia, and, ultimately, to a single-flowered inflorescence (as in the carnation).

The flowers are regular and usually bisexual. The calyx consists of four or five free sepals (subfamily Alsinoideae) or of united sepals with a four- or five-lobed apex (subfamily Silenoideae); a number of subtending bracts are present at the base of the calyx in some genera, notably *Dianthus*. The corolla consists of four or five petals which are free from each other (petals absent in part of subfamily Paronychioideae, and some other species) and often sharply differentiated into limb and claw; two small outgrowths (ligules) may be present at the junction of the two parts on the inner surface. The apexes of the petals are often notched or deeply cut, producing more or less bilobed or even fringed petals. The stamens are typically twice as many as the petals, but may be reduced to as many, or even fewer (eg *Stellaria media*). They are usually free from each other and attached directly to the receptacle, but in some apetalous members of subfamily Paronychioideae they are attached to the sepals, rendering the flower perigynous. The ovary is superior, of two to five united carpels; usually it has a single locule with free central placentation, but in a few species of *Silene* and *Lychnis* it is septate at the base. The styles are free, as many as there are carpels. The ovules are usually numerous, but may be reduced to one, when the placentation is basal. The fruit is most frequently a capsule, dehiscing by means of teeth at the apex; these may be as many as, or twice as many as, the number of carpels. More rarely, in single-ovuled genera, the fruit is an achene. Seeds are usually numerous, with the embryo curved around the food-reserve material, which is usually perisperm (tissue derived from the diploid nucleus) rather than endosperm (derived from the triploid nucleus of the fertilized embryo sac). In *Silene* and *Lychnis* the petals, stamens and ovary are separated from the calyx by a shortly extended internode (anthophore).

Classification. The family is usually divided into three subfamilies:

ALSINOIDEAE. Stipules absent; sepals free from each other. This subfamily contains many well-known and widely distributed genera, such as *Arenaria, Minuartia, Honkenya, Stellaria, Cerastium, Sagina, Colobanthus* and *Lyallia*.

SILENOIDEAE. Stipules absent; sepals connate. This subfamily is of about the same size as the Alsinoideae, and contains equally well-known genera: *Silene, Melandrium, Dianthus, Gypsophila, Agrostemma, Lychnis* etc. Both of these subfamilies are well distinguished and easily recognized, though the recognition of genera within them is taxonomically difficult and controversial.

1

3b

3c

3d

3e

2b

3a

5

6b

2a

4

6a

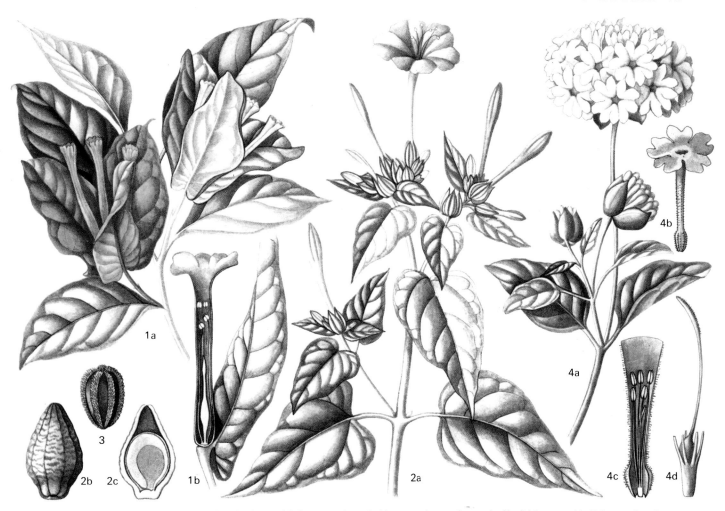

Nyctaginaceae. 1 *Bougainvillea spectabilis* (a) leafy shoot with flowers subtended by conspicuous bracts ($\times\frac{2}{3}$); (b) bract and half flower showing petaloid tubular calyx and no petals ($\times 2$). 2 *Mirabilis jalapa* (a) leafy shoot with each flower enclosed by a calyx-like involucre of bracts ($\times\frac{2}{3}$); (b) indehiscent fruit ($\times 3\frac{1}{3}$); (c) vertical section of fruit showing single seed ($\times 3\frac{1}{3}$). 3 *Pisonia aculeata* glandular fruit that is dispersed by birds ($\times 1$). 4 *Abronia fragrans* (a) shoot bearing dense clusters of flowers ($\times\frac{2}{3}$); (b) flower ($\times 1$); (c) section of base of perianth-tube showing stamens and style ($\times 2$); (d) gynoecium with elongate, hairy stigma ($\times 4$).

PARONYCHIOIDEAE. Stipules present, usually scarious; sepals free or connate. This subfamily is more variable than the other two, and consists essentially of two groups of genera: (a) Those in which a corolla is present, the flower being hypogynous and the fruit is usually a several- to many-seeded capsule. This is a group consisting of the tribes SPERGULEAE and POLYCARPEAE, containing, among others, the genera *Spergula*, *Spergularia* and *Polycarpon*. These plants are very similar to members of the Alsinoideae, differing only in the possession of

Caryophyllaceae. 1 *Stellaria graminea* shoot with opposite leaves, swollen nodes and cymose inflorescence ($\times\frac{2}{3}$). 2 *Telephium imperati* (a) shoot with flowers and fruits ($\times\frac{2}{3}$); (b) flower with five sepals, five petals, five stamens and three styles ($\times 4$). 3 *Dianthus deltoides* habit ($\times\frac{2}{3}$); (b) half flower with fused sepals, deeply notched petals, stamens twice as many as petals and superior ovary crowned by two styles ($\times 3$); (c) cross section of ovary ($\times 8$); (d) vertical section of ovary ($\times 8$); (e) fruit ($\times 3$). 4 *Arenaria purpurascens* habit ($\times\frac{2}{3}$) 5 *Silene dioica* inflorescence bearing flowers with deeply cleft limb and white claw to each petal ($\times\frac{2}{3}$). 6 *Herniaria ciliolata* (a) shoot with small axillary inflorescences ($\times\frac{2}{3}$); (b) flower with clawed petals ($\times 12$).

stipules. (b) Those in which the corolla is absent, the flower being perigynous and the fruit usually single-seeded and indehiscent. This group contains the tribe PARONYCHIEAE and one or two others, and is sometimes recognized as a separate family, the Illecebraceae. Its best-known genera are *Paronychia*, *Herniaria* and *Corrigiola*. Its status is unsettled, but it appears to be only distantly related to the Sperguleae.

The family is generally grouped with a number of others (Chenopodiaceae, Aizoaceae, Phytolaccaceae, etc) in a group known as the Centrospermae (Caryophyllales). This disposition was based on morphological structure, in particular that of the embryo, which is usually strongly curved. The discovery that most of the Centrospermae (but not the Caryophyllaceae) contain a group of chemical pigments known as betalains, instead of the more usual anthocyanins, has led to a separation of the Caryophyllaceae from the rest of the group. In spite of this difference, however, the Caryophyllaceae still shows a great deal of similarity to the betalain-containing families, even though this may not imply as close a relationship as was once thought.

Economic uses. The Caryophyllaceae provides a large number of widely cultivated garden ornamentals. The most important single species is the carnation (*Dianthus caryophyllus*), which is now found in numerous garden forms (cultivars), and forms a specialized crop for the cut-flower market. Other widely cultivated genera are *Dianthus* (pinks), of which many species are cultivated, including alpines, *Silene* (catchfly, campion), *Gypsophila* (baby's breath), *Agrostemma* (corn cockle), *Lychnis* and *Saponaria* (soapworts).

Several species, notably *Stellaria media*, are widespread annual weeds of fields, gardens, and other disturbed places. *Agrostemma githago* was at one time a troublesome weed of grain fields, but, with the use of selective herbicides, this species is no longer a considerable problem.

Spergula arvensis var *sativa* is occasionally used as a fodder plant in dry, sandy areas.   J.C.

NYCTAGINACEAE
Bougainvilleas

The Nyctaginaceae is a family of chiefly tropical herbs, shrubs and trees.

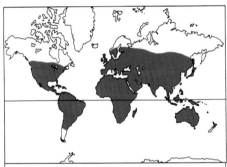

Number of genera: 30
Number of species: about 290
Distribution: pantropical, particularly America.
Economic uses: *Bougainvillea* and *Mirabilis* cultivated as ornamentals; *Pisonia* used as vegetables.

Distribution. The family is found throughout the tropics, particularly in America.

Diagnostic features. The leaves are alternate or opposite, simple and without stipules. The inflorescence is usually cymose and the flowers are bisexual or unisexual, and are sometimes surrounded by colored bracts which resemble a calyx. The perianth is usually petal-like, tubular, and often the lower part persists into fruiting time. There are no petals and the one to many stamens, usually five, alternate with the five perianth lobes, the filaments being free or fused together at the base, or sometimes branched above. The ovary is superior, comprising a single carpel with a single basal erect ovule; it is surmounted by a long style. The fruit is an indehiscent achene, sometimes enclosed by the persistent base of the calyx which may serve to assist fruit dispersal. The seeds have endosperm, perisperm and a straight or curved embryo.

Classification. *Mirabilis*, including *Oxybaphus*, comprises about 60 American species. The base of the flower is surrounded by a five-part involucre of bracts which greatly resembles a calyx. The derivation of the involucre is from a much-condensed three-flowered cyme, with only one of the flowers developed. Evidence for this is seen in species such as *Mirabilis coccinea* where the involucre encloses more than one flower. In *Mirabilis* the involucre has taken on the role of a parachute-like fruit dispersal structure. The flowers of *Mirabilis jalapa* open in the evening, whence one of the common names, four o'clock. Another common name, marvel of Peru, relates to the polychromic flowers, which are white, yellow or red.

In *Bougainvillea*, a genus of 18 South American species, the three decorative and colored "sepals" are in fact bracts which subtend groups of three inconspicuous tubular flowers.

Pisonia comprises 50 tropical and subtropical species, and the fruits are glandular so that they adhere to animals and are dispersed.

Other genera in the family include the monotypic southern North American and Mexican *Nyctaginia*; the 40 tropical and subtropical species of herbs in the genus *Boerhavia*; 35 North American species of the genus *Abronia*; and *Neea*, comprising some 80 tropical American species.

The Nyctaginaceae belongs to a group of families often referred to as the Centrospermae (Caryophyllales).

Economic uses. Bougainvilleas are often grown as defensive and decorative hedges in warmer climates, and as greenhouse plants farther north. The two most commonly grown species are *Bougainvillea glabra* and *B. spectabilis*. From these, and from *B. peruviana* and *B. × buttiana*, many cultivars have been produced. *Mirabilis jalapa* and *M. coccinea* are amongst many species of *Mirabilis* cultivated for their ornamental value as garden plants. The tuberous roots of *M. jalapa* are the source of a purgative drug used as a substitute for jalap. The leaves of the brown cabbage tree (*Pisonia grandis*) and the lettuce tree (*P. alba*) can be used as a vegetable. Decoctions of the leaves of *P. aculeata* and of the fruits of *P. capitata* are used medicinally to treat a range of complaints. B.M.

AMARANTHACEAE
Cockscombs and Celosias

Number of genera: 65
Number of species: 900
Distribution: cosmopolitan, with tropical members centered in Africa and America.
Economic uses: widely cultivated as garden ornamentals and a few used as pot herbs and vegetables.

The Amaranthaceae is a large family of herbs and shrubs containing several well-known species of horticultural importance such as the cockscombs (*Celosia* species) and love lies bleeding (*Amaranthus caudatus*).

Distribution. The family of about 65 genera and 900 species grows in tropical, subtropical and temperate regions, the tropical members occurring mainly in Africa and America.

Diagnostic features. Most members are herbs or shrubs, rarely climbers, with entire, opposite or alternate leaves without stipules. The flowers may be solitary or in axillary dichasial cymes arranged in spike-like or head-like, usually bracteate, inflorescences. They are bisexual, rarely unisexual, normally regular with four to five perianth segments which are sometimes united; stamens are one to five, free or often united at the base in a tube from which petaloid appendixes arise in some genera between the stamens; the ovary is superior, comprising two to three fused carpels that are free from or united with the perianth; it has a single locule containing one to numerous ovules. The perianth is often dry, membranaceous and colorless. Sometimes the lateral flowers are sterile and develop spines, wings or hairs which serve as a dispersal mechanism, as in *Froelichia*. The flowers are subtended by well-developed dry, chaffy scales (bracteoles) and in the mass are often very showy. The fruit may be a berry, pyxidium or nut; the seeds usually have a shiny testa and the embryo is curved.

Classification. The family may be divided into two subfamilies, each containing two tribes, as follows:

AMARANTHOIDEAE. Stamens are four-locular and the ovary has one to many ovules; tribe CELOSIEAE, main genera *Celosia* and *Deeringia*; tribe AMARANTHEAE, main genera *Amaranthus, Ptilotus, Achyranthes*.

GOMPHRENOIDEAE. Stamens are bilocular and the ovary has a single ovule; tribe BRAYULINEAE containing the two small genera *Brayulinea* and *Tidestromia*; tribe GOMPHRENEAE including *Froelichia, Pfaffia, Alternanthera, Gomphrena* and *Iresine*.

The Amaranthaceae belongs to the group of families known as the Centrospermae, and in common with most other members of the group contains betalain pigments instead of the customary anthocyanins found in most other angiosperm families. It is closely related to the Chenopodiaceae but differs in having a scarious perianth and the stamens frequently united in a ring.

Economic uses. The family contains many weedy species but several are widely cultivated as garden ornamentals and a few are used as pot herbs or as vegetables. The edible seeds of some species of *Amaranthus* were widely used, especially in Central and South America, and a few are still grown today. Celosias are often grown as pot plants or as tender bedding plants. *Celosia cristata* is the cockscomb, a tropical herbaceous annual. *Alternanthera* species from the New World tropics are grown for their ornamental leaves. The fleshy leaves of *A. sessilis* are eaten in various tropical countries. Also grown for their colorful, usually scarlet leaves as house or tender bedding plants are the iresines, especially *Iresine herbstii* and *I. linderii*, both from South America. Some species are reputed to have medicinal properties. The Australian *Ptilotus* (*Trichinium*) *manglesii*, with globose heads of feathery pink and white flowers, is sometimes cultivated as a tender bedding plant or under glass. *Gomphrena globosa*, a tropical annual with white, red or purple heads, is grown as an "everlasting." V.H.H.

Amaranthaceae. 1 *Amaranthus retroflexus* (a) leafy shoot with flowers in axillary tassels (×⅔); (b) fruit dehiscing by lid to disperse globular seed (×6). 2 *A. caudatus* (a) flower with reddish subtending bracteoles and reddish perianth (×14); (b) seed (×14); (c) leaf (×⅔); (d) vertical section of male flower (×12); (e) vertical section of female flower (×4). 3 *Deeringia amaranthoides* inflorescence with fruits at the base (×3). 4 *Froelichia gracilis* (a) shoot with large lateral, hairy, sterile flowers (×⅔); (b) inflorescence (×⅔); (c) vertical section of sterile flower (×⅔).

PHYTOLACCACEAE
Pokeweed and Bloodberry

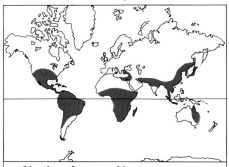

Number of genera: 22
Number of species: about 125
Distribution: chiefly tropical and subtropical, America and W Indies
Economic uses: many medicinal uses, yield red dyes and are used as ornamentals and potherbs.

The Phytolaccaceae is a family of trees, shrubs, woody climbers and herbs, including some medicinal plants and ornamentals.

Distribution. Most members of the family are native to tropical America and the West Indies, but some are found in Central and temperate South America, the eastern Mediterranean area, in tropical and South Africa, Madagascar, the Indian subcontinent. Malaysia, China, Japan and Australasia.

Diagnostic features. The leaves are alternate, simple and entire, typically without stipules or with minute stipules. The flowers are small, mostly in terminal or axillary racemes or cymes. They are regular, bisexual (rarely irregular), rarely unisexual, then with both sexes on one plant (monoecious) or on different plants (dioecious). The perianth is almost always of one whorl of four or five usually free and persistent segments, but sometimes disciform; petals are sometimes present. The stamens are usually hypogynous, sometimes united at the base, as many as the perianth lobes or more numerous, often as a result of branching. The ovary is usually superior, sometimes raised on a gynophore, rarely more or less inferior; it comprises one to many separate or united carpels, each carpel typically with a single basal or axillary ovule. Styles may be as many as the carpels, short or more or less filiform, or absent. The fruit is a fleshy berry, dry nut or, rarely, a loculicidal capsule; the seed has mealy perisperm and the curved embryo characteristic of the order.

Classification. The family is divided into four subfamilies. The subfamily PHYTO-LACCOIDEAE (perianth single; one ovule per carpel, apotropous) has four sections; PHYTOLACCEAE (*Anisomeria, Ercilla, Phytolacca*); BARBEUIEAE (*Barbeuia*); GYROSTEMONEAE (*Gyrostemon, Codonocarpus, Didymotheca*); RIVINEAE (*Hilleria, Ledenbergia, Monococcus, Petiveria, Rivina, Seguieria, Trichostigma*); and AGDESTIDEAE (*Agdestis*). Subfamily STEGNOSPERMATOIDEAE (perianth double; ovules epitropous, fruit capsular, with red aril; glands with oxalate deposits) contains one genus, *Stegnosperma*. Subfamily MICROTEOIDEAE (perianth single; gynoecium with one locule but two to four stigmas and a single basal ovule; fruit dry) includes *Microtea* and *Lophiocarpus* (sometimes united with *Microtea*). Subfamily ACHATOCARPOIDEAE (flowers unisexual, plants dioecious; ovary with one locule of two fused carpels with two stigmas, containing one ovule; fruit a berry) includes *Achatocarpus* and *Phaulothamnus*).

In recent years, the woody climber *Barbeuia madagascariensis* has been made by some authorities the only species of the family Barbeuiaceae. Another monotypic family (Agdestidaceae) has been proposed for *Agdestis clematidea*. The family Stegnospermataceae has also been proposed for the

Phytolaccaceae. 1 *Lophiocarpus burchellii* (a) leafy shoot and inflorescences ($\times\frac{2}{3}$); (b) flower with single whorl of five perianth segments ($\times 10$); (c) vertical section of ovary showing curved basal ovule and forked styles ($\times 20$); (d) fruit—a nut ($\times 10$). 2 *Phytolacca clavigera* (a) shoot with axillary leaf-opposed racemose inflorescence bearing flowers and fruits ($\times\frac{2}{3}$); (b) flower with numerous stamens with swollen bases and seven free carpels ($\times 6$); (c) fleshy fruit ($\times 3$); (d) vertical section of fruit ($\times 4$). 3 *Seguieria coriacea* (a) shoot with pairs of thorny stipules and axillary inflorescence ($\times\frac{2}{3}$); (b) flower ($\times 4$); (c) vertical section of winged fruit with curved embryo ($\times 1$).

three species of the genus *Stegnosperma*. Section Gyrostemoneae (five genera) has also been recognized as a family, the Gyrostemonaceae, as has Achatocarpoideae (Achatocarpaceae), with two genera. Finally, the whole section Rivineae (single carpellate ovary, styloid oxalate cells in the leaves, and unusual wood anatomy) may be separated as the family Petiveriaceae.

With its curved embryo, perisperm and betalain pigments, the Phytolaccaceae is properly included among the Centrospermae (Caryophyllales). The family has a close affinity with the Nyctaginaceae and the subfamily Microteoideae is held to show a transition to the family Chenopodiaceae.

Economic uses. *Rivina humilis*, the bloodberry or rouge plant, is grown in greenhouses and a red dye is extracted from the berries. *Petiveria alliacea*, remarkable for its smell of onions, is used medicinally in South America. *Trichostigma peruvianum* is often grown as a hothouse plant. *Phytolacca americana* (*P. decandra*), the pokeweed or red ink plant, is cultivated as an ornamental shrub and like some other *Phytolacca* species yields edible leaves, sometimes used as potherbs, and, from the berries, a red dye.

The medicinal uses are many and varied, from treatment of rabies, insect bites, lung diseases and tumors by species of *Phytolacca*, mainly in root preparations, to the treatment of syphilis by *Agdestis*, again in root preparations.   F.B.H.

CHENOPODIACEAE
Sugar Beet, Beetroot and Spinach

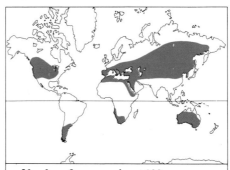

Number of genera: about 100
Number of species: about 1,500
Distribution: temperate and subtropical, principally in saline habitats.
Economic uses: sugar beet, beetroot, leaf beets and spinach beet.

The Chenopodiaceae is a large family of perennial herbs (and rarely shrubs or trees) which are halophytic, that is adapted to live in soils containing an unusually high percentage of inorganic salts. Thus they are dominant components of salt marshes, and since saline soils are often associated with arid conditions, many species exhibit xerophytic adaptations.

Distribution. The family is widely distributed in temperate and subtropical saline habitats, particularly around the Mediterranean, Caspian and Red seas, the salt-rich steppes of central and eastern Asia, the edge of the Sahara desert, the alkaline prairies of the United States of America, the Karroo of South Africa, Australia and the Pampas of Argentina. They also grow as weeds in salt-rich soils around human habitations.

Diagnostic features. Typically, members of the family have deep penetrating roots to obtain any available water supply, and small, mealy-textured or hair-covered, lobed or spiny alternate leaves without stipules. Some genera, eg *Salicornia*, have fleshy jointed stems with no leaves at all, which gives the plants a curious cactus-like appearance. The inconspicuous flowers, arranged into spike-like or cymose inflorescences,

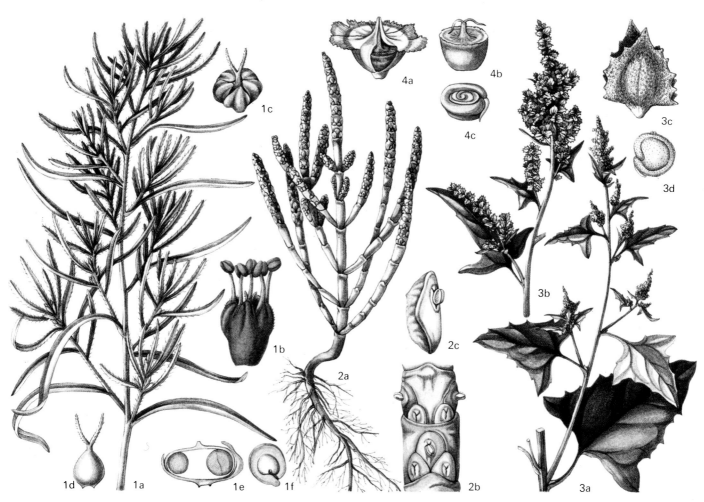

Chenopodiaceae. 1 *Kochia scoparia* (a) leafy shoot with inconspicuous flowers (×⅔) ; (b) bisexual flower with five perianth-segments and conspicuous stamens (×8) ; (c) female flower (×8) ; (d) gynoecium of female flower with two styles (×8) ; (e) vertical section of fruit (×8) ; (f) section of seed with circular embryo surrounding endosperm (×16). 2 *Salicornia europaea* (a) habit showing fleshy leafless stem (×⅔) ; (b) part of flowering shoot (×4); (c) flower sunk in stem (×8). 3 *Atriplex triangularis* (a) flowering shoot (×⅔); (b) fruiting stem (×⅔); (c) enlarged bracteoles enclosing the fruit (×4) ; (d) fruit (×4). 4 *Salsola kali* (a) fruit with one segment of persistent bracteole removed (×4); (b) fruit (×6); (c) seed (×6).

are small, usually regular, bisexual or unisexual and wind-pollinated. The sepals and petals are very similar to one another in appearance and usually consist of five, three or two brown or greenish lobes. There are usually the same number of anthers as perianth segments, sometimes fewer, arranged on top of the ovary or on a disk. The ovary is superior (semi-inferior in *Beta*) and consists of three fused carpels and a single locule containing a single basal ovule. There is a terminal style with two (rarely one or three) stigmas. The fruit is a small round nut or achene.

Classification. The 100 genera can be divided up into two main tribes on the basis of embryo shape.

CYCLOBEAE. Embryo ring-shaped, horseshoe-shaped or semicircular, wholly or partially enclosing the endosperm; important members of this group include the temperate and subtropical genera *Chenopodium*, *Kochia* and *Atriplex*, the salt marsh herbs of *Salicornia*, *Halocnemum* and *Arthrocnemum* and the well-known food-plant genera *Beta* and *Spinacia* (spinach).

SPIROLOBEAE. Embryo spirally twisted, and endosperm divided into two halves by the embryo or entirely wanting; important members of this group include the coastal salt marsh and steppe genera *Salsola*, *Anabasis*, *Halimione*, *Haloxylon* and *Suaeda*.

The family belongs to the assemblage of families commonly known as the Centrospermae (Caryophyllales).

Economic uses. *Beta vulgaris* is really the only species of any major agricultural importance; it includes amongst its many different varieties the sugar and fodder beets. Today, sugar beet serves as a source of sugar in almost every country in Europe, in the USSR, the United States of America, Turkey, Iran, parts of Africa, Korea, Japan and parts of Australia. In South America, sugar beets are cultivated in Argentina, Chile and Uruguay, but the major source of sucrose there is still sugar cane. Other varieties of *B. vulgaris* include the deep-red beetroot and mangel-wurzels, the large leaved spinach beet or perpetual spinach and seakale beet or Swiss chard.

Other cultivated plants of the family include quinoa, *Chenopodium quinoa*, which is grown for its edible leaves and seeds to provide a staple diet for Andean Peruvians, *C. anthelminticum* which is used as a vermifuge and *C. amaranticolor*, with its decorative green and violet-red colored foliage, is used as a border plant in gardens.

C.J.H.

DIDIEREACEAE

The Didiereaceae is a curious family of chiefly columnar cactus-like plants.

Distribution. The four genera of the family are confined to semi-desert areas in Madagascar.

Diagnostic features. The leaves are alternate, simple, entire and without stipules, and in some species wither and fall off to expose the spiny stems. The flowers are unisexual and borne on different plants (bisexual and female in *Decaryia*), the males consisting of two opposite petal-like sepals and four overlapping petals surrounding the eight to ten stamens which are shortly united at the base. The female flowers have a perianth like the males, and a superior ovary of three fused carpels comprising three locules, only one of which is fertile, containing a single basal ovule. The style is single and usually expanded into three or four irregular stigmatic lobes. The triangular dry fruits do not dehisce and the seed has a folded embryo,

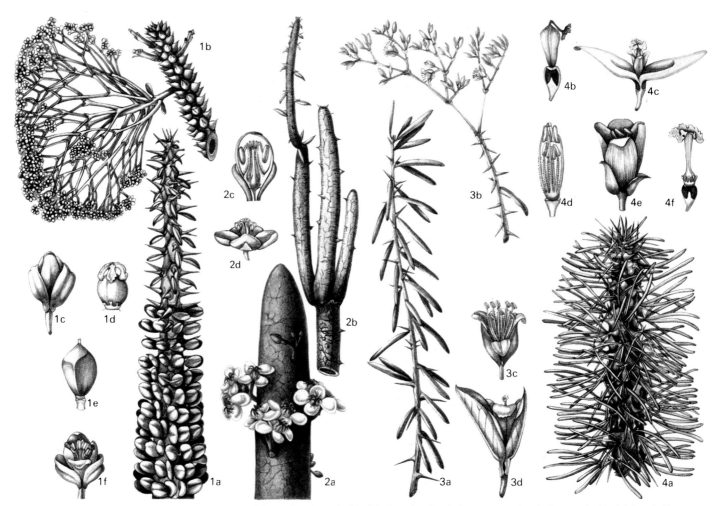

Didiereaceae. 1 *Alluaudia procera* (a) upper portion of flowering shoot ($\times\frac{1}{3}$); (b) shoot bearing inflorescence of male flowers ($\times\frac{1}{9}$); (c) female flower ($\times 4$); (d) gynoecium ($\times 7$); (e) fruit ($\times 7$); (f) male flower ($\times 2$). 2 *A. dumosa* (a) upper portion of flowering shoot ($\times\frac{2}{3}$); (b) spiny branches ($\times\frac{1}{3}$); (c) vertical section of male flower bud ($\times 3\frac{1}{2}$); (d) male flower ($\times 1\frac{1}{2}$). 3 *Alluaudiopsis fiherenensis* (a) spiny shoot ($\times\frac{1}{3}$); (b) shoot with male flowers ($\times\frac{1}{3}$); (c) male flower ($\times 1\frac{2}{3}$); (d) female flower ($\times 1\frac{1}{3}$). 4 *Didierea madagascariensis* (a) upper portion of branch ($\times\frac{1}{9}$); (b) fruit ($\times 3$), (c) female flower opened out ($\times 2$); (d) androecium ($\times 2$); (e) male flower ($\times 2$); (f) gynoecium ($\times 3\frac{1}{2}$).

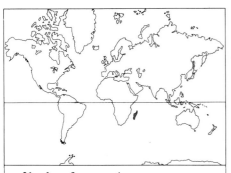

Number of genera: 4
Number of species: 11
Distribution: dry parts of Madagascar.
Economic uses: rarely cultivated.

fleshy cotyledons and little or no endosperm.
Classification. There are four genera in the family: *Alluaudia* (six species), *Alluaudiopsis* (two species), *Decaryia* (one species) and *Didierea* (two species). The strangest species is perhaps *Alluaudia procera*. It looks like a bent and thorny telegraph pole up to 50ft (15m) high, with flowers produced in incongruous apical clusters.

The two species of *Didierea* are a little more conventional, reminiscent of certain arborescent euphorbias. *Didierea madagascariensis* has erect branches 13ft–20ft (4m–6m) tall, while *D. trollii* is smaller with branches which spread horizontally. The internal structure of the stem is divided into a series of chambers by transverse diaphragms of pith which confer light weight but rigidity to the member. The single species of *Decaryia* is characterized by its spreading branches and thorny zig-zag twigs.

The Didiereaceae is one of the group of families known as the Centrospermae (Caryophyllales) containing betalain pigments rather than anthocyanins. It has earlier been placed in the Euphorbiales.
Economic uses. The plants occasionally appear in succulent collections.   B.M.

PORTULACACEAE
Lewisias and Portulacas
The Portulacaceae is a medium-sized family of annual or perennial more or less succulent herbs or subshrubs, several of which are valued as ornamentals.
Distribution. The family is cosmopolitan, but is especially well represented in South Africa and America.
Diagnostic features. The leaves are more or

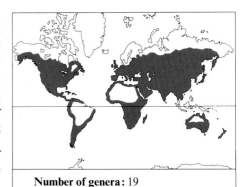

Number of genera: 19
Number of species: about 500
Distribution: cosmopolitan, but centered in S Africa and America.
Economic uses: several ornamentals and a potherb.

less fleshy, alternate or opposite, entire and bear stipules which may form hairs or membranous scales that may envelop the whole stem and leaves (*Anacampseros papyracea*). The flowers are rather small, except in a few species cherished by the gardener (*Portulaca grandiflora, Lewisia tweedyi*). They are regular, bisexual and typically composed of two green sepals, five (sometimes four or six) free petals and stamens and

Portulacaceae. 1 *Lewisia cotyledon* (a) habit showing basal rosette of leaves and inflorescence (×⅔) ; (b) vertical section of ovary with basal ovules (× 3). 2 *Portulaca grandiflora* (a) flowering shoot showing hairy stipules (×⅔) ; (b) cross section of unilocular ovary (× 4) ; (c) half flower showing overlapping petals (× 4). 3 *Montia fontana* (a) habit (×⅔), (b) fruit—a capsule dehiscing by three valves (× 6) ; (c) flower (× 6). 4 *Claytonia perfoliata* (a) habit showing flower stalks erect before and curved downwards after pollination, and erect when bearing fruit (×⅔) ; (b) mature capsule with one of two persistent sepals removed (× 6) ; (c) flower with petals partly removed (× 12).

a more or less superior ovary of three (sometimes four or five) fused carpels containing a single locule with two to numerous ovules on a central basal placenta. The style is usually divided. Some authorities consider the two green sepals to be bracts and the corolla to be a perianth. Nectar is present and pollination is by insects. *Anacampseros papyracea* only rarely opens a flower and is almost wholly cleistogamous. The fruit is a capsule dehiscing by two or three valves or a lid, and the seeds have a large embryo coiled around the endosperm.

Classification. The most recent classification splits the family into seven tribes and 19 genera. Some genera are ill-defined and can be distinguished from one another only by microscopic characters of the seed. The Portulacaceae is placed in the Centrospermae (Caryophyllales), sharing with other families of that order the possession of betalains in place of anthocyanin in the flowers. Morphologically it comes closest to the Caryophyllaceae and Basellaceae, and is linked to the Aizoaceae by the many-stamened genera *Portulaca* and *Lewisia*.

Economic uses. *Portulaca oleracea*, the common purslane, has been cultivated since classical times as a salad and pot herb, and is still so used in some countries. The plant long known as *P. grandiflora*, although now thought by some to be a cultivar of hybrid origin, is much in demand as a summer bedding annual, and has been bred for a wide range of colors as well as double flowers. Species of *Lewisia* are collectors' pieces for the alpine garden or cold house. The starchy rootstocks of *Lewisia rediviva* are eaten by the American Indians. Several tender genera are popular in collections of succulent plants; for example the African *Anacampseros* with over 50 miniature rosette species, the shrubby *Ceraria* and *Portulacaria*, and the leafy caudiciform American and African *Talinum*. Several species of *Claytonia* are grown in rock gardens.   G.D.R.

BASELLACEAE
Madeira Vine

The Basellaceae is a small family of climbing vines, mostly from tropical America.

Distribution. Apart from America, species are also found in tropical Africa, Madagascar, southern Asia, New Guinea and some Pacific islands.

Diagnostic features. The leaves are mostly simple, broadly-ovate and fleshy, without stipules and arranged alternately on the long climbing stem of the vine. The rootstock is often tuberous. The flowers are small, regular, bisexual or unisexual, supported by a pair of bracts and arranged in spikes or in racemes in the leaf axils. The floral organs are usually arranged perigynously. The perianth has five segments which may be partially fused at their bases and in some species may be colored. There are five stamens, each opposite a perianth segment and adnate, or partially fused, to its base. The ovary is superior and comprises three fused carpels which form a single locule containing one basal ovule. There is usually one style and three stigmas. The fruit is a drupe and usually enclosed within the persistent fleshy perianth. The seed usually has copious endosperm and a twisted or ring-like embryo.

Classification. The four genera can be grouped into two tribes:

BASELLEAE. Filaments erect and straight in bud; *Basella*, or Malabar nightshade, with two principal species, *Basella rubra* and *B. alba*, bearing red and white flowers respectively; *Tournonia*; *Ullucus* (ulluco).

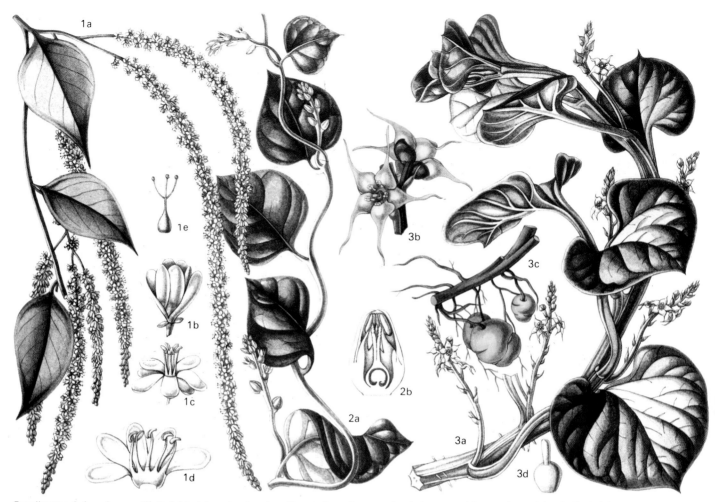

Basellaceae. 1 *Anredera cordifolia* (a) twining stem bearing alternate broadly ovate simple leaves and flowers in panicles ($\times\frac{2}{3}$); (b) flower partly open showing pair of bracteoles below the flower ($\times4$); (c) fully open flower with five perianth segments and five stamens ($\times4$); (d) perianth opened out to show stamens attached to its base ($\times6$); (e) gynoecium with terminal style deeply-divided into three stigmas ($\times3$). 2 *Basella alba* (a) twining stem ($\times\frac{2}{3}$); (b) half flower bud showing ovary with single locule containing one ovule ($\times6$). 3 *Ullucus tuberosus* (a) twining stem ($\times\frac{2}{3}$); (b) flowers with brightly colored bracteoles and five greenish perianth segments ($\times2$); (c) tuberous roots ($\times\frac{2}{3}$); (d) gynoecium ($\times6$).

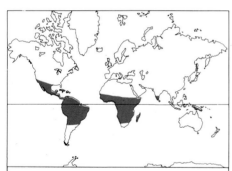

Number of genera: 4
Number of species: 22
Distribution: mainly tropical America.
Economic uses: limited uses as vegetables and ornamentals.

ANREDEREAE. Filaments curved outwards in bud; *Anredera* (*Boussingaultia*), Madeira vine.

The family is related to the Portulacaceae and the other families in the group known as the Centrospermae (Caryophyllales).
Economic uses. The leaves of *Basella rubra* and *B. alba* are sometimes eaten like spinach, and ulluco produces small tubers which are eaten as a substitute for potatoes. *Anredera*

baselloides is grown for its decorative value for covering porches, arbors etc. It is fast growing and mainly propagated by means of the small bulbils produced in the leaf-axils.
B.N.B.

BATALES

BATIDACEAE
Saltwort

The Batidaceae is a family consisting of only a single species, the saltwort (*Batis maritima*).

Distribution. The saltwort is found in the coastal regions of the West Indies and Brazil, as well as in the Pacific from California to the Galapagos Islands and Hawaii.

Diagnostic features. Saltwort is a straggly shrub with rather fleshy leaves which are opposite, simple, narrow, and without stipules. The flowers are unisexual, and male and female are borne on separate plants. In both types, the flowers are very small with very short stalks and are arranged in cone-like spikes. The male flowers arise in the axils of bracts and consist of a two-lipped calyx and four petals (sometimes described as stami-

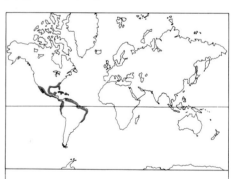

Number of genera: 1
Number of species: 1
Distribution: coastal regions of the W Indies, Brazil, California, Central America and Hawaii.
Economic uses: minor use in salads.

nodes), which are fused at the base and alternate in position with four free stamens. The spike bearing the female flowers is rather fleshy and the bracts are smaller than those of the male-flowered spikes. There is no indication of either calyx or petals in the female flowers, which essentially consist of only an ovary divided into four locules, each of which contains a single ovule inserted at

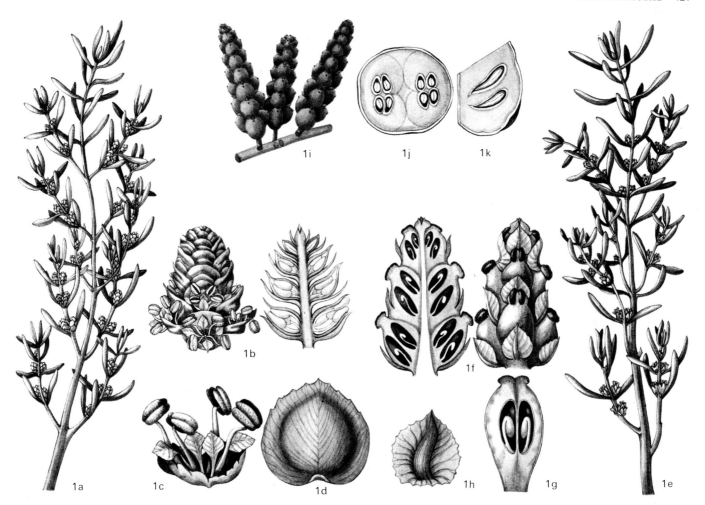

Batidaceae. 1 *Batis maritima* (a) male flowering shoot ($\times\frac{2}{3}$); (b) male inflorescence entire (left) and vertical section (right) ($\times 7$); (c) male flower with two-lipped calyx, four petals and four stamens ($\times 20$); (d) bract from male inflorescence ($\times 14$); (e) female flowering shoot ($\times\frac{2}{3}$); (f) female inflorescence entire (right) and in vertical section (left) ($\times 10$); (g) half female flower with sessile stigma and single basal ovules in each chamber ($\times 14$); (h) bract from female inflorescence ($\times 14$); (i) ripe fruit ($\times 3$); (j) cross section of fruiting spike showing two individual fruits each with four seeds ($\times 12$); (k) vertical section of fruit ($\times 20$).

the base. There is no distinct style and the flattened stigma sits directly on top of the ovary. As the fruits of the four up to 12 flowers in each spike ripen into berries, they often become fused into a fleshy structure. The seed contains a large straight embryo but no endosperm.

Classification. The relationships of the Batidaceae are uncertain, but it seems to have some affinities with a number of families in a group known as the Centrospermae (Caryophyllales), and in particular with the Amaranthaceae and the Chenopodiaceae, which also contain species to be found in coastal regions. There is also evidence to suggest that it ought to be separated into an order of its own, as followed here.

Economic uses. The leaves of saltwort are edible and are sometimes eaten raw in salads.

S.R.C.

POLYGONALES

POLYGONACEAE
Buckwheats, Rhubarb and Sorrels

The Polygonaceae is a very large cosmopolitan family of herbs, some shrubs and a few trees, with a number of cultivated ornamentals and plants with edible seeds (buckwheat), stalks (rhubarb), leaves (sorrel) or berries (*Coccoloba*).

Distribution. Most genera inhabit the temperate northern regions. A few are tropical or subtropical, notably *Antigonon* (Mexico and Central America), *Coccoloba* (tropical America and Jamaica) and *Muehlenbeckia* (Australasia and South America).

Diagnostic features. The leaves are usually alternate and simple, with a characteristic ochrea or membranous sheath uniting the stipules. The small white, greenish or pinkish flowers are solitary or grouped in racemose inflorescences and are usually bisexual; occasionally the sexes are separate. There are three to six sepals that often become enlarged and membranous in the fruit. Petals are absent. The six to nine stamens have bilocular anthers opening lengthwise. The ovary is superior and composed of two to four carpels united into one locule containing a single basal ovule. There are two to four usually free styles. The fruit is a triangular nut; the seeds have abundant endosperm and a curved or straight embryo.

Classification. Three major groups of genera

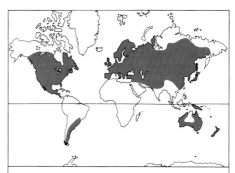

Number of genera: about 30
Number of species: about 750
Distribution: cosmopolitan, but chiefly in northern temperate regions.
Economic uses: ornamentals and crop plants (buckwheat, rhubarb).

may be distinguished. The first comprises plants which are tropical, or half-hardy in temperate zones. *Antigonon* has three or four species of flamboyant climbers. *Brunnichia* is a genus of two deciduous climbers closely related to *Polygonum*. The large genus *Coccoloba* comprises some 125 species of tropical trees, shrubs and climbers. *Muehlenbeckia* includes about 15 species of climbing or woody, hardy, half-hardy and greenhouse plants related to *Coccoloba*. Notable in the second group of desert-loving hardy and half-hardy shrubs and subshrubs are *Atraphaxis*, the shrubby buckwheats from semidesert regions of southeast Europe and central Asia; *Calligonum*, 100 species of broom-like xerophytic shrubs from central Asia; *Padopterus*, whose single species *Podopterus mexicanus* is an attractive spiny pink-flowered shrub, cultivated in dry greenhouse conditions; and *Eriogonum*, a genus of over 100 species of annual or perennial herbs and subshrubs mostly from the dry, warm regions of western North America: most species are densely woolly and have clusters of small white flowers. The third group of genera, whose typical habitat is in temperate regions, includes edible species, vigorous ornamental herbs and shrubs and weeds. *Fagopyrum* has 15 perennial and annual herbaceous species often with succulent stems, native to temperate regions of Eurasia. The 50 species of *Rheum*, strong, large-leaved herbs, come from Siberia, the Himalayas and eastern Asia. *Polygonum* comprises 150 vigorous and often invasive species of mainly perennial and hardy herbs

with a few woody climbers. The often pink or white flowers are pollinated by insects. The greenish, occasionally reddish or yellowish flowers of *Rumex* (150 northern temperate species) are wind-pollinated.

The Polygonaceae is most closely related to the Plumbaginaceae; both families have affinities with the Caryophyllaceae.

Economic uses. Cultivated ornamentals include *Antigonon leptopus* (coral vine or rosa de montaña), *Muehlenbeckia axillaris*, a small creeping rock garden shrub, *Atraphaxis frutescens*, grown for its pink and white flowers, the rock garden species of *Eriogonum*, grown for their gray and white foliage, the waterside *Rheum palmatum* and *Rumex hydrolapathum*, and many fast-growing border, ground cover and rock garden species of *Polygonum*. The purple berries of the West Indian seaside grape *Coccoloba uvifera* are eaten, as are the leaves of the common sorrel (*Rumex acetosa*), used as a salad and potherb, and the stalks of the common rhubarb *Rheum rhaponticum*. *Fagopyrum esculentum* (common buckwheat) is widely cultivated for its seeds and as a manure and cover crop and similar but less extensive uses are made for *F. tataricum*

(tartary buckwheat) although the seeds are not eaten by Man.   T.J.W.

PLUMBAGINALES

PLUMBAGINACEAE
Sea Lavender and Thrift
The Plumbaginaceae is a medium-sized family of annual or perennial herbs and shrubs or climbers, many of which are cultivated as garden ornamentals.

Distribution. The family is cosmopolitan but especially frequent in dry or saline habitats such as sea coasts and salt steppes.

Diagnostic features. The leaves are either arranged in a basal rosette or alternately on the aerial branched stems. They are simple, glandular and without stipules. The inflorescence is cymose or racemose (eg *Limonium*), spicate (eg *Acantholimon*) or in dense, capitulate clusters (eg *Armeria*). The bracts are scarious and sometimes form an involucre. The flowers are bisexual and regular, with their parts in fives. The five persistent sepals are fused to form a five-toothed or five-lobed tube which is often

Polygonaceae. 1 *Rumex hymenosepalus* (a) leafy shoot with flowers and winged fruit ($\times\frac{2}{3}$); (b) mature fruits showing persistent perianth ($\times\frac{2}{3}$); (c) cross section of fruit ($\times$1); (d) flower ($\times$2). 2 *Oxyria digyna* (a) habit ($\times\frac{2}{3}$); (b) winged fruit ($\times$4); (c) cross section of fruit ($\times$4). 3 *Polygonum amplexicaule* (a) flowering spike showing sheathing stipules or ochreas clasping the stem above the leaf bases ($\times\frac{2}{3}$); (b) perianth opened out to show eight stamens ($\times$2); (c) vertical section of ovary ($\times$4). 4 *Coccoloba platyclada* (a) flowering shoot ($\times\frac{2}{3}$); (b) flower buds and young fruits ($\times$4); (c) mature fruit ($\times$4); (d) seed ($\times$4); (e) cross section of seed ($\times$4); (f) flower viewed from above ($\times$7).

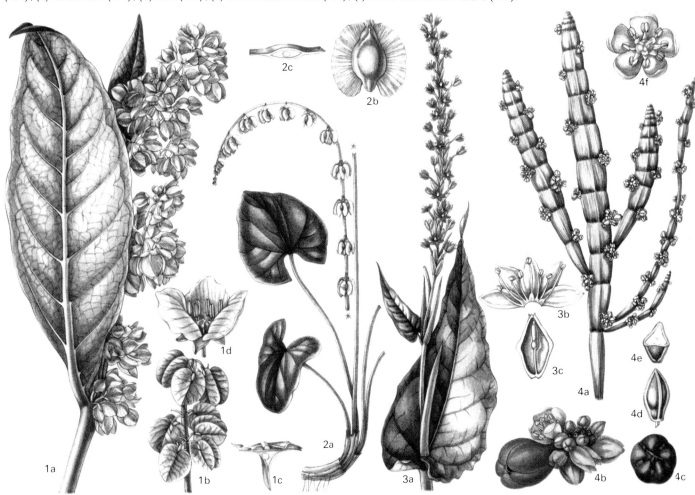

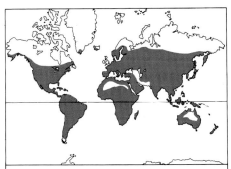

Number of genera: 10
Number of species: about 560
Distribution: cosmopolitan, particularly in dry or saline habitats.
Economic uses: garden ornamentals (thrift, *Plumbago*) and medicinal uses.

membranous, ribbed and colored. The five petals are free, connate only at the base or fused into a long tube. The five stamens, which are arranged opposite the petals, are free or inserted at the base of the corolla. The anthers are bilocular and split open longitudinally. The ovary is superior, of five fused carpels and a single locule. It contains a single basal anatropous ovule and is sur-

mounted by five styles or five sessile stigmas. The fruit is usually enclosed by the calyx and is normally indehiscent. The seed contains a straight embryo surrounded by mealy endosperm.

Classification. The chief genera are *Limonium* (about 300 species), *Acantholimon* (150 species), *Armeria* (80 species), *Plumbago* (12 species), *Limoniastrum* (10 species), and *Ceratostigma* (eight species). *Plumbago* is similar to *Ceratostigma* in that it has leafy stems, but differs in having free stamens and a glandular calyx as opposed to the epipetalous condition and non-glandular calyx in species of the latter. *Limonium*, *Armeria* and *Acantholimon* usually have radical leaves. Species of *Armeria* and *Acantholimon* generally possess tighter flower heads than those of *Limonium* but can be distinguished from each other on various floral and vegetative features.

The family is related to the Polygonaceae, and both families have affinities with the order Caryophyllales. Relationships have also been suggested with the Primulaceae and Linaceae.

Economic uses. A number of species yield extracts that are used medicinally. For

example those from the subshrub *Plumbago europaea* and the herbaceous climber *P. scandens* are used to treat dental ailments while extracts from the leaves and roots of the tropical *P. zeylanica* are used to treat skin diseases. Extracts from the roots of the European *Limonium vulgare* are used to treat bronchial haemorrhages.

Many members of the family are grown in gardens. For example, many species of *Armeria* (sea pink or thrift) are grown in borders and as rock plants. They are tufted perennials with moss-like leaves and globose white or pink flowering heads on wiry stems.

Many species of *Limonium* (sea lavender) are grown in borders and beds and for cut flowers which may be dried and used as everlastings. *Acantholimon glumaceum* and *A. venustum* are grown in rock gardens, producing loose spikes of small rose-colored flowers. Two climbing species, *Plumbago auriculata* (pale blue flowers) and *P. rosea* (red flowers) are grown in warm glasshouses; *P. europaea*, a perennial herb with violet flowers and *P. micrantha*, a white-flowered annual, are hardy in cool temperate conditions. *Ceratostigma willmottianum* is a popular ornamental garden shrub. S.R.C.

Plumbaginaceae. 1 *Limonium imbricatum* (a) habit showing part of tap root, rosette of leaves and flowers in branched panicles ($\times\frac{1}{3}$); (b) part of inflorescence ($\times 2$). 2 *L. tunetanum* (a) half flower showing stamens inserted at base of corolla tube ($\times 8$); (b) cross section of ovary with a single ovule ($\times 40$). 3 *L. thouini* vertical section of fruit ($\times\frac{2}{3}$). 4 *Aegialitis annulata* indehiscent fruit with persistent calyx ($\times 1$). 5 *Armeria pseudarmeria* habit showing radical leaves and flowers in dense capitulate clusters ($\times\frac{2}{3}$). 6 *A. maritima* (a) half flower with lobed petals, epipetalous stamens and gynoecium with simple hairy styles and a single basal ovule ($\times 4$). 7 *Plumbago auriculata* shoot bearing simple leaves and inflorescences ($\times\frac{2}{3}$).

Dilleniaceae. 1 *Hibbertia tetrandra* (a) flowering shoot ($\times\frac{2}{3}$); (b) half flower showing lobed petals and free carpels with one basal ovule ($\times 3$). 2 *Dillenia indica* (a) gynoecium showing ovoid ovary and free styles and stigmas ($\times\frac{2}{3}$); (b) cross section of ovary showing numerous partly united carpels ($\times 1$). 3 *Dillenia suffruticosa* (a) shoot with wing-like stipules on leaf-stalks ($\times\frac{2}{3}$); (b) cross section of ovary with united carpels ($\times 1$); (c) gynoecium ($\times\frac{2}{3}$). 4 *Tetracera masuiana* (a) flowering shoot ($\times\frac{2}{3}$); (b) vertical section of gynoecium with free carpels ($\times 6$).

DILLENIIDAE

DILLENIALES

DILLENIACEAE
Dillenias and Hibbertias
This large family of tropical trees, shrubs and climbers contains a number of handsome species, some with large white or yellow flowers.

Distribution. The family is almost pantropical, though only one genus, *Tetracera*, has members in Africa. Among the major genera with 40 or more species, *Dillenia* (including *Wormia*) is found in Asia, New Guinea, Australia, Fiji and Madagascar, and *Hibbertia* is native to Australasia and Madagascar.

Diagnostic features. Most plants in the family have deciduous alternate leaves with prominent lateral veins (resembling those of the loquat); stipules may be present or absent. The white or yellow flowers are usually regular and bisexual, borne solitary or in cymes. There are five persistent

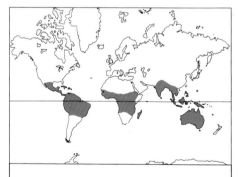

Number of genera: 18
Number of species: 530
Distribution: almost pantropical, but centered in Asia and Australasia.
Economic uses: *Dillenia* and *Hibbertia* are cultivated as ornamentals.

overlapping sepals, five free overlapping deciduous petals (often crumpled in the bud) and numerous stamens often persisting on the fruit. The numerous carpels are free or slightly fused (rarely completely fused), each carpel containing one or more erect ovules. The styles are separate and divergent, each with a single stigma, and fruits may be dehiscent or berry-like. There are one to few seeds with an aril which is convolute or fringe-like; the seed coat is crusty, the endosperm fleshy and the embryo very small.

Classification. The Dilleniaceae is here allied with the Crossosomataceae and Paeoniaceae within the order Dilleniales, and although each of the families is sharply set off from the others, they have a unique combination of features in common. This group is related to the Magnoliales, and allied orders.

Economic uses. Some species are decorative climbers or trees, the rough leaves of others are used in rural economies as a sandpaper, and the timber of *Dillenia* species is used in general construction and boat building. The flowers of *Dillenia* are like "gigantic buttercups" to quote E. J. H. Corner; in *Dillenia obovata* they are about 6in (15cm) in diameter and yellow, and in *D. indica* about 8in (20cm) across and white. Such flowers

Paeoniaceae. 1 *Paeonia peregrina* (a) shoot with upper leaves and solitary terminal flower ($\times\frac{2}{3}$); (b) young fruit comprising three follicles ($\times\frac{2}{3}$); (c) dehisced fruit ($\times\frac{2}{3}$); (d) vertical section of seed with copious endosperm and a small embryo ($\times 2$); (e) young leafy shoots ($\times\frac{1}{2}$). 2 *P. wittmanniana* (a) cross section of carpel ($\times\frac{2}{3}$); (b) vertical section of carpel ($\times\frac{2}{3}$); (c) young fruit ($\times\frac{2}{3}$). 3 *P. mascula* fruit of five follicles ($\times\frac{2}{3}$). 4 *P. emodi* fruit ($\times\frac{2}{3}$). 5 *P. tenuifolia* flower ($\times\frac{2}{3}$).

last only one day and are borne on the leafless tree in *D. obovata*, but when new leaves are emerging in *D. ovata*.

A group of *Dillenia* species, with dehiscent fruits which open on the tree, has sometimes been separated as the genus *Wormia*, but shares the colloquial name simpoh. Of these *D. excelsa*, an 80ft (25m) tree with red fruit buds, yellow flowers to 4in (10cm) across with purple anthers is one of the most noble.

The Australian *Hibbertia scandens* is often encountered as a glasshouse climber or outdoors in warmer climates. *Tetracera sarmentosa* is also an evergreen climber often grown in the semishade.   B.M.

PAEONIACEAE
Peonies

The family Paeoniaceae comprises one genus (*Paeonia*) of 33 species of perennial, rhizomatous herbs or shrubs, including many popular ornamentals, cultivated for their showy flowers and attractive foliage.

Distribution. The family is native to north temperate regions, chiefly south Europe, China and northwestern America.

Diagnostic features. The leaves are composed of several leaflets which may be lobed. They are alternate and without stipules. The

Number of genera: 1
Number of species: 33
Distribution: north temperate, chiefly southern and central Europe, China and NW America.
Economic uses: ornamental herbs and shrubs (peony) and some local medicinal uses.

large conspicuous flowers are regular and bisexual, rather globular in appearance. Leafy bracts may be present, which by reduction of the blade and expansion of the base pass into five green, persistent sepals. The five to ten petals are large, with a gradual transformation into successively narrower forms. The many anthers are centrifugally arranged and bear anthers with two locules

opening lengthwise by slits which face outward. The two to five carpels are free and borne on a fleshy nectar disk. They are themselves fleshy, each surmounted by a thick stigma and containing numerous ovules in a double row. The fruit consists of two to five large, leathery follicles containing several large red seeds which turn shiny black on maturity. The seeds have arils, copious endosperm and a small embryo.

Most species of peony, such as *Paeonia officinalis*, possess large flowers up to 5.5in (14cm) across. There is substantial variation in the degree of subdivision of the leaves, and this can be of diagnostic value in separating the various species and subspecies.

Classification. At one time *Paeonia* was placed in the Ranunculaceae, where it was anomalous in possessing persistent sepals, petals with a sepalar rather than staminodial derivation, a perigynous disk and seeds with arils. Corner in 1946 first pointed out that the Paeoniaceae was much closer to Dilleniaceae, and recent research supports his view.

Economic uses. Many species are grown as garden flowers, making attractive border plants. There are a number of varieties of *P. officinalis* (native to southern Europe) including 'Alba-plena' (double white-flowered), 'Rosea-plena' (double pink-flowered) and 'Rubra-plena' (double crimson-red-flowered).

A species native to Siberia, *P. lactiflora*, produces scented, pure white single flowers but is rarely cultivated as such, having been superseded by a range of forms often with double flowers, such as 'Albert Crousse' (double pink, carmine at the center), 'Bower of Roses' (double rose-crimson) and 'Bowl of Beauty' (semi-double pink with prominent gold/yellow stamens). Other popular cultivated species are the southern European *P. arietina* with hairy stems and single pink flowers and *P. mlokosewitschii* (Caucasus) with single yellow cup-shaped flowers.

A number of shrubby species are also popular ornamentals. *P. lutea* (China) is a deciduous wide-spreading shrub with deeply segmented pale-green leaves and fragrant yellow single flowers. 'Chromatella' and 'L'Esperance' are hybrids between this species and *P. suffruticosa* with double or semi-double yellow flowers. *P. suffruticosa* (*P. moutan*), moutan or tree peony, also native to China, grows to 8.0ft (2.5m) with large bluish-pink flowers up to 7in (18cm) across.   S.R.C.

CROSSOSOMATACEAE

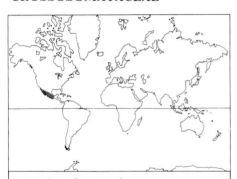

Number of genera: 1
Number of species: 4
Distribution: southern N America.
Economic uses: limited use as ornamentals.

The Crossosomataceae is a small family of New World shrubs with conspicuous white or purplish flowers.
Distribution. The family comprises the single genus *Crossosoma* of four species, restricted to dry habitats in the southwest United States of America and Mexico.
Diagnostic features. The shrubs are glabrous and sometimes spiny. The leaves are simple, alternate, without stipules and more or less glaucous, sometimes deciduous or retained whilst dead (ie marcescent, like the leaves of seedling beech trees). The flowers are superficially very like those of the Dilleniaceae. They are solitary, regular and bisexual, with five sepals, five petals and numerous stamens. The ovary is superior, with three to six carpels, each with a short style, capitate stigma and numerous ovules. The fruit is a stalked dehiscent follicle of many seeds,

which have conspicuous fringed arils, thin endosperm and a slightly curved embryo.
Classification. The absence of stipules and the presence of other characters have suggested to some that *Crossosoma* is allied to the subfamily Spiraeoideae of the Rosaceae, but the family is usually allied to Dilleniaceae particularly on the basis of seed characters, and has been included in it by some workers.
Economic uses. Some species are cultivated for ornament in sunny situations in Europe.
                                          D.J.M.

THEALES

THEACEAE
Tea, Camellias and Franklinia

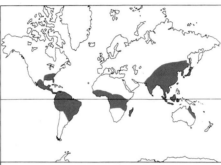

Number of genera: about 29
Number of species: about 1,100
Distribution: tropical and subtropical, centered in America and Asia.
Economic uses: tea (*Camellia sinensis*), tea-seed oil (*C. sasanqua*), timber and ornamentals (camellias).

The Theaceae, formerly called the Ternstroemiaceae by some authorities, is a medium-sized family of trees and shrubs, rarely scrambling vines. The former type genus *Thea*, now merged in the older name *Camellia*, includes the economically important tea plant, *Camellia sinensis*.
Distribution. The family is mainly restricted to tropical and subtropical regions, and centered chiefly in America and Asia.
Diagnostic features. The leaves are alternate (rarely opposite), often evergreen and leathery, and usually without stipules. The flowers are regular, usually bisexual, generally solitary but occasionally in a branched inflorescence, and are often very showy; there are four to seven sepals and petals while there may be four, eight or, more generally, numerous stamens which may be free or in bundles or united into a tube. The ovary is superior (rarely inferior or semi-inferior) and has three to five (rarely two or eight to 25) fused carpels and a corresponding number of locules, each of which contains two to numerous ovules (rarely one) on axile placentas. There are as many styles as locules, free or united (rarely a single style). The fruit is a capsule, berry or achene with the sepals persistent at the base. The

seed usually has little or no endosperm and a straight or curved embryo which may be folded or spirally twisted.
Classification. As described here the family comprises about 29 genera and almost 1,100 species. However, many authorities have split it into a number of small families. In its narrowest sense (16 genera and 500 species) it comprises two tribes:
CAMELLIEAE. Anthers versatile and the fruit usually a loculicidal capsule; chief genera *Camellia*, *Gordonia*, *Stewartia*.
TERNSTROEMIEAE. Anthers basifixed and the fruit a berry or achene; chief genera *Ternstroemia*, *Adinandra*, *Eurya* (in *Annesleya* and *Visnea* the ovary is semi-inferior, while in *Symplococarpon* it is inferior).

The small families now generally accepted as being included within the Theaceae are:
ASTEROPEIACEAE (one genus, seven species, Madagascar). Stamens nine to 15, ovary of three (rarely two) carpels, ovules two to numerous in each locule, style single.
BONNETIACEAE (three genera, 22 species, tropical Asia and America). Stamens numerous, ovary of three to five carpels, ovules numerous in each locule, styles three to five.
PELLICIERACEAE (one genus, one species, tropical America). Stamens five, ovary of two carpels, one ovule in each locule, style single.
PENTAPHYLACACEAE (one genus, two species, Southeast Asia). Stamens five, ovary of five carpels, two ovules in each locule, style single.
TETRAMERISTICACEAE (one genus, three species, Malaysia). Stamens four, ovary of four carpels, one ovule in each locule, style single.

More debatable is the inclusion of the following families:
MEDUSAGYNACEAE (one genus, one species, Seychelles). Leaves opposite or whorled, stamens numerous, ovary of 17–25 carpels, two ovules in each locule, styles 17–25.
STACHYURACEAE (one genus, 10 species, eastern Asia). Leaves with stipules, stamens eight, ovary of four carpels, numerous ovules in each locule, style single.
CARYOCARACEAE (two genera, 25 species, tropical America). Leaves opposite or alternate with stipules, stamens numerous, ovary of four or eight to 20 carpels, ovules solitary in each locule, styles four to 20.
SYMPLOCACEAE (two genera, 500 species, tropics and subtropics, except Africa). Corolla of five or ten petals, stamens five, 10, 15 or more numerous, ovary inferior or semi-inferior, of two to five carpels, ovules two to four in each locule, style single. (The position of this family is the most debatable and several systems place it within the Ebenales.)

Within the Theales, the Theaceae is most closely related to the Dipterocarpaceae, Guttiferae and Marcgraviaceae, while the order Theales appears to be the stock for a number of other orders including the Capparales, Ebenales, Ericales, Malvales, Primulales and Violales.

Economic uses. *Haploclathra paniculata* yields a handsome red wood, mura piranga. The seeds of *Camellia sasanqua* yield tea-seed oil. Among the various ornaments is *Franklinia altamaha*, originally distributed over a very small area near Forth Barrington in Georgia in the southern United States of America, but now cultivated in North America and Europe. The best-known ornamentals are cultivars of *Camellia japonica*, which have long been grown in the Far East for their beautiful, often scented, flowers. They are now popular garden plants in many temperate regions, but the flowers are sensitive to frost damage.

The tea plant, *C. sinensis*, is native to Southeast Asia and has long been cultivated in China, probably at first for medicinal use, but subsequently as a beverage plant. The distinctive flavor of the stimulant beverage is due to the constituents caffeine, polyphenols and essential oils, the proportions of which vary according to the age of the leaves and the method by which they are processed after picking. Tea is used by about half of the world's population. The chief producers are India and Sri Lanka, with East Africa, Japan, Indonesia and Russia next. B.S.F.

OCHNACEAE
African Oak and Ochnas

The Ochnaceae is a large tropical family of trees, shrubs and some herbs which includes a number of hothouse ornamentals.

Distribution. The family is pantropical with the greatest concentration of genera and species in tropical South America.

Diagnostic features. The family has alternate, simple leaves with stipules (*Godoya splendida* is an exception with large pinnate leaves). Regular, bisexual flowers are borne in panicles, racemes or false umbels. The calyx is free or united at the base. The corolla has five, rarely 10–12, contorted petals. The five or ten or numerous stamens are hypogynously arranged or on an elongated axis. The ovary is superior, of two to five (rarely 10–15) carpels which are often free below, but have a common style. There are one or two or numerous erect (rarely pendulous) ovules in each carpel. The axis of some genera swells and becomes fleshy under the fruit, which is usually a cluster of drupes, or sometimes a berry or capsule. The seed may or may not contain endosperm and the embryo is usually straight.

Classification. The major genera are distin-

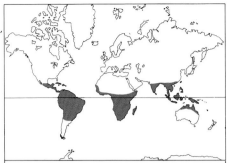

Number of genera: about 40
Number of species: about 600
Distribution: tropical, chiefly S America.
Economic uses: timber (African oaks), hothouse and tropical garden ornamentals (*Ochna* and *Cespedesia*).

guished mainly on floral characters. *Ochna* (85 species of deciduous trees) has an indefinite number of stamens with filaments as long or longer than the anthers and a three- to 15-carpelled ovary with numerous ovules in each carpel. The genus has a characteristic colored calyx which does not enlarge in fruit as in some members of the

Theaceae. 1 *Camellia rosiflora* flowering shoot (×⅔). 2 *C. japonica* cv 'Kimberley' half flower with semi-inferior ovary and numerous stamens, united at their bases (×⅔). 3 *C. salicifolia* (a) gynoecium with three-lobed stigma (×4); (b) cross section of trilocular ovary (×6); (c) stamens with fused filaments (×3); (d) stamen (×4); (e) fruit—a capsule (×2). 4 *Symplocarpon hintonii* (a) half flower showing inferior ovary (×6); (b) dry indehiscent fruit (×1). 5 *Eurya macartneyi* (a) leafy shoot with female flowers (×⅔); (b) female flower (×6); (c) male flower (×6); (d) epipetalous stamens with lengthwise dehiscence (×12). 6 *E. japonica* fruit—a berry.

family and is a brilliant red or purple. The petals are greenish yellow. Each carpel forms a drupe, the receptacle becoming fleshy beneath it. *Ouratea* (300 mostly South American evergreen tree and shrub species) has only 10 stamens, with filaments shorter than the anthers, and a five-lobed ovary. Most species have yellow flowers, and fruit consisting of five or fewer drupes borne sessile on an enlarged disk. *Euthemis* (two Asian species) has five stamens and five staminodes; the ovary comprises four or five locules with only one or two ovules in each locule. *Godoya*, a genus of trees, is represented by five species from Peru and Columbia, with pure white fragrant flowers. *Sauvagesia* comprises 30 species of chiefly South American herbs and shrubs, with ciliate stipules and white, pink or purple flowers with convolute petals and five fertile stamens surrounded by numerous staminodes.

The Ochnaceae is most closely related to the Dipterocarpaceae.

Economic uses. The family includes few plants of economic value. The only genus with commercial timber is *Lophira*, whose two species, *Lophira alata* and *L. lanceolata*, are both commonly called the African oak,

meni oil tree or red iron tree. Plants cultivated in tropical gardens and in hothouses in temperate zones include *Ochna kibbiensis* and *O. flava*, *Sauvagesia erecta* (the West Indian iron shrub), *Cespedesia bonplandii* and *C. discolor*. S.A.H.

DIPTEROCARPACEAE

The Dipterocarpaceae is a family of small to very lofty trees which dominate the lowland rain forests of Asia and which are among the grandest in the tropics and a major source of hardwood. (See also p. 834.)

Distribution. Concentrated in Malaya, Indonesia, Borneo and Palawan, the family is distributed throughout tropical Asia and Indomalaysia, with two genera in tropical Africa. Many species are gregarious; in the monsoon region of India and Burma there are vast forests comprised almost entirely of a single species, such as *Shorea robusta* or *Dipterocarpus tuberculatus*, while the moist evergreen forests of Malaysia are dominated by members of this family. (See p. 878.)

Diagnostic features. Dipterocarps tend to share a characteristic shape: the trunk is buttressed at the base and then rises, often to a great height, smooth and unbranched, before reaching the open, cauliflower-

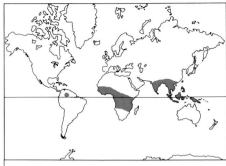

Number of genera: about 15
Number of species: about 580
Distribution: centered in tropical rain forests of Malaysia.
Economic uses: the world's main source of hardwood timber.

shaped crown. Except in African species, all parts of the plant contain special resin canals and most species exude an oily aromatic resin called dammar from wounds.

The leaves are simple, entire and alternate, and subtended by stipules, although these often fall early on. The flowers are regular, bisexual, usually borne in racemes, and are adapted for insect pollination, being large, showy and often scented. The calyx and

Ochnaceae. 1 *Luxemburgia ciliosa* (a) leaf ($\times\frac{2}{3}$); (b) flower ($\times 1$); (c) fruit ($\times 1$); (d) cross section of fruit ($\times 2$). 2 *Ochna atropurpurea* (a) flowering shoot ($\times\frac{2}{3}$); (b) stamen with apical pores on anthers ($\times 8$); (c) fruit—a cluster of drupes on a fleshy receptacle, with a persistent colorful calyx ($\times 1$); (d) gynoecium ($\times 6$). 3 *Ouratea intermedia* (a) leafy shoot with terminal inflorescence ($\times\frac{2}{3}$); (b) flower with cluster of ten stamens ($\times 2$); (c) flower with perianth removed to show stamens (with filaments much shorter than anthers) and gynoecium ($\times 4$).

corolla each consist of five parts which may be free or connate at the base. The stamens vary in number from five to many, and the anthers are distinctive in having a sterile tip. The ovary is superior of three carpels; it has three locules, each with two pendulous ovules. Only one ovule develops, the fruit being a single-seeded nut enclosed in the persistent winged and membranous calyx. The seed has no endosperm.

Classification. The Dipterocarpaceae is divided into two subfamilies: MONOTOIDEAE (all African species) and DIPTERO-CARPOIDEAE (all Asian species). However, a new species of an undescribed genus and subfamily has recently been discovered in the highlands of South America.

The Dipterocarpaceae is related to members of the Theales, especially the Ochnaceae, Guttiferae and Theaceae.

Economic uses. Many closely related species of several genera (principally *Dipterocarpus*, *Hopea*, *Shorea* and *Vatica*) grow together in mixed dipterocarp rain forests. These forests are the world's main source of hardwood timber. However, they are doomed largely to disappear by the end of the century unless present conservation and replanting programs are invigorated and extended. Dip-terocarp timber can be grouped for sale into a few grades, which immeasurably assists marketing. Clear cylindrical boles of 65ft–98ft (20m–30m) length and girths of 6.5ft–13ft (2m–4m) are common. The wood is light in weight and pale in color and therefore in great demand in modern conditions. Much is processed into plywood either locally or in Korea and Japan. The principal market is North America. Minor products are the resin (damar) used for special varnishes; and a substitute for cocoa butter from Bornean *Shorea* species.

GUTTIFERAE
Mangosteen and Mammey Apple

The Guttiferae is a large cosmopolitan family of trees and shrubs many of which produce timber, drugs, dyes and fruits.

Distribution. The family is almost worldwide in distribution, although only *Hypericum* (widespread) and *Triadenum* (Asia and North America) occur outside the tropics.

Diagnostic features. Most members have simple, usually opposite, entire leaves without stipules. The flowers may be bisexual or unisexual and borne on separate plants, and single or grouped in a cymose or thyrsoid inflorescence. The perianth most often has

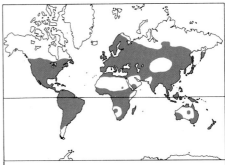

Number of genera: about 40
Number of species: about 1,000
Distribution: cosmopolitan, but centered in the tropics.
Economic uses: timber, fruits (mangosteen, mammey apple), drugs and gums, and cosmetics from essential oils.

whorls in five or four parts, usually of distinct sepals and petals, the latter being free and either imbricate or contorted when in bud. The androecium consists basically of two whorls, each of five stamen-bundles with filaments free almost to the base; the outer antisepalous whorl is usually sterile and may be absent, whereas the inner whorl is always fertile (except in female flowers), modified by

Dipterocarpaceae. 1 *Shorea ovalis*, tree in leaf. 2 *Monoporandra elegans* (a) leafy twig with fruit and inflorescence (×⅔); (b) flower dissected to show sepal (left), petals and gynoecium in vertical section (center), and stamens fused at the base and anthers with long connectives (right) (×6); (c) cross section of ovary (×6). The fruits are often enclosed in winged extensions of the calyx; shown here are 3 *Dipterocarpus incanus* (×⅔), 4 *Doona ovalifolia* (×1½) and 5 *Monentes tomentellus* (×⅔). 6 *Dipterocarpus oblongifolia* vertical section of single-seeded fruit (×1).

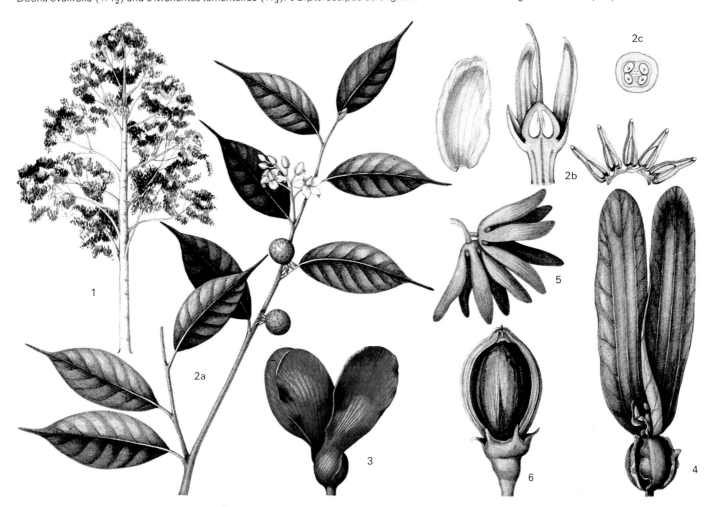

fusion or reduction to form masses of united anthers or more or less numerous apparently free stamens. (In *Hypericum gentianoides* each stamen bundle is often reduced to a single stamen.) The ovary is superior and consists of usually five to three, rarely two or up to 13, united carpels and one to many locules, each containing one to many ovules on axile or parietal placentas. There are as many stigmas as placentas, and the styles may be free, united or totally lacking. The fruit is usually a capsule (usually dehiscing lengthwise along the compartment walls) but may be berry- or drupe-like. The seeds, sometimes winged or with an aril, lack endosperm and usually have a straight embryo with cotyledons either well-developed or reduced and replaced in function by a swollen hypocotyl.

Glandular secretions are produced in canals or lacunae within stems, leaves and floral parts. They consist of essential oils and fats, anthocyanins and resins.

Classification. The subdivision of the Guttiferae into five subfamilies is based primarily on sex-distribution, androecium, ovary, fruit and seeds. Hypericoideae has often been treated as a separate family

Hypericaceae; but this segregation does not appear to be warranted unless each subfamily is similarly treated, for they are all quite distinct.

KIELMEYEROIDEAE. Flowers usually bisexual, stamens "free," styles elongate and wholly united; the many seeds without an aril, the embryo with thin free cotyledons; includes *Kielmeyera, Mahurea, Caraipa.*

HYPERICOIDEAE. Flowers bisexual, the outer stamen whorl sterile or absent, and styles elongate, free or more or less united; the fruit is normally either a capsule or a berry, rarely a drupe; the five to many seeds have no aril; the embryo has thin free cotyledons; includes *Hypericum, Cratoxylum, Vismia.*

CALOPHYLLOIDEAE. Flowers unisexual, bisexual or polygamous (male, female and bisexual on same plant); the outer stamen whorl is absent, the styles elongate and free; the fruit is capsular or usually drupaceous; the one to four seeds have no aril; the embryo is enlarged, usually with united cotyledons (including *Mesua, Calophyllum, Endodesmia*).

MORONOBEOIDEAE. Flowers bisexual, the outer androecium whorl sterile, the styles elongate, more or less united; the fruit is

berry-like, the many, or rarely solitary, seeds have no aril, and the embryo is undifferentiated; includes *Pentadesma, Montrouziera, Symphonia.*

CLUSIOIDEAE. The two tribes in Engler's treatment of this subfamily appear to be quite distinct and each may deserve subfamilial status. CLUSIEAE has flowers unisexual or rarely polygamous; the outer androecium whorl fertile or sterile; styles short and free to completely united or absent; the fruit is capsular (rarely berry-like); the five to many seeds have an aril; the embryo has an enlarged hypocotyl and vestigial or no cotyledons; includes *Clusia, Tovomita,* possibly also *Decaphalangium, Allanblackia.* GARCINIEAE has unisexual or rarely bisexual flowers; the outer androecium whorl sterile or absent; styles very short and united or usually absent; the fruit is drupaceous; the one to five (sometimes up to 13) seeds have no aril; the embryo has an enlarged hypocotyl and no cotyledons; includes *Garcinia, Mammea.*

The Guttiferae is related to the Bonnetiaceae (here included within the Theaceae) and through them to the Dilleniaceae, differing from these families in having

Guttiferae. 1 *Symphonia globulifera* (a) leafy shoot and terminal inflorescence ($\times\frac{2}{3}$); (b) androecium, comprising tube of fused stamens, surrounding a five-lobed stigma ($\times 3$); (c) fruit—a berry ($\times 1\frac{1}{3}$). 2 *Hypericum calycinum* (a) shoot with decussate leaves and terminal solitary flower ($\times\frac{2}{3}$); (b) half flower with stamens in bundles and numerous ovules on axile placentas ($\times 1$); (c) fruit—a capsule ($\times 1$). 3 *H. frondosum* cross section of ovary showing single locule with ovules on three parietal placentas ($\times 3$). 4 *Calophyllum inophyllum* (a) shoot with inflorescences in axils of terminal leaves ($\times\frac{2}{3}$); (b) gynoecium showing long, curved style ($\times 4$); (c) stamen ($\times 4$).

glandular secretions, leaves usually opposite and petals usually contorted in bud. It may also be related to the Myrtaceae.

Economic uses. The Guttiferae have been used as a source of: hard and/or durable wood (species of *Cratoxylum*, *Mesua*, *Calophyllum*, *Montrouziera*, *Platonia*); easily worked wood (species of *Harungana*, *Calophyllum*); drugs or dyes from bark (species of *Vismia*, *Psorospermum*, *Harungana*, *Calophyllum*); gums, pigments and resins from stems (including species of *Garcinia*, gamboge, and *Clusia*, healing gums); drugs from leaves (species of *Hypericum*, *Harungana madagascariensis*); drugs and cosmetics from flowers (*Mesua ferrea*); edible fruits (species of *Garcinia* including *Garcinia mangostana*, mangosteen, and of *Mammea* including *Mammea americana*, mammey apple; *Platonia insignis*); fats and oils from seeds (species of *Calophyllum*, *Pentadesma*, *Allanblackia*, *Garcinia*, *Mammea*).

N.K.B.R.

ELATINACEAE

The Elatinaceae is a widespread family of herbs and shrub-like plants found in aquatic and semi-aquatic or dry habitats.

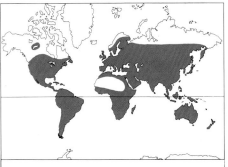

Number of genera: 2
Number of species: about 33
Distribution: cosmopolitan, centered in temperate and subtropical regions.
Economic uses: weeds in ricefields and irrigation ditches.

Distribution. The genus *Elatine* is almost cosmopolitan with the majority of species in temperate regions. *Bergia* is found throughout warmer regions of the world with a few species in temperate zones.

Diagnostic features. The species of Elatinaceae are annual or perennial herbs or occasionally somewhat woody shrub-like plants. The leaves are opposite and decussate in all species except *Elatine alsinastrum* which has leaves in whorls. A pair of small stipules is present at the base of each leaf; the leaf blade is simple and linear to ovate in shape. The flowers are bisexual, regular, either solitary in leaf axils or in cymes, and usually inconspicuous. The sepals are two to five in number and are free or united at the base. The petals are free and as many as the sepals. The ovary is superior, with two to five locules, and numerous ovules on axile placentas. The fruit dehisces septicidally (along a wall dividing compartments). The seed wall bears a characteristic complex net-like pattern. The seeds have a curved or straight embryo and very little or no endosperm.

Classification. The genus *Bergia* is characterized by having five free, acute sepals with a distinct vein or midrib and flowers in dense clusters. Of the 20 species about half are aquatic or semiaquatic while the other species grow in dry regions. The species of *Bergia* are robust and conspicuous while those of *Elatine* are small and inconspicuous. *Elatine* has two to four sepals which are united at the base, obtuse at the apex and without a distinct vein. Most species are

Elatinaceae. 1 *Bergia ammannioides* (a) habit (×⅔); (b) inflorescences in axils of leaves (×1⅓); (c) flower viewed from above with three each of sepals, petals and stamens and a four-lobed ovary (×8); (d) dehiscing capsule with seeds exposed (×20); (e) cross section of fruit (×20). 2 *B. capensis* (a) part of creeping stem with adventitious roots (×⅔); (b) fruit (×20). 3 *Elatine hydropiper* (a) habit showing long adventitious roots (×⅔); (b) solitary flower in leaf axil (×4); (c) flower with four sepals and petals, eight stamens and globose, superior ovary (×8); (d) dehiscing fruit (×8); (e) curved seed (×20).

adapted to fluctuating water levels and are found in shallow water that seasonally dries out. They are particularly common in ricefields and periodically drained fishponds.

The Elatinaceae has been little studied and its relationship to other families is not clear. It shows similarities with the Guttiferae, Frankeniaceae, Lythraceae and Haloragaceae.

Economic uses. *Elatine* is usually considered beneficial as it effectively consolidates mud. However, *Elatine* and *Bergia* are frequently found as weeds in ricefields and irrigation ditches.   C.D.C.

QUIINACEAE

The Quiinaceae is a family of little-known trees and large shrubs native to the tropical forests of South America and the West Indies.

The leaves are opposite or in whorls, simple or pinnately divided, with a smooth satiny texture. Stipules are present, in one to four pairs at the nodes. The flowers are small, bisexual or sometimes unisexual, in racemes or panicles, with four or five sepals and four or five or eight petals; there are 15–20 or many (160–170) stamens; the ovary is superior, has three, or seven to 11, locules,

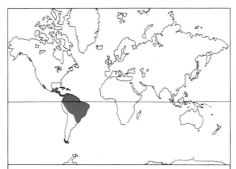

Number of genera: 4
Number of species: 52
Distribution: tropical S America.
Economic uses: none, but potentially useful as timber.

with the same number of long curving styles each with an oblique stigma; each locule contains two ovules. The fruit is a single berry with one to four seeds, or three separate carpels each with one seed; the seed has no endosperm and the seed coat is often velvety.

Quiina is the largest genus, with 35 species. The other genera are *Touroulia* (four species), *Lacunaria* (11 species) and *Froesia* (two

species). There are some similarities between the Quiinaceae and Guttiferae and Ochnaceae, but the relationships between the families are not well defined.

The heartwood of some species could prove to be a useful timber but at present is of no economic importance.   S.W.J.

MARCGRAVIACEAE

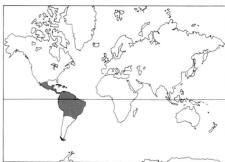

Number of genera: 5
Number of species: about 125
Distribution: tropical America.
Economic uses: none.

The Marcgraviaceae is a family of tropical climbers with a number of interesting

Marcgraviaceae. 1 *Marcgravia umbellata* (a) climbing stem with juvenile foliage and adventitious roots ($\times\frac{2}{3}$); (b) nectar cup ($\times\frac{2}{3}$); (c) flower with petals united into deciduous cap ($\times 2$). 2 *M. exauriculata* (a) tip of shoot with adult leaves and inflorescence ($\times\frac{2}{3}$); (b) young flower ($\times 1\frac{1}{3}$). 3 *Norantea peduncularis* flower and nectar cup ($\times\frac{2}{3}$). 4 *Ruyschia clusiifolia* (a) flower ($\times 2$); (b) stamen ($\times 4$); (c) fruit ($\times 1\frac{1}{3}$). 5 *Souroubea* sp cross section of ovary ($\times 3$). 6 *Marcgravia nepenthoides* (a) shoot with adult foliage and inflorescence with infertile flowers bearing conspicuous nectar cups ($\times\frac{2}{3}$); (b) half flower ($\times 1\frac{1}{3}$); (c) gynoecium ($\times 2$); (d) cross section of ovary ($\times 2$). 7 *M. affinis* half flower ($\times 1\frac{1}{3}$).

features including highly modified nectaries.

Distribution. The family is restricted to tropical America.

Diagnostic features. Members of the family are climbing shrubs, often epiphytic. The leaves are simple, often leathery, and without stipules. In some genera (including *Marcgravia* and *Norantea*) the climbing shoots bear different leaves from the mature shoots (dimorphic foliage). The flowers are bisexual and borne in pendulous racemes or racemose umbels, with the bracts of sterile flowers modified into variously shaped pitchers which secrete nectar. The flowers have four or five imbricate sepals, and five free, or fused petals forming a cap which falls off when the flower opens (*Marcgravia*). There are three to many stamens which are free or variously fused. The ovary is superior and has at first one, but later two to many, locules with multiple ovules by ingrowth of the parietal placentas. The stigma has a short style and radiates out in five lobes. The fruits are globose, fleshy and thick, often indehiscent, and contain many small seeds lacking endosperm. Each seed has a somewhat curved embryo, a large radicle and small cotyledons.

Classification. *Marcgravia*, the type-genus, commemorates Georg Marcgraaf (b.1610), an early writer on Brazilian natural history. The 55 or so species in this interesting genus are climbing epiphytes with dimorphic foliage, the climbing shoots having small, two-ranked, rounded, sessile, often reddish leaves pressed against the surface up which the shoot is climbing. Such leaves are regarded as juvenile. The stem, meanwhile, puts out adventitious roots onto this surface. With increasing age or environmental factors not yet fully understood, the mature shoot develops, the stem becoming pendulous, and the leaves change gradually to a stalked, green, leathery, lanceolate condition. Should the mature shoot be required to climb once more, the leaves switch back to the juvenile form: the process is reversible.

The mature shoot is terminated by dense racemes of green flowers with stalked pitcher-like nectaries borne at the very tip. In species such as *Marcgravia rectiflora* the inflorescence is erect, the flowers erect but nectaries hanging down; in others the inflorescence hangs down. The pollination of some species involves the visits of hummingbirds, bananaquits and todies, while others are visited by lizards and bees, and some are self-pollinated before the flower opens. Only in *Marcgravia* are there four not five sepals and the petals form a fused cap over the flower.

Ruyschia comprises 10 species, with petals slightly fused at the base, five stamens, an ovary with two locules, and trilobed solid nectaries which are globose or spoonshaped. The numerous fragrant flowers are borne in elongated racemes.

In *Norantea* (about 35 species) the stamens are often many, the nectaries spoon- or pitcher-like, the ovary with three to five locules, and the flowers borne in umbel-like clusters. *Souroubea* (about 25 species) has three to five stamens, three-lobed bracts and an ovary with five locules. *Caracasia* (two species) has three stamens and free petals and filaments.

The Marcgraviaceae is thought to be related to the Theaceae.

Economic uses. There are no known uses for this family.   B.M.

MALVALES

SCYTOPETALACEAE

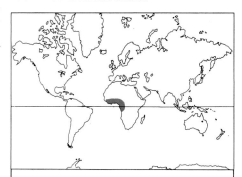

Number of genera: 5
Number of species: 20
Distribution: tropical W Africa.
Economic uses: wood used locally in house building.

The Scytopetalaceae is a small family of tropical trees and shrubs.

Distribution. The family is native to tropical West Africa.

Diagnostic features. The leaves are without stipules, alternate, often in two ranks, simple, sometimes toothed and asymmetrical at the base.

The flowers are bisexual, regular, often with long pedicels, borne either on the old woody stems or terminally (in panicles) or in the axils of leaves (in racemes) on young stems. The calyx has three or four sepals, fused into a cup-shaped structure, which is either entire or toothed. The petals are three to 16, either free or joined at the base, valvate. The petals are sometimes thick and they either become reflexed as the anthers mature, or do not separate and fall off the flower as a cap. The flower has a disk on which the numerous stamens are inserted in three to six series; the filaments are sometimes joined below; anthers dehisce by means of longitudinal slits or by apical pores. The ovary is superior, with three to eight locules and two or more pendulous ovules in each locule borne on axile placentas. The ovary is surmounted by a simple style with a small stigma.

The fruit is normally a woody capsule, but in a few cases is drupe-like. The seeds vary in number from one to eight and are sometimes covered with mucilaginous hairs. The seed contains a narrow embryo surrounded by copious endosperm which may have a rough or mottled appearance.

Classification. The five genera, *Oubanguia*, *Scytopetalum*, *Rhaptopetalum*, *Brazzeia* and *Pierrina*, can be classified on features of inflorescence and flowers. For example, *Oubanguia* has long, lax panicles and has stamen filaments joined at the base, in contrast to the other genera which have flowers either in fascicles (close clusters) on old woody branches (*Brazzeia*) or in racemes in the axils of leaves, as in *Scytopetalum* (petals several to many and stamen filaments unequal in length) and *Rhaptopetalum* (free petals and stamen filaments all the same length).

Various affinities have been suggested for this family, notably with Tiliaceae, Sterculiaceae, Malvaceae or Olacaceae. The features that Scytopetalaceae shares with all these families are the woody habit, the alternate, simple leaves, the bisexual flowers with usually numerous stamens, sometimes partly fused, and a several-loculed ovary.

Economic uses. There are no known economic uses for this family apart from *Scytopetalum tieghemii*, a medium-sized tree reaching about 80ft (25m) in height, whose wood is resistant to decay and is used as poles for house-building in Ghana and Sierra Leone.   S.R.C.

ELAEOCARPACEAE
Crinodendrons and Aristotelias

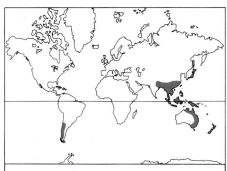

Number of genera: 12
Number of species: about 350
Distribution: tropics and subtropics.
Economic uses: limited as ornamentals and local uses of edible fruits.

The Elaeocarpaceae is a smallish family of tropical and subtropical trees and shrubs, some of which are cultivated as ornamentals.

Distribution. Members of the family are found in eastern Asia, Indomalaysia, Australasia, the Pacific area, South America and the West Indies.

Diagnostic features. The leaves are alternate or opposite, and have stipules. The flowers are regular, bisexual, borne in racemes, panicles or cymes, and have four or five sepals, free or partly united. The petals are usually free, either four or five in number or absent altogether; they are often

Elaeocarpaceae. 1 *Aristotelia racemosa* (a) shoot with axillary racemes of flowers (×⅔); (b) male flower with three-lobed petals and numerous stamens (×3); (c) gynoecium with free curled styles (×6); (d) fruits (×⅔). 2 *Elaeocarpus dentatus* (a) shoot with inflorescence (×⅔); (b) bisexual flower (×2); (c) bilocular ovary in vertical (left) and cross (right) section (×6). 3 *Muntingia calabura* half flower (×2). 4 *Sloanea jamaicensis* (a) half flower with numerous stamens having short filaments and large anthers (×1½); (b) cross section of ovary with four locules and numerous ovules on axile placentas (×3); (c) dehiscing fruit (×⅓).

fringed or lacerated at their tips. There are numerous free stamens, and the anthers have two locules which release pollen through two apical pores. The ovary is superior and contains two to many locules (rarely one only), and each locule contains two to many pendulous ovules. The style is simple and sometimes lobed at the tip. The fruit is a capsule or drupe; the seeds contain straight embryos and abundant endosperm.

Classification. The largest genus, *Elaeocarpus*, comprises about 200 species from eastern Asia, Indomalaysia, Australasia and the Pacific area. The other large genus in the family is *Sloanea*, with about 120 species of tropical Asian and American trees. It differs from *Elaeocarpus* in not having a succulent fruit, but a hard capsular one covered with rigid bristles. The best known of the small genera are *Aristotelia*, with five species from Australasia and South America, and *Crinodendron*, with two species from temperate South America.

The family is related to the Tiliaceae and to the Combretaceae and Rhizophoraceae. Also associated with the family are the Sarcolaenaceae (Chlaenaceae) and the Sphaerosepalaceae (Rhopalocarpaceae).

Economic uses. Several species of *Elaeocarpus*, *Crinodendron* and *Aristotelia* are cultivated. *Elaeocarpus reticulatus* (*E. cyaneus*), a native of Australia with cream flowers and blue drupes, and *E. dentatus* from New Zealand, with straw-colored flowers, are both known in cultivation in Europe. Better known, however, are the two ornamental evergreen species in the genus *Crinodendron*. The pendulous, urn-like, crimson flowers of *Crinodendron hookerianum*, about 1in (2.5cm) long on crimson stalks to 3in (7cm) long, are complemented by dark green narrow leaves to 4in (10cm) long. It grows to 30ft (9m) tall and is a spectacle in flower. The leaves of *C. patagua* are smaller and more oval, and the flowers white and bell-shaped. Both species are frost-tender, and require moist acid soils. The Chilean *Aristotelia chilensis* (*A. macqui*) grows to about 10ft (3m) and has insignificant green-white flowers, and black pea-sized fruits.

Aristotelia chilensis produces maqui berries which are said to have medicinal properties and are made into a local wine in Chile. The fruits and seeds of several *Elaeocarpus* species are eaten, eg *E. calomala* (Philippines), *E. dentatus* (New Zealand), *E.*

serratus (Ceylon olives). The West Indian *Sloanea berteriana* (motillo) and *S. woollsii* (gray or yellow carabeen) yield a heavy and a light timber respectively. The New Zealand *Aristotelia racemosa* and Australian *Elaeocarpus grandis* produce wood used for cabinet-making. B.M.

TILIACEAE
Limes, Lindens, Basswoods and Jute

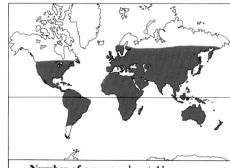

Number of genera: about 41
Number of species: about 400
Distribution: tropical with a few temperate species.
Economic uses: jute, timber and ornamental trees.

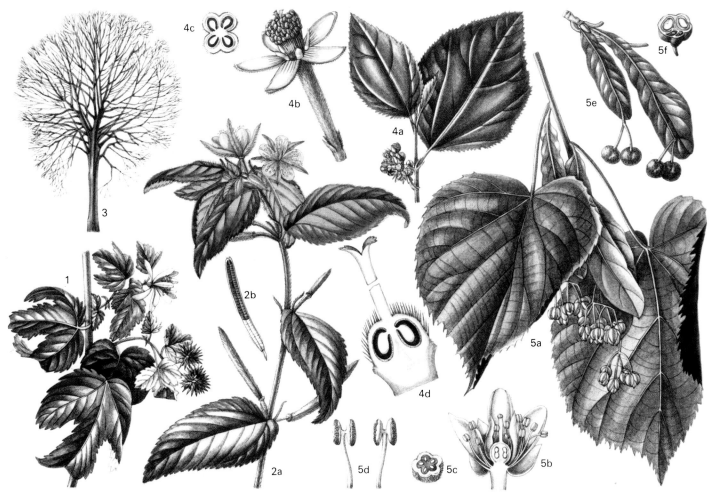

Tiliaceae. 1 *Triumfetta subpalmata* leafy shoot with flowers and fruits (×⅔). 2 *Corchorus bullatus* (a) leafy shoot with narrow stipules, flowers and fruits (×⅔); (b) fruit (a capsule) with wall removed to show seeds (×⅔). 3 *Tilia platyphyllos* leafless tree. 4 *Grewia parvifolia* (a) flowering shoot (×⅔); (b) flower with sepals fused into a tube and small free petals (×5); (c) cross section of ovary with four locules (×10); (d) vertical section of gynoecium (×15). 5 *Tilia petiolaris* (a) flowering shoot (×⅔); (b) half flower (×4); (c) cross section of ovary (×6); (d) anthers (×12); (e) fruits with persistent bract (×⅔); (f) cross section of fruit (×1½).

The Tiliaceae is a medium-sized family of tropical and temperate trees and shrubs. It includes the lindens (limes) and the economically important jute.

Distribution. This family is widely distributed throughout the tropical regions of the world, especially South America, Africa and Southeast Asia. The largest genus, *Grewia*, occurs in tropical Africa, Asia and Australasia. *Triumfetta* is an important genus of the New World tropics. *Corchorus*, the only genus which contains herbaceous species, is found in Africa and Asia, and *Sparmannia* is a tropical African genus which extends into the temperate region of the Cape of Good Hope. The genus *Tilia* also extends into temperate regions of Europe and North America.

Diagnostic features. The leaves are alternate in two ranks, both tending to lie towards the upper side of the horizontally spreading shoots which bear them. They are usually deciduous, simple and asymmetrical and have branched hairs; their bases bear small stipules. The bark is often fibrous and mucilaginous.

The flowers are borne in complex cymes in the leaf-axils, and are normally bisexual, regular, small and green, yellow or white. They often secrete scent and nectar. There are five sepals which are either free and valvate or united, and usually five free petals, with glandular hairs at their bases; in a few species the corolla may be absent. The many stamens are arranged in groups, or fascicles, of five to ten which are inserted at the bases of the petals or on an androphore. The ovary is superior with two to ten or many locules each containing one to many ovules. The style is simple with a capitate or lobed stigma.

The several-seeded fruits take various forms, from the globose, indehiscent, nutlike fruits of *Tilia* to the spheroidal, dehiscent capsules of *Corchorus* and *Sparmannia*. The seeds contain endosperm and well-differentiated, straight embryos.

Classification. The family is related to the Malvaceae from which it differs in having anthers with two locules (not one), and to the Bombacaceae and Vitaceae.

Economic uses. The genus *Tilia* contains several woodland trees which yield valuable timber. These are *Tilia cordata*, *T. × platyphyllos* and *T. vulgaris*, the European limes or lindens, *T. americana*, the American basswood, and *T. japonica*, the Japanese linden. The wood of *T. cordata* is particularly good for making furniture and musical instruments since it is easily cut and carved. Bees produce an excellent honey from lime flowers. The decorative leaves and perfumed flowers of these species have also made them popular as ornamental trees for the public squares, parks and streets of many European towns. *Sparmannia africana*, the rumslind tree, is grown in South Africa for its beautiful clusters of white flowers.

Jute is obtained from the bast fibers of *Corchorus capsularis*, grown chiefly in the Ganges-Brahmaputra delta, and to a lesser extent from *C. olitorius* grown in Africa. The leaves of *C. olitorius* are used for food in eastern Mediterranean countries. The bark of many tropical trees and shrubs in this family, such as species of *Grewia*, *Triumfetta* and *Clappertonia*, is also used as a source of fibers for rope-making. B.N.B.

STERCULIACEAE
Cocoa and Kola

The chiefly tropical family Sterculiaceae consists of soft-wooded trees and shrubs, and a few herbaceous and climbing species.

Sterculiaceae. 1 *Dombeya burgessiae* (a) inflorescence and leaf with stipules ($\times \frac{2}{3}$); (b) two outer sterile stamens (staminodes) and three fertile stamens ($\times 1\frac{1}{2}$); (c) gynoecium with five-lobed stigma ($\times 1\frac{1}{2}$); (d) cross section of ovary with five locules and ovules on axile placentas ($\times 4$). 2 *Melochia depressa* habit ($\times \frac{2}{3}$). 3 *Theobroma cacao* (a) unripe fruit cut away to show seeds—the cocoa beans of commerce ($\times \frac{2}{3}$); (b) flowers and young fruits which form on old wood ($\times \frac{2}{3}$). 4 *Cola acuminata* (a) flowering shoot ($\times \frac{2}{3}$); (b) male flower ($\times \frac{2}{3}$); (c) stamens united into a column ($\times 2$); (d) gynoecium ($\times 2$); (e) cross section of ovary ($\times 2$). 5 *Sterculia rupestris* tree in leaf.

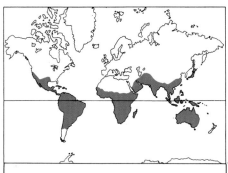

Number of genera: about 60
Number of species: about 700
Distribution: pantropical.
Economic uses: cocoa and cola, with a number of ornamental shrubs.

It includes the economically important genera *Cola* and *Theobroma* (cocoa).

Distribution. The family is pantropical, extending into subtropical regions.

Diagnostic features. The leaves are alternate, with stipules, and simple or partly divided into lobes. Many species bear star-shaped hairs on their parts. The flowers are regular and borne in complex cymes, and are bisexual or unisexual on the same plant.

There are three to five sepals more or less united, and five petals which are free or fused together by a staminal tube. The petals are often small, and occasionally absent altogether. An outer whorl of stamens is often reduced to staminodes or quite lacking, while the inner whorl bears the anthers with two locules each. The ovary is superior and with usually two to 12 carpels, rarely more, or rarely reduced to one. Each locule contains two or more ovules on axile placentas, and the style is simple or divided into lobes, or rarely free to the base. The fruits may be dry or rarely berry-like, and often dehiscent. The seeds contain fleshy, little or no endosperm and the embryo is curved or straight.

Classification. *Sterculia*, the largest genus, comprising about 300 species, derives its name from the Roman god of privies, Sterculius (Latin, *stercus* = dung), on account of the smell of the flowers and leaves of certain species. *Cola* is another large genus of about 125 African species. The 30 or 50 species of *Theobroma* are native to America. *Dombeya*, comprising some 350 species from Africa, Madagascar and the Mascarene Islands, commemorates J. Dombey

(1742–94), a French botanist who accompanied Ruíz and Pavón on their South American expedition from Spain. Other major genera include *Pterospermum* and *Reevesia*, with 40 and 15 Asian species respectively, *Firmiana* (15 species from Africa and Asia) and *Brachychiton* (11 species from Australia). The family is closely related to the Tiliaceae, Malvaceae and Bombacaceae.

Economic uses. The two economically important products from this family are cocoa (*Theobroma cacao*) and kola (*Cola nitida* and *C. acuminata*).

There are a number of ornamental genera in the family, the best-known being the attractive shrubs of the two small genera *Fremontodendron* from California and Mexico and *Abroma* from Asia and Australia. There are several attractive *Dombeya* species and hybrids: large, rounded shrubs with mallow-like flowers borne in pink or white erect or pendulous heads. *Pterospermum acerifolium* from India has remarkable large, erect, brown-felted flower buds which open lily-like to reveal a boss of stamens about 5in (12cm) long. The foliage is bold, tough and felted bronze when young, gray

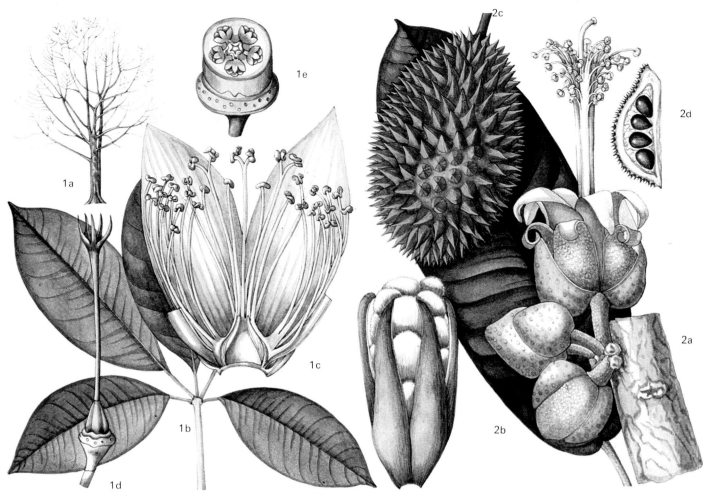

Bombacaceae. 1 *Bombax ceiba* (a) habit; (b) digitate leaf ($\times\frac{2}{3}$); (c) flower dissected to show petals and numerous bundles of stamens ($\times\frac{2}{3}$); (d) gynoecium with superior ovary, simple style and divided stigma ($\times\frac{2}{3}$); (e) cross section of ovary ($\times3$); (f) fruit with seeds embedded in hairs ($\times\frac{2}{3}$); 2 *Durio zibethinus* (a) flowers arising from old wood showing the pair of sepal-like appendages subtending the whorls of sepals and petals, and the stamens united into a tube surrounding the style ($\times\frac{2}{3}$); (b) leaf ($\times\frac{2}{3}$); (c) spined fruit (the evil smelling durian) ($\times\frac{1}{2}$); (d) vertical section of part of fruit showing seeds ($\times\frac{1}{4}$).

beneath when mature, making it a splendid specimen tree. *Reevesia thyrsoidea*, native to Hong Kong, is an evergreen shrub with scented white heads of 45–50 flowers borne at the shoot tips. *Firmiana* and *Bracychiton* species are also cultivated.   B.M.

BOMBACACEAE
Baobab, Durian and Balsa Trees

The Bombacaceae is a small family of tropical flowering trees, whose members include the well-known baobab, balsa, durian and kapok trees.

Distribution. Most species are found in South America, above all in Brazil. A few occur in Southeast Asia, and some unusual ones in Africa and Madagascar. They live mostly in dense rain forest in South America, and in open savanna and weedy habitats in Africa. (See p. 834.)

Diagnostic features. Several of the trees (eg *Adansonia digitata* – baobab, *Cavanillesia platanifolia* – Colombian ciupo, and *Chorisia* species) which have adapted to dry places have a peculiar appearance, with small apical crowns and unusually thick bottle-shaped, egg-shaped or barrel-shaped trunks – an adaptation for water storage. Many

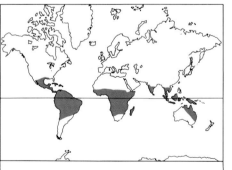

Number of genera: 20
Number of species: about 180
Distribution: tropics especially rain forests of S America.
Economic uses: baobab used locally in Africa, silk cotton tree yields kapok, and durian fruits from *Durio zibethinus*.

species are deciduous and their entire, palmate or digitate leaves and stipules are shed at the end of each rainy season. During this leafless period the flowers open. They are massive for most genera of the family, and even when small they are showy, with white or brightly colored flowers. They are always

bisexual and frequently emerge from the branches and trunks and even near the base in some tropical forest genera such as *Durio*. The calyx and corolla respectively consist of five separate sepals and petals, which are sometimes fused into a tube. The whole flower is subtended by another whorl of sepal-like appendages – the epicalyx. There are five to numerous stamens, free or joined into a tube. The ovary is superior with two to five fused carpels and many locules, with two to numerous erect ovules in each locule. The style is simple, lobed or capitate. The fruit is a capsule containing smooth seeds often with long cotton-like fibers, as in *Ceiba*, giving the kapok of commerce. The seeds have little or no endosperm.

Several species of the Old World genus *Adansonia* and their allies are pollinated by ants, and have ant colonies living within the spines of the branches, the extrafloral nectaries of the leaves, calyx and flower stalks providing a valuable food source for the ants, which protect the flowers from predators.

Classification. Important genera of the family include *Adansonia*, the kapok or silk cotton trees (*Bombax* and *Ceiba*), the

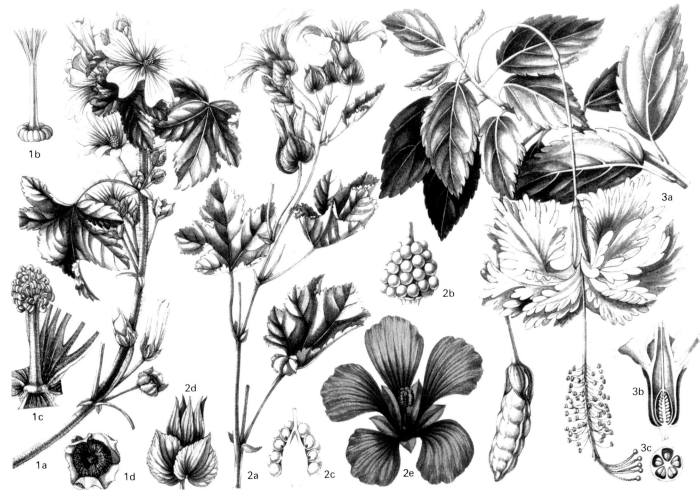

Malvaceae. 1 *Malva sylvestris* (a) flowering shoot (×⅔); (b) gynoecium (×4); (c) androecium and base of corolla (×4); (d) fruit and persistent calyx viewed from above (×1½). 2 *Malope trifida* (a) flowering shoot (×⅔); (b) young fruit with remains of styles and stigmas removed (×2); (c) vertical section of young fruit (×2); (d) ripe fruit enclosed in calyx and epicalyx (×⅔); (e) flower (×1). 3 *Hibiscus schizopetalus* (a) leafy shoot bearing flower and fruit—a capsule (×⅔); (b) vertical section of lower part of flower showing ovary containing ovules on axile placentas (×1); (c) cross section of ovary showing five locules (×2).

Southeast Asian durians (*Durio*) and the tropical South American trees of *Eriotheca*, *Chorisia*, *Cavanillesia*, *Ochroma* and *Matisia*.

The Bombacaceae is very closely related to the Malvaceae and has occasionally been placed in it, but, because it forms a group of closely related trees with smooth instead of rough pollen grains, it is kept distinct.

Economic uses. Perhaps the most important species commercially is *Ochroma pyramidale* or balsa. Other light timbers used for matchstick manufacture, boxes and veneers are obtained from various species of *Bombax*. The baobab tree plays an important role in African life. The fruit fibers of *Ceiba pentandra* and *Bombax ceiba* (*B. malabaricum*) constitute the valuable filling material kapok. The edible arils of the evil-smelling *Durio zibethinus* are the much-sought-after durian fruit of Malaya. C.J.H.

MALVACEAE
Cotton, Mallows and Hollyhocks

The Malvaceae is a cosmopolitan family of herbs, shrubs and trees. Its most important members are cotton, okra and China jute. It is also the mallow family, producing many popular garden plants, including the holly-

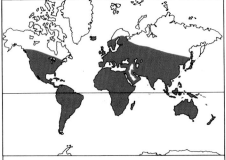

Number of genera: about 80
Number of species: over 1,000
Distribution: cosmopolitan, but centered in S America.
Economic uses: fiber crops (cotton, China jute, aramina), fruits (okra) and ornamentals (mallows, hollyhock).

hock (*Althaea*), mallows (*Malva*) and *Hibiscus*.

Distribution. Members of this family occur over most of the world, except the very cold regions, and are particularly abundant in tropical South America. *Hibiscus* is the largest genus with some 300 species widely distributed, although most are tropical; *Hibiscus trionum* and *H. roseus* are the only

European species. *Abutilon* is basically tropical and *Lavatera* Mediterranean. *Althaea* is cosmopolitan in temperate and warm regions, *Althaea rosea* being the garden hollyhock native to the eastern Mediterranean. *Malva* itself comes from north temperate regions.

Diagnostic features. The leaves are alternate, with stipules; often stellate hairs are present. The flowers are bisexual and regular, with parts usually in fives. The calyx is composed of five sometimes joined sepals, and is often subtended by an epicalyx. This has been interpreted both as fused bracteoles and as stipules. The corolla consists of five free petals, usually convolute. The numerous stamens are monadelphous, that is united below into a tube basally joined to the corolla. Division of the filaments has resulted in the anthers being unilocular. The ovary is superior and composed of five or more fused carpels with axile placentation. The style is branched. The fruit is dry, capsular or schizocarpic, except in *Malvaviscus* where it is a berry. The seeds are often covered in fine hairs, which may be tufted, as in *Gossypium*. They have little or no endosperm and a straight or curved embryo.

Classification. The classification of the Malvaceae poses many problems, and opinions differ as to delimitation of genera and tribes. Most modern treatments recognize five tribes:

MALOPEAE. Carpels in two or more superposed or spirally arranged whorls; *Malope*, *Palaua* and *Kitaibelia*.

HIBISCEAE. Fruit a capsule, the carpels persistent; *Hibiscus* and *Gossypium*.

MALVEAE. Fruit a schizocarp and stigmas decurrent on the style-branches; *Malva*, *Malvastrum*, *Lavatera*, *Althaea*, *Sidalcea*, and *Hoheria*.

ABUTILEAE. Fruit a schizocarp and stigmas apical or nearly so; *Abutilon*, *Sphaeralcea*, *Modiola*, and *Sida*.

URENEAE. Style-branches and stigmas twice as many as carpels; *Malvaviscus*, *Pavonia* and *Urena*.

The Malopeae with the carpels in two or more superposed or spirally arranged whorls is the most primitive tribe. All other members have carpels in a single whorl. Hibisceae, Malveae and Abutileae have equal numbers of style-branches or stigmas and carpels, but the tribe Ureneae, possibly the most recently evolved, has style-branches twice the number of carpels.

The Malvaceae is related to the Tiliaceae, but differs in the possession of one-celled anthers and monadelphous stamens. It probably represents a climax group derived from ancestral woody Tiliaceous stock.

Economic uses. *Gossypium* provides cotton and is by far the most important genus of the whole family. The young fruits of *Hibiscus esculentus* are known as okra, a common vegetable in warm climates. Several species yield tough fibers, notably *Abutilon avicennae* (China jute) and *Urena lobata* (aramina). *Abutilon*, *Althaea*, *Hibiscus*, *Lavatera*, *Malope*, *Malva*, *Malvastrum*, *Pavonia*, *Sida* and *Sidalcea* species are among those grown as ornamentals.   S.L.J.

SPHAEROSEPALACEAE

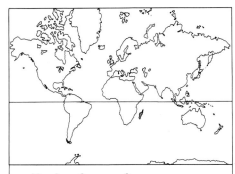

Number of genera: 2
Number of species: 14
Distribution: Madagascar.
Economic uses: none.

The Sphaerosepalaceae (Rhopalocarpaceae) is a small family of trees and shrubs native to Madagascar. The leaves are simple and possess stipules. The flowers are regular,

bisexual, in terminal and axillary panicles or cymes, with four or six unequal sepals, and four (rarely three) petals. Sepals and petals are imbricate. The stamens are numerous with slender filaments which are more or less joined at the base: the anthers have two widely separated locules. A single style rises between the two lobes of the ovary which is superior and comprises two (rarely three) united carpels partly sunk in a large cup-like disk. There are two locules each with about three erect, anatropous, basal ovules. The one- or two-seeded fruit is round or didymous, covered in short, stout spines. The seeds have a more or less ruminate endosperm and a minute embryo.

Rhopalocarpus has 13 species, *Dialyceras*, the only other genus, one. It has been suggested that the family is related to Thymelaeaceae, resembling particularly the tropical Asian *Gonystylus* in its leaves and flowers. *Gonystylus* differs, however, in having no stipules, five valvate sepals and petals, and a disk outside rather than inside the stamens; it also differs in many features of the fruit. Others have allied the family to the Malvaceae or to the Sarcolaenaceae, which is also restricted to Madagascar. Sometimes the family is submerged in the Cochlospermaceae or allied to the Guttiferae or Flacourtiaceae. No economic uses are known.   D.J.M.

SARCOLAENACEAE

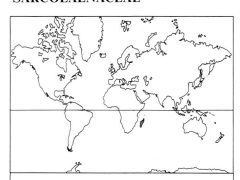

Number of genera: 8
Number of species: 39
Distribution: eastern Madagascar.
Economic uses: wood used locally in house-building.

The Sarcolaenaceae (Chlaenaceae) is a small family of beautiful trees mostly restricted to the rain forest of eastern Madagascar; the forests of the western slopes of the high plateaus were dominated by them until they were destroyed by persistent burning and replaced by *Heteropogon* grassland. The trees have simple alternate leaves with stipules, regular, often showy flowers with three to five sepals, five or six large petals, sometimes a disk, five to ten or many stamens and a superior ovary of one to five united carpels containing one to five locules with few to several anatropous basal, apical or axile ovules in each locule. The fruit is a

many-seeded capsule or single-seeded and indehiscent, often surrounded by woody bracts. The seeds have a straight embryo and fleshy or horny endosperm.

The largest genera are *Sarcolaena* (10 species), *Leptolaena* (12 species) and *Schizolaena* (7 species). The family is usually allied with the Malvaceae with which it shares mucilage cells in the pith, though the petiole structure suggests some closer relationship with the Dipterocarpaceae, from which it differs in having no resin canals; the pollen is unlike that of any of these families or their allies, however, and although it is included here doubtfully in the Malvales, the Sarcolaenaceae is possibly more allied to the Theaceae in the order Theales.

Apart from local use of the wood of *Leptolaena pauciflora* in house-building, no uses are recorded.   D.J.M.

URTICALES

ULMACEAE
Elms and Hackberries

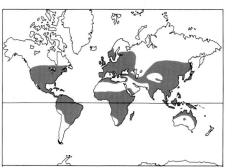

Number of genera: 16
Number of species: about 2,000
Distribution: two groups, north temperate, and tropical and subtropical.
Economic uses: major source of superior hardwood timber and valued ornamental trees.

The Ulmaceae is a family of tropical and temperate trees and shrubs whose best-known members are the elms.

Distribution. The two tribes into which the Ulmaceae are customarily divided have different patterns of distribution. The Ulmeae are mainly a north temperate group, one genus, *Ulmus*, occurring in all three northern continents, while the other genera are less wide-ranging, such as *Hemiptelea* and *Pteroceltis* in China, and *Planera* in North America. *Holoptelea* has a disjunct distribution in peninsular India and West Africa. The Celtideae are mainly tropical or subtropical, with *Celtis* also represented in temperate regions. *Trema* occurs throughout the tropics; three of the smaller genera are restricted to tropical Asia and the Malaysian regions, three to tropical and subtropical America, and one to Africa.

Diagnostic features. All members of the family are trees or shrubs. The leaves are usually alternate and simple, with stipules that are shed as the leaves unfold. The flowers may be either bisexual or unisexual; they are typically green and inconspicuous and borne in clusters. There is a calyx at the base of which the stamens arise, usually one stamen opposite each calyx-lobe; petals are absent. The ovary is superior (rudimentary in the male flowers) of two carpels usually forming one locule (rarely two) with a single pendulous ovule. There are two styles with the stigmatic surface on inner face. The fruit is a nut, samara or drupe, containing a single seed with a straight embryo and little or no endosperm. The anatomy of the wood is variable. Several genera include species in which the vessels are arranged in wavy concentric bands, the so-called ulmiform pattern. Chemically, the family is distinguished more by the absence of diagnostic substances than by their presence. Leucoanthocyanins are, however, usually present.

Classification. The Ulmaceae is divided into two tribes: the ULMEAE with pinnately veined leaves and the flat seeds without endosperm, and the CELTIDEAE which includes species with both pinnately veined leaves and, more typically, leaves having three main veins

diverging from the base; the seeds are usually rounded and with at least some endosperm. The principal genera of the Ulmeae are *Holoptelea*, *Planera*, *Ulmus* and *Zelkova*, and of the Celtideae, *Aphananthe*, *Celtis*, *Gironniera* and *Trema*.

The Ulmaceae are similar in basic floral structure to the large families Moraceae and Urticaceae. The former differs in the presence of milky latex, the latter in its generally herbaceous habit. Also possibly related is the family Eucommiaceae.

Economic uses. The economic significance of the family is mainly in its timber. Most species of *Ulmus* produce a superior timber with a distinctive patterned grain. It is much used for furniture-making and for posts. The timber is resistant to decay under waterlogged conditions and is used for underwater piles. Some species of *Aphananthe*, *Celtis*, *Holoptelea*, *Trema* and *Zelkova* also produce good timber. The leaves of some *Celtis* species and formerly of *Ulmus* have been used as a forage. Coarse fibers from the inner bark of species of *Celtis*, *Trema* and *Ulmus* are in local use. The only edible fruits of any consequence are those borne by *Celtis* (hackberries). The principal

medicinal product is the mucilaginous inner bark of *Ulmus rubra*, the slippery elm.

R.H.R.

MORACEAE
Fig, Hemp and Mulberries
The Moraceae is an economically important and scientifically interesting family of mainly tropical and subtropical trees and shrubs.

Distribution. The family is widely distributed in the tropics, subtropics and some temperate regions of both hemispheres.

Diagnostic features. All are trees or shrubs except *Cannabis*, *Dorstenia* and *Humulus*. The character which distinguishes them most clearly from related families is the presence of milky sap containing latex. Latex production begins in the embryo and continues throughout the plant's life, yet despite its apparent importance its function is still unknown. The leaves are alternate, spiral or opposite, entire or lobed, the margins entire or toothed. Stipules are present. Throughout the family the flowers are unisexual, borne on the same or separate plants, small, with four perianth segments (five in *Cannabis* and *Humulus*), and are arranged in heads on flattened or hollowed

Ulmaceae. 1 *Ulmus campestris* (a) habit; (b) leafy shoot (×⅔); (c) flowering shoot (×⅔); (d) flower with calyx, no petals, five stamens and two styles (×8); (e) anther posterior (right) and anterior (left) view (×24); (f) gynoecium crowned by two styles with stigmas on inner faces (×12); (g) winged fruit (×1). 2 *Trema orientalis* (a) leafy shoot with flowers (×⅔); (b) fruit (×6). 3 *Celtis integrifolia* (a) male flower with five stamens and hairy vestige of ovary (×6); (b) bisexual flower with five stamens and gynoecium crowned by two styles forked at apices (×4); (c) vertical section of ovary with single pendulous ovule (×4).

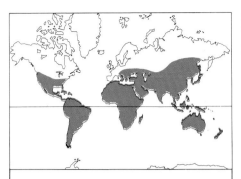

Number of genera: 75
Number of species: about 3,000.
Distribution: centered in tropics and subtropics but some temperate.
Economic uses: important fruits (figs, mulberries, breadfruit), fiber crops (hemp), narcotic drugs (cannabis) and hops.

receptacles or in catkins. A solitary flower is found in only one genus, *Chlorophora*. In *Cannabis* and *Humulus* female flowers are surrounded by large, persistent bracts. The male flower has four stamens, rarely one or two, and five in *Cannabis* and *Humulus*. The female flower has two carpels of which one is usually abortive, the style remaining. The ovary contains a single pendulous ovule. Within the Moraceae can be seen a transition from a superior ovary to an inferior ovary. For example, *Artocarpus* has a superior ovary whereas *Castilla* has an inferior ovary. Intermediate states can clearly be seen in related genera. The same trend is repeated in other parts of the family.

The infructescences are remarkably variable and the ripe fruit is often fleshy and edible. The fleshy parts are produced not by the ovary but by the swollen receptacle in which the seeds are embedded, eg *Ficus*, *Artocarpus, Morus*. Sometimes the fruit is an achene, covered by persistent perianth segments, eg *Humulus*, *Cannabis*. The seed is with or without endosperm.

Classification. The most important scheme of classification is based on inflorescence types, and divides the family into six tribes. The Moraceae has been included in the Urticaceae, but the latter can readily be distinguished from the Moraceae by the single style and stigma, basal ovule and clear sap (two styles, apical ovule and milky sap in Moraceae). However, the boundary between the two families is not entirely clear, because there are some transitional genera which do not produce latex but still possess latex ducts. *Cannabis* and *Humulus* are often considered to be a distinct family (Cannabaceae), differing most notably from the Moraceae by their five floral parts instead of four.

Economic uses. Most important are the fig (*Ficus*), mulberry (*Morus*) and breadfruit or jackfruit (*Artocarpus*). Other useful fruits come from species of *Brosimum* (breadnut) and *Pseudolmedia* (bastard breadnut). *Cannabis sativa* provides hemp fiber and narcotic drugs. Hops (*Humulus lupulus*) are cultivated for their use in brewing, giving the characteristic bitter taste to beer. *Castilloa elastica* (Panama rubber) and some species of *Ficus* were formerly used as latex sources in rubber manufacture. Useful timbers include osage orange (*Maclura*), iroko-wood (*Chlorophora excelsa*) or fustic (*Chlorophora tinctoria*).

S.W.J.

URTICACEAE
Stinging Nettles and Ramie Fiber
The Urticaceae is a medium-sized family which includes *Urtica* and related genera, the

Moraceae. 1 *Ficus religiosa* (a) shoot with drip tip leaf and fruits ($\times\frac{2}{3}$); (b) fruit from below ($\times\frac{2}{3}$); (c) stalked and sessile female flowers ($\times 5$); (d) sterile female or gall flower ($\times 5$); (e) male flower ($\times 5$); 2 *Morus nigra* (a) shoot with fruit, the mulberry—an aggregation of achenes and the fleshy perianth ($\times\frac{1}{3}$); (b) female inflorescence ($\times 1\frac{1}{2}$); (c) female flower ($\times 3$). 3 *Ficus benghalensis*—the banyan tree. 4 *Ficus carica*—the fig, a multiple fruit of numerous achenes and the swollen receptacle ($\times\frac{1}{2}$). 5 *Artocarpus communis* (a) multiple fruit comprising numerous achenes, swollen perianth and swollen receptacle ($\times 1$); (b) female inflorescence ($\times\frac{1}{2}$); (c) leaf ($\times\frac{1}{4}$).

stinging nettles of north temperate regions.

Distribution. The family is found in most tropical and temperate regions, although it is relatively poorly represented in Australia.

Diagnostic features. Most genera are herbs or small shrubs, although one of the tribes contains primarily trees. The leaves may be alternate or opposite, and have stipules; the epidermis is usually marked with prominent cystoliths. The inflorescence is basically cymose and is often condensed into heads. The flowers are greenish, regular and unisexual (male and female being borne on the same individuals), although rarely bisexual, and usually have four or five sepal-like lobes. The male flowers have four or five stamens, usually bent downwards and inwards in bud and exploding when ripe. The female flowers possess a superior ovary which has one locule containing a single erect basal ovule. There is a single style. The fruit is usually dry, an achene, with the seed rich in oily endosperm, and with a straight embryo.

Classification. The family is divided into six tribes, based mainly on floral differences. The URTICEAE, however, is distinguished by its characteristic stinging hairs. This tribe contains *Urtica* (50 species) and the wide-

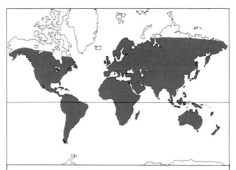

Number of genera: about 45
Number of species: over 1,000
Distribution: most tropical and temperate regions
Economic uses: ramie fiber and several troublesome weeds.

spread tropical and subtropical genus *Urera* (35 species) with its persistent, fleshy perianth making a berry-like fruit. *Laportea*, containing the stinging trees of Australia, also belongs here. The largest tribe is the PROCRIDEAE; the perianth of the female flowers is three-lobed, and the stigma has the characteristic appearance of a paint brush. *Pilea*, the widespread tropical genus contain-

ing the "artillery plant", so-named because of the puffs of pollen released when the anthers explode, *Elatostema* and the tropical Asian and Polynesian *Pellionia* belong here. The small tribe FORSKOHLEEAE, containing *Forskohlea* with six species from the Canary Islands to western India, has very reduced male flowers consisting of a single stamen. The two tribes BOEHMERIEAE and PARIETARIEAE are distinguished from each other by the presence of an involucre of often united bracts in the latter, with its principal genus *Parietaria* of 30 species possessing bisexual flowers (an unusual feature for the family). The former of these two tribes contains the tropical and northern subtropical genus *Boehmeria*, with 100 species, and *Maoutia*, from Indomalaya and Polynesia, unusual in its 15 species having no perianth in the female flowers, The sixth tribe, the CONOCEPHALEAE, includes *Cecropia*, trees with light wood used for making floats, and *Poikilospermum*, 20 species from the eastern Himalayas to southern China extending into Malaysia. They differ from the other genera in the family in having straight stamens, and because of this and some other similarities, used to be placed in a neighboring family, the

Urticaceae.1 *Pilea microphylla* (a) bud of male flower (×10); (b) male flower (×12); (c) perianth of female flower (×24); (d) gynoecium (×24); (e) vertical section of ovary (×24). 2 *Parietaria judaica* (a) bisexual flower (×4); (b) perianth opened out to show single style and hairy capitate stigma (×6). 3 *Forskohlea angustifolia* male flower (×6). 4 *Myrianthus serratus* (a) part of shoot with inflorescences in leaf axil (×⅔); (b) vertical section of ovary (×8); (c) dehiscing stamen (×18); (d) fruits (×⅔). 5 *Urtica magellanica* (a) flowering shoot (×⅔); (b) bud of male flower (×10); (c) male flower (×12); (d) vertical section of male flower with cup-like vestige of ovary (×12); (e) female flower (×12).

Moraceae. This affinity is still generally recognized, but the presence of latex in most genera of the Moraceae is a useful diagnostic feature, along with details of the fruit structure. The Ulmaceae is also closely related.

Economic uses. As well as being a well-known and noxious weed, *Urtica dioica*, the common stinging nettle, contains some small amount of silky bast-fiber. Fiber from other members of this family is used in the textile industry, notably *Boehmeria nivea* (ramie fiber or China grass) from Southeast Asia.

I.B.K.R.

LECYTHIDALES

LECYTHIDACEAE
Brazil Nuts and Cannonball Tree

The Lecythidaceae is a family of tropical trees, the best known of which is *Bertholletia excelsa*, which gives Brazil nuts.

Distribution. The family is centered in the wet regions of tropical South America, with some genera in Africa and Asia.

Diagnostic features. Tree size ranges from very small to very large. The leaves are

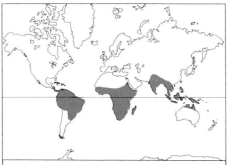

Number of genera: about 20
Number of species: about 450
Distribution: tropical, centered in S America.
Economic uses: nuts (Brazil nuts, sapucaia nuts) and useful timber.

spirally arranged in clusters at the tips of the twigs, each leaf large, simple, usually without gland-dots. Stipules are very rarely present. The flowers are bisexual, and borne in spikes (up to 3ft (1m) long, as in *Couroupita guianensis*), terminally, on side shoots, or on the older parts of the stems. They are generally large and showy, in shades of red, pink, yellow or white, and have an attractive,

fluffy appearance due to numerous stamens. They seldom last long (in *Barringtonia* remaining open for only one night before stamens and petals fall at dawn). The flowers are regular or irregular, with four to six calyx segments and four to six petals (absent in *Foetidia*) free or united into a ribbed tube. The stamens also are joined to each other and to the petals at their base in one or more rings. The ovary is inferior of two to six fused carpels, totally fused with the top of the receptacle or partially sunk into it. There are two to six or more locules, each with one to many ovules, a long simple style and a lobed or disk-shaped stigma. Pollination is frequently by bats, attracted by the sweet-smelling flowers. The usually large fruits have fleshy outer layers, hard and woody inner layers, and are indehiscent, with a lid through which the seeds leave the fruit. The seed is large, woody and lacks endosperm.

Classification. *Barringtonia* is the most important Old World genus, a well-known tree throughout Southeast Asia and Africa; others include *Careya*, *Combretodendron*, *Crateranthus*, *Foetidia*, *Napoleona* and *Planchonia*. However, the majority of the Lecythidaceae and those of the greatest

Lecythidaceae. 1 *Gustavia pterocarpa* (a) flowering shoot (×⅔) ; (b) flower with stamens and petals removed to show simple style surmounted by a lobed stigma (×⅔). 2 *Napoleona imperialis* (a) petal-less flower showing several whorls of stamens and outer ring of staminodes forming a corolla-like saucer-shaped body (×⅔) ; (b) half flower with calyx and staminodes removed, showing fertile outer whorls of stamens within which are outgrowths (disk) of the receptacle and short flat-topped style (×1⅓) ; (c) berry-like fruit with apical lid (×⅔). 3 *Barringtonia racemosa* (a) spike bearing flowers with many stamens (×⅔) ; (b) vertical section of flower base showing ovary fused into the receptacle (×2) ; (c) fruit (×⅔).

Violaceae. 1 *Anchietea salutans* shoot with alternate leaves and fruit (×⅔). 2 *Rinorea moagalensis* half flower showing stamen filaments fused at the base and the anthers with a membraneous extension to the connective (×10). 3 *Viola hederacea* (a) habit (×⅔); (b) vertical section of flower showing irregular petals and anthers in a close ring around the ovary (×4). 4 *Corynostylis hybnanthus* (a) shoot with leaf and inflorescence (×⅔); (b) cross section of ovary with one locule containing numerous ovules on parietal placentas (×4). 5 *Hybanthus (Ionidium) enneaspermum* var *latifolium* dehiscing fruit—a capsule (×4). 6 *Hymenanthera obovata* leafy shoot with fruit (×⅔).

economic importance are natives of South America. These include *Bertholletia, Couroupita, Grias, Gustavia* and *Lecythis*. Some classification schemes assign the African and Asian genera to a separate family, the Barringtoniaceae. Hutchinson combined the African genera *Crateranthus* and *Napoleona* with an American genus, *Asteranthus*, in another separate family, Napoleonaceae.

By tradition, the family has generally been associated with, or even included in, the Myrtaceae, the two families sharing many characters, particularly of the flowers. However, there are important differences of development and anatomy. Closer relatives might be found in the order Malvales, for, besides similarities of the flowers, the mucilage canals which are so characteristic of that order are also found in some genera of the Lecythidaceae.

Economic uses. *Bertholletia excelsa* is the source of Brazil nuts or para nuts. Sapucaia or paradise nuts, from several species of *Lecythis*, such as *Lecythis zabucajo*, are reputedly superior to Brazil nuts. The fruits are woody fibrous capsules resembling pots with a terminal lid. After the nuts are shed the empty pots are used as traps for wild

monkeys (hence the common name monkey-pots). *Couroupita guianensis* (cannonball tree), a native of tropical South America, is grown as an ornamental for its large 4in (10cm) waxy, sweet-smelling red and yellow flowers which are followed by spectacular spherical fruits 6in–8in (15cm–20cm) in diameter, the "cannonballs" borne on the trunks. Useful timber comes from *Lecythis grandiflora* (wadadura wood), *Careya* (tummy wood) from Malaya and India and from *Bertholletia excelsa*.   S.W.J.

VIOLALES

VIOLACEAE
Violets and Pansies
The Violaceae is a medium-sized family of perennial (rarely annual) herbs or shrubs, including the violets and pansies.

Distribution. The family is cosmopolitan, but more typical of the temperate regions; in the tropics it tends to be restricted to higher mountainous areas.

Diagnostic features. Most species have simple alternate leaves, with small stipules. Only *Hybanthus* and *Ionidium* have species

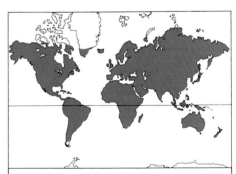

Number of genera: 22
Number of species: about 900
Distribution: cosmopolitan, chiefly temperate.
Economic uses: valued garden ornamentals (violets and pansies) and uses in perfumery and flavoring.

with opposite leaves. The flowers are in racemes, or solitary in the leaf-axils. They are regular (except in *Viola*), bisexual, and have five sepals and five petals. There are five stamens which usually have their filaments fused at the base to form a ring around the ovary. The ovary is superior, consisting of three fused carpels, with one locule contain-

Flacourtiaceae. 1 *Oncoba spinosa* (a) flowering shoot armed with axillary spines ($\times\frac{2}{3}$); (b) cross section of fruit ($\times\frac{2}{3}$); (c) entire fruit with remains of flower below ($\times\frac{2}{3}$). 2 *Idesia polycarpa* (a) pendulous inflorescence ($\times\frac{2}{3}$); (b) cross section of unilocular ovary with ovules on five large parietal placentas ($\times 2$); (c) vertical section of female flower showing branched style ($\times 2$); (d) male flower with numerous short stamens ($\times 2$); (e) ripe fruit ($\times\frac{2}{3}$). 3 *Azara microphylla* (a) flowering shoot ($\times\frac{2}{3}$); (b) vertical section of flower with single style and large stamens ($\times 9$); (c) part of inflorescence ($\times 3$); (d) cross section of unilocular ovary ($\times 18$).

ing numerous ovules arranged on a parietal placenta. The style and stigma are usually simple. The fruit is a capsule which usually dehisces, often explosively, along lateral lines into three or five valves. The seeds are usually spherical, and winged in some tropical climbing species. They contain a straight embryo and a fleshy endosperm.

All species of *Viola* have unequal petals with the lowermost pair, often the largest, forming a prominent spur. Their colored petals and scent attract pollinating insects which are said to be guided into the spur by linear markings, or honey guides, on the petals. Nectar is secreted into the spur from the bases of the two lowermost stamens. To reach it the insect's body must touch the stigma, so pollinating it with the pollen it may be carrying. The insect also touches the spurs on the anthers which shower pollen onto its back which it then carries to the stigma of another flower. Many species of *Viola* have small, insignificant, cleistogamous flowers which never open and are self-pollinating.

Classification. The chief genera are *Viola* (about 400 species, mainly north temperate herbs but some small shrubs), *Rinorea* (*Alsodeia*, about 340 species of tropical and warm temperate shrubs), *Hymenanthera* (seven species of shrubs from Australia, New Zealand and Norfolk Island), *Paypayrola* (seven species of tropical South American trees), *Hybanthus* (about 150 species of herbs from tropics and subtropics), *Anchietea* (eight species of shrubs and climbers from tropical South America), *Leonia* (six species of tropical South American shrubs) and *Corynostylis* (four species of tropical American shrubs).

The Violaceae has its closest affinities with the Flacourtiaceae but some links with the Resedaceae are probable.

Economic uses. The Violaceae has little commercial significance except for *Viola*, which contains *Viola odorata*, grown in the south of France for essential oils used in manufacture of perfumes, flavorings, toiletries and the very sweet, violet-colored liqueur *parfait amour*; the flowers are also preserved in sugar as crystallized violets used largely for decoration. Many species of *Viola* are grown as ornamentals (pansies and violets). The garden pansies are a hybrid group (*Viola* × *wittrockiana*).

Some species are of limited medicinal importance: the root of *Hybanthus ipecacuanha* is used as a substitute for true ipecacuanha as an emetic; the roots of *Anchietea salutaris* are used as an emetic and to treat sore throats and lymphatic tuberculosis; and the roots of *Corynostylis hybanthus* are used as an emetic. B.N.B.

FLACOURTIACEAE
Chaulmoogra Oil and West Indian Boxwood

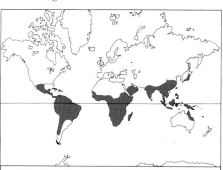

Number of genera: 89
Number of species: about 1,250
Distribution: tropical and subtropical, with some in temperate regions.
Economic uses: a few ornamentals; chaulmoogra oil and timber.

The Flacourtiaceae is a large family, chiefly of trees and shrubs, and of limited economic importance.

Distribution. The family is widespread in the tropics and subtropics, with some species in temperate regions.

Diagnostic features. The leaves are simple, alternate, opposite or in whorls, toothed or entire. The branches are sometimes spiny, and flowers are regular, bisexual or unisexual with the sexes on separate plants. They are solitary or borne in axillary or terminal inflorescences which may be racemose, corymbose, paniculate, in bundles. There are two up to 16 sepals, free, overlapping or contorted, sometimes intergrading with the petals in appearance. The usually overlapping or contorted petals, sometimes united, are normally rather small and the same number as the sepals, rarely more and then not arranged in relation to the sepals, or rarely absent altogether. The petals are usually hypogynous or more or less perigynous, and each may or may not have a scale-like outgrowth inside the base.

The stamens are frequently numerous' or sometimes the same number as and opposite the petals. The filaments may be free, fused in bundles and alternating with glands, or rarely fused into a tube. The anthers usually open by slits, rarely by pores. The ovary position varies from superior through semi-inferior to inferior, and comprises two to ten united carpels with a single locule containing several ovules on one or more parietal placentas. The styles may be fused or free, rarely much branched or lacking, and are the same in number as placentas, the stigmas likewise. The fruits are capsules, berries, drupes, dry indehiscent and winged, horny or prickly, and containing seeds sometimes with arils or silky hairs and usually with much endosperm. There is a straight or curved embryo and the cotyledons are broad.

Classification. On the basis of floral characters 12 tribes have been recognized. Chief genera are: *Erythrospermum* (six species, Madagascar, Sri Lanka, Burma, China, Malaysia, Polynesia); *Hydnocarpus* (40 species, Indomalaysia); *Scolopia* (45 species, tropical and South Africa, Asia and Australia); *Homalium* (200 species, tropical and subtropical); *Flacourtia* (15 species tropical and South Africa, Mascarene Islands, Southeast Asia, Malaysia and Fiji); *Azara* (10 species, southern Bolivia and Brazil to Chile and Argentina); *Xylosoma* (100 species warm regions); *Casearia* (160 species tropical).

In evolutionary terms, the Flacourtiaceae lies between the Dilleniaceae and Tiliaceae, and is the most primitive family within the Violales, although this does not mean that it is the ancestor of other families in the group, rather that it is the least advanced of a series of parallel evolutionary lines.

Economic uses. The family contains few plants of economic importance. Notable ornamentals are *Oncoba spinosa*, *Berberidopsis corallina*, *Carrierea calycina*, *Idesia polycarpa* and *Azara* species. *Hydnocarpus wightiana* (southwestern India) and *Taraktogenos kurzii* (Burma) have seeds which yield chaulmoogra oil of use in the treatment of leprosy. The few timber trees include *Gossypiospermum praecox*, West Indian boxwood.   B.M.

LACISTEMATACEAE

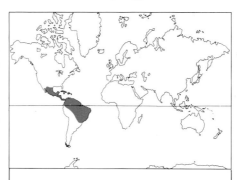

Number of genera: 2
Number of species: 27
Distribution: tropical America, W Indies.
Economic uses: none.

The Lacistemataceae is a small family of tropical shrubs.

Distribution. The family is native to the West Indies and tropical America.

Diagnostic features. The leaves are simple and alternate, with two small deciduous stipules or without stipules. The flowers are very small and inconspicuous, without petals. They are unisexual or bisexual, closely clustered into axillary spikes or racemes. Each flower is subtended by a concave overlapping bract and there are also two bracteoles at the base of each flower. Sepals are four to six in number and unequal in size, or absent. The axis is expanded into a fleshy concave disk on which is inserted a single stamen. The two anthers are separate, sometimes borne on a short stalk. The ovary is superior, of two or three fused carpels forming a single locule with two or three parietal placentas each bearing one or two pendulous ovules. There are two or three stigmas borne on a short style. The fruit is a capsule bearing one to three seeds each of which has a straight embryo surrounded by copious fleshy endosperm.

Classification. The two genera in this family can be distinguished on the basis of both vegetative and floral characters. *Lacistema* (20 species) has entire leaves, conspicuous bracts and spike-like inflorescences, while *Lozania* (seven species) has dentate leaves, small bracts and racemose inflorescences.

The family shows marked similarities with a number of other families in the order Violales, especially the Flacourtiaceae.

Economic uses. There are no known economic uses for this family.   S.R.C.

PASSIFLORACEAE
Passion Flowers and Granadillas

The Passifloraceae is a medium-sized family of vines, trees, shrubs and herbs, some species producing showy flowers and edible berries.

Distribution. The family is native to the tropics and subtropics. *Passiflora* itself is widely distributed, with 400–500 species in the warmer parts of America, a few species in Asia and Australasia, and one in Madagascar; it is widely cultivated throughout the world. *Adenia* has about 80 species in tropical Africa and Asia. Thirteen genera are found only in tropical and subtropical Africa.

Diagnostic features. The plants are trees, shrubs, herbs or frequently climbers with axillary coiled tendrils, corresponding to sterile pedicels. The leaves are alternate, entire or lobed, and have small, often deciduous stipules. The flowers are regular and usually bisexual; when they are unisexual they are usually borne on the same plant, rarely (in *Adenia* only) on separate plants. The single-flowered peduncle is jointed and furnished with three bracts. The five sepals are distinct or fused at the base. The petals are usually five, occasionally absent, and like the sepals may be distinct or basally connate. The receptacle is often terminated by one or more rows of petal-like or stamen-like filaments forming a corona. The stamens are usually equal in number to the petals and often opposite them, but frequently arising from a gynophore or androphore. The ovary is superior, with one locule containing three to five parietal placentas and numerous ovules. The styles are free or united. The three to five stigmas are capitate or discoid. The fruit is an indehiscent berry or capsule. The seeds are surrounded by a pulpy aril, and contain fleshy endosperm and a large, straight embryo.

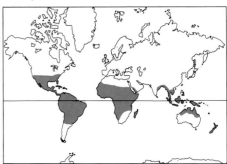

Number of genera: 20
Number of species: about 600
Distribution: tropical and subtropical, chiefly in America and Africa.
Economic uses: several species of *Passiflora* cultivated for edible fruit (passion fruit, granadilla) and as ornamentals.

Classification. *Passiflora* is the only genus of importance. The genera *Smeathmannia*, *Soyauxia* and *Barteria*, erect shrubs lacking tendrils from Africa, are considered the most primitive members of the family. They relate the Passifloraceae to the Flacourtiaceae. Both families have ovaries with parietal placentation, but the Passifloraceae is more advanced in possessing a perigynous calyx and corolla, a corona and tendrils for climbing. The family is also considered closely related to the Cucurbitaceae and Loasaceae. Recent works regard all these families as very closely related.

Economic uses. Between 50 and 60 species of *Passiflora* have edible fruits, but few are commercially cultivated. *Passiflora quadrangularis*, (the giant granadilla) is cultivated throughout the tropics for its juicy edible fruits up to 10in (25cm) long. In Hawaii, *P. edulis* var *flaviocarpa*, the yellow passion fruit, forms the basis of the entire passion fruit juice industry. In Australia, India and Sri Lanka it is *P. edulis*, passion fruit, or purple granadilla, that is cultivated. In Australia both species are grown, but the former is used solely as a stock on which the latter is grafted. The purple granadilla is

used in beverages, candy and sweets. *Passiflora maliformis* (West Indies) is the sweet calabash which has grape-like juice. Other species are used locally in the South American tropics.

About twenty species of *Passiflora* are cultivated for their attractive and unusual flowers. The family has no other species of economic or domestic importance. S.L.J.

TURNERACEAE

The Turneraceae is a family of mostly shrubs or small trees and a few herbs with no significant economic importance.

Distribution. The family is confined to tropical and subtropical parts of the New World, Africa, Madagascar and the Mascarene Islands.

Diagnostic features. The leaves are alternate, usually without stipules, often with glandular teeth on the margin. The flowers, which are usually solitary in the leaf axils, are bisexual and regular. The five regularly overlapping sepals usually have a swelling on the inner surface; the petals and stamens also each number five; all are united below into a cup which surrounds the ovary. The ovary is superior and formed of three united carpels

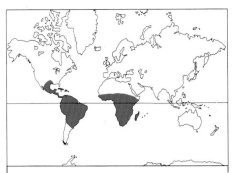

Number of genera: 8
Number of species: about 100
Distribution: tropical and subtropical regions, mainly in America.
Economic uses: limited medicinal and flavoring uses.

with a single locule and three parietal placentas bearing three to many ovules; it is surmounted by three styles. The fruit is a capsule splitting into three parts; the seeds have an aril and contain copious endosperm.

Most species have two types of flower, some with short, and some with long styles. Many species have nectaries on parts of the plant other than in the flowers. Self-

Passifloraceae. 1 *Passiflora caerulea* (a) twining stem with coiled tendrils, solitary flower with conspicuous filamentous corona and five-lobed leaves subtended by leafy bracts ($\times \frac{2}{3}$); (b) vertical section of flower with, from the base upwards, subtending bracts, hollowed-out receptacle bearing spurred sepals, petals and filaments (the latter forming the corona) and a central stalk (androphore) with at the apex the ovary bearing long styles with capitate stigmas and at the base downward curving stamens ($\times 1\frac{1}{2}$); (c) fruit ($\times \frac{2}{3}$); (d) cross section of fruit containing numerous seeds ($\times 1\frac{1}{2}$); (e) seed ($\times 6$).

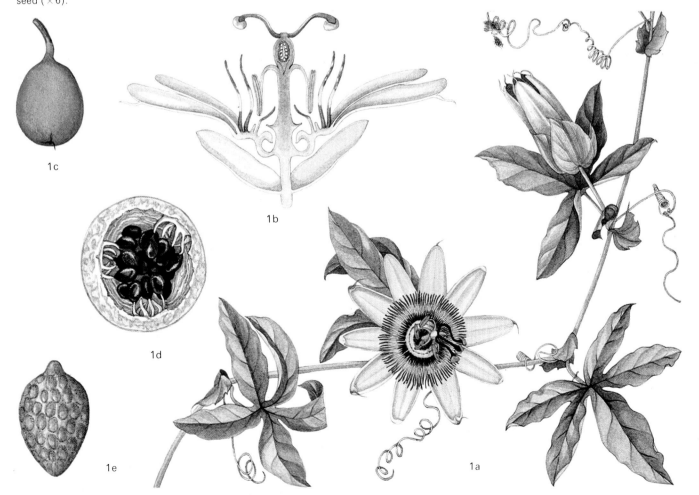

1c

1b

1d

1e

1a

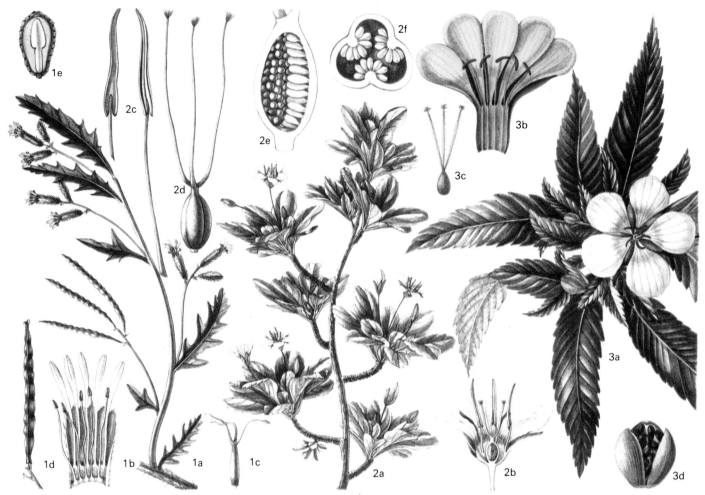

Turneraceae. 1 *Wormskioldia heterophylla* (a) shoot with alternate leaves, flowers in racemes and elongate fruits (× ⅔); (b) perianth opened out (× 2);
(c) gynoecium (× 2); (d) fruit—a capsule (× 1); (e) vertical section of seed (× 4). 2 *Turnera berneriana* (a) shoot with leaves and solitary flowers
(× ⅔); (b) half flower (× 3); (c) bilocular anthers (× 8); (d) gynoecium showing fringed stigmas (× 8); (e) vertical section of ovary (× 15); (f) cross
section ovary with ovules on three parietal placentas (× 15). 3 *Turnera angustifolia* (a) flowering shoot (× ⅔); (b) perianth opened out (× ⅔); (c)
gynoecium (× 1); (d) fruit dehiscing by three valves (× 1½).

fertilization occurs in the absence of insect
visits, by the corolla withering and pressing
anthers and stigmas together.

Classification. The eight genera may be
distinguished on a number of characters.
Flowers are pendulous and the seeds have an
aril covered in long thread-like hairs in
Mathurina. A corona is present within the
calyx of *Erblichia* and *Piriqueta*, the former
genus having leaves with minute stipules and
the latter lacking them altogether. Of the
genera that lack a corona *Hyalocalyx* has
sepals united only halfway, *Turnera* has
solitary flowers with variously lobed stigmas, *Loweia* has solitary flowers and leaves
with resin glands and stellate hairs, *Streptopetalum* is a herb with flowers in a raceme,
petals inserted in the throat of the calyx tube
and short fruits, and *Wormskioldia* is as
Streptopetalum except that the petals are
inserted in the calyx tube and fruits are
elongate.

The affinities of the family lie with the
Passifloraceae and neighboring families.

Economic uses. The leaves of a few species of
Turnera have medicinal uses locally. They
are also used in Mexico as a tea substitute
and to flavor wines, etc.   I.B.K.R.

MALESHERBIACEAE

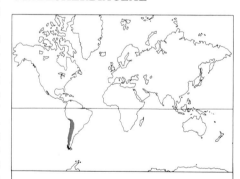

Number of genera: 1 or 2
Number of species: 27
Distribution: western S America.
Economic uses: none.

The Malesherbiaceae is a small family of
herbs and undershrubs.

Distribution. The family is native to western
South America.

Diagnostic features. The leaves are alternate,
simple, without stipules, and frequently
covered with a dense mat of hairs. The
flowers are bisexual, regular and arranged in
racemes, cymes or panicles. The calyx is five-
lobed and with a long tube; the five petals are
valvate, as are the sepals.

The ovary is superior, borne on a hairy
stalk from which also arise the five stamens
(androgynophore). The anthers have two
locules which open lengthwise. The ovary is
formed of three fused carpels forming one
locule with three or four parietal placentas
bearing numerous ovules, and is surmounted
by three or four slender, thread-like styles
separated at the base. The fruit is a capsule
enclosed by the persistent calyx. The seed
contains a straight embryo surrounded by
fleshy endosperm.

Classification. Opinions vary as to whether
all the species belong to a single genus
(*Malesherbia*) or whether some can be
ascribed to another genus (*Gynopleura*). The
basis for such a division lies in floral
characters: species belonging to *Malesherbia*
have flowers in racemes with petals smaller
than the calyx lobes, while those belonging
to *Gynopleura* have flowers in panicles or
dense clusters with petals larger than the
calyx lobes.

This family is closely related to the passion
flower family (Passifloraceae) and to the
Turneraceae, but differs from the former in

having more widely separated styles and from the latter in having a persistent receptacle. A further distinction is that in the Maleesherbiaceae the seeds do not possess an aril.

Economic use. The family is of no economic importance.   S.R.C.

FOUQUIERIACEAE
Ocotillo

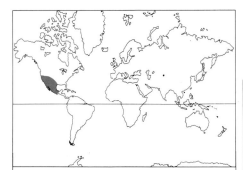

Number of genera: 2
Number of species: 8
Distribution: Mexico and SW USA.
Economic uses: limited uses as hedging and as a source of wax.

The flowering, spiny trees or shrubs that make up this family are a familiar sight in the dry southwest of North America.

Distribution. The family occurs only in Mexico and bordering states of the United States of America.

Diagnostic features. The leaves are small, succulent, are borne in groups or singly and are without stipules. The showy flowers are yellow (*Idria*) or red (*Fouquieria*). Borne in panicles or spikes, they are regular, bisexual, with five imbricate sepals, five hypogynous petals fused into a tube at the base, and 10 or more hypogynous stamens in one or more series with free or slightly fused filaments. The ovary is superior comprising three fused carpels and has a single locule with axile placentation below, but with septiform parietal placentation above dividing it incompletely into three locules. The style is branched (*Fouquieria*) or entire (*Idria*). The fruit is a capsule with oblong, winged and compressed seeds containing thin endosperm and a straight embryo with thick flat cotyledons.

Classification. The Fouquieriaceae comprises two genera, the monotypic *Idria* (stem usually branched), and the seven species of *Fouquieria* (usually unbranched stem).

Fouquieria splendens (ocotillo) a characteristic plant of parts of the Mojave and Colorado deserts, flowers between March and July. The leaves are deciduous on the few branched or cane-like stems to 23ft (7m) tall, being only briefly replaced after the spring and late summer rains. *Idria columnaris* has a weird habit with a thick trunk at the base, conical and often hollowed out, with a few long erect branches which may

become top heavy and fall over sideways to assume fantastic shapes.

The family is of disputed affinity, being sometimes placed in the Violales, as here, regarded as a peripheral member of the Centrospermae (Caryophyllales) or as closely allied to the Polemoniaceae.

Economic uses. With its curious spiny habit, *F. splendens* is sometimes used for hedging or boundary fences. Local use is made of wax obtained from the bark or stem of some *Fouquieria* species.   B.M.

CARICACEAE
Papaw

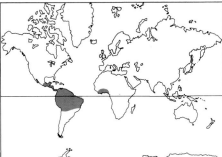

Number of genera: 4
Number of species: 30
Distribution: tropical America and tropical W Africa, centered in S America.
Economic uses: *Carica papaya* grown for fruit (papaw, papaya) and latex containing enzyme papain; other fruits eaten locally.

The Caricaceae is a tropical family of small trees, famous for the edible fruit of *Carica papaya*, grown throughout the tropics and widely known as the papaw, pawpaw, papaya or melon tree.

Distribution. The family is almost confined to the New World, where it is most abundant in South America, but with representatives also in Central America. *Cylicomorpha*, with two species, is native to parts of tropical West Africa.

Diagnostic features. The plants are small, sparsely branched trees, with soft wood; all parts contain milky latex in articulated laticifers which may be pungent. The leaves are alternate, crowded at branch tips, digitately lobed or foliolate and without stipules. The flowers are unisexual, rarely bisexual, the trees being usually dioecious, rarely monoecious or polygamous. The flowers are regular, with the parts in fives; the sepals are more or less free; the corolla is contorted or valvate with the corolla tube long in male, short in female flowers. The stamens are attached to the petals and the anthers open inward. The ovary is superior, of five fused carpels, has one to five locules, with many anatropous ovules on parietal placentas. The style is short and crowned by five stigmas. The fruit is a berry. The numerous seeds each have a gelatinous

envelope, oily endosperm and a straight embryo.

The stem of *Carica papaya* is very unusual in that there is little development of secondary xylem. The wood is formed largely from the phloem, which gives the soft, large-pithed trunk much of its rigidity.

Classification. There are four genera. *Jacaratia* (six species, tropical America and Africa) has sepals opposite the petals, and digitate leaves. In the spiny *Cylicomorpha* (two species, Africa) the sepals alternate with the petals and the leaves are mostly entire. *Jarilla* (one species, Mexico) has fruits with five protruding basal horns. The fruit of *Carica* (21 species) is without horns.

The Caricaceae is related most closely to the Passifloraceae, with which it has sometimes been united, and perhaps to the Cucurbitaceae.

Economic uses. The family's economic importance resides largely in *Carica papaya*, which has a large, bland juicy fruit and is extensively cultivated throughout the tropics. This species has nocturnal, sweet-scented, moth-pollinated flowers. As with many other cultivated plants, its origin is unknown and it may have arisen from hybridization. The fresh fruit is eaten with lemon or lime juice or in fruit salad; it may be tinned, crystallized or made into jam, ice cream, jellies, pies or pickles; when unripe, it is used like marrow or apple sauce. The green fruit produces latex which contains the proteolytic enzyme papain that breaks down proteins, and leaves are sometimes wrapped round meat to soften it. Commercial grade papain will digest 35 times its own weight of lean meat and is an important article of commerce for medicinal and industrial usages (for example, in canned meat and leather tanning). A few other species of *Carica* are cultivated in Latin America for their edible pericarp or the sweet, juicy seed envelopes, including *C. chrysophila* (higicho) and *C. pentagona* (babaco) both from Colombia and Ecuador, and *C. candicans* from Peru.

The mountain papaw is *C. cundinamarcensis* of the Andes: it has smaller fruits than the papaw and is successfully grown at altitudes in the tropics where *C. papaya* would fail. The fruits of *Jarilla caudata* and *Jacaratia mexicana* are eaten locally.
                                           T.C.W.

BIXACEAE
Annatto

The Bixaceae is a family consisting of a single tropical genus (*Bixa*) of shrubs and small trees.

Distribution. The family is native to tropical America and the West Indies and one species, *Bixa orellana*, is naturalized in tropical West Africa.

Diagnostic features. The leaves are alternate, simple, entire, palmately nerved and with stipules. They have long petioles and are

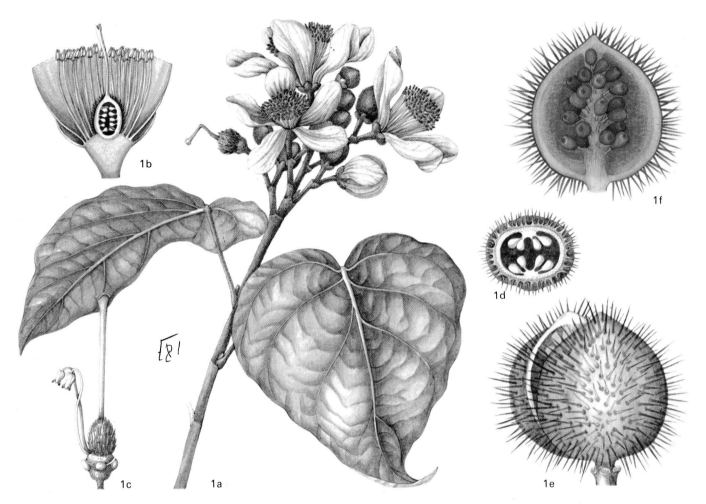

Bixaceae. 1 *Bixa orellana* (a) shoot with alternate leaves and flowers in a terminal panicle (×1); (b) half base of flower showing numerous stamens and ovary with numerous ovules on parietal placentas (×2); (c) stamens dehiscing by short slits and ovary crowned by long style and bilobed stigma (×3); (d) cross section of ovary showing ovules on parietal placentas (×8); (e) capsule dehiscing by two valves (×1); (f) vertical section of fruit with numerous red seeds (×1).

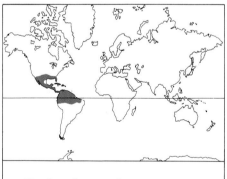

Number of genera: 1
Number of species: 1 or 4
Distribution: S America and W Indies.
Economic uses: *Bixa orellana* cultivated for annatto dye and as an ornamental.

covered with tufted hairs. Both leaves and stems contain reddish sap. The flowers are regular, bisexual and borne in showy, paniculate inflorescences. They have five imbricate, deciduous sepals. There are five large petals, imbricate and twisted in the bud. The stamens are numerous with free filaments and with two-celled, horseshoe-shaped anthers which dehisce by short slits at the apex. The ovary is superior, of two to four fused carpels with one locule and two parietal placentas bearing numerous ovules. It is surmounted by a long slender style which terminates in a two-lobed stigma. The fruit dehisces along the two valves of the capsule and is often covered with hairs or stout prickles. It contains many obovoid seeds, with a bright red, rather fleshy testa. The seeds contain a large embryo surrounded by copious starchy or granular endosperm.

Classification. The genus *Bixa* consists of one or four species, depending on taxonomic interpretation. The Bixaceae is perhaps related to the Cochlospermaceae, which also has alternate leaves with stipules, and sometimes orange or reddish sap. Both families have showy flowers, but the Cochlospermaceae differs mainly in having palmately lobed, not entire, leaves, three- to five-valved (not two-valved) fruits and oily endosperm within the seeds. The Bixaceae may also have affinities with the more primitive Dilleniaceae. The horseshoe-shaped anthers are also to be found in the Thymelaeaceae.

Economic uses. Economically the family is important for the species *Bixa orellana* (annatto) which is often cultivated as a quick-growing ornamental shrub in warm countries.

The testa is the source of a reddish-yellow dye, used for coloring foodstuffs such as cheese and butter. On a plantation scale, where the trees are grown at spaces of about 16ft (5m), mature specimens yield 4cwt–5cwt of seed per acre (some 80kg–100kg per hectare). The brown or dark red ovoid fruits are borne in large clusters at the ends of branches. Harvesting takes place when the fruits are nearly ripe. When the capsule splits open on drying the seeds are either dried and sold as annatto seed or paste.

S.R.C.

COCHLOSPERMACEAE
Rose Imperial

This small family of tropical trees and shrubs contains a number of species with attractive large yellow flowers.

Distribution. Members of the family are native to the tropics, often in drier parts, in America, western central Africa, Indo-malaysia and northern and western Australia.

Diagnostic features. The Cochlospermaceae are mostly trees and shrubs which may

Cochlospermaceae. 1 *Cochlospermum tinctorium* (a) flowering shoot ($\times\frac{2}{3}$); (b) shoot bearing old flowers and alternate, palmately-lobed leaves ($\times\frac{2}{3}$); (c) stamen with anther opening by apical, pore-like slits ($\times 6$); (d) gynoecium ($\times 2$); (e) cross section of unilocular ovary ($\times 3$); (f) seed covered with woolly hairs ($\times 2$); (g) seed with hairs removed ($\times 4$). 2 *Amoreuxia schiedeana* (a) flowering shoot ($\times\frac{2}{3}$); (b) half fruit showing three locules and valves formed by separation of inner and outer layers of the fruit ($\times\frac{2}{3}$); (c) vertical section of fruit ($\times\frac{2}{3}$); (d) entire fruit ($\times\frac{2}{3}$).

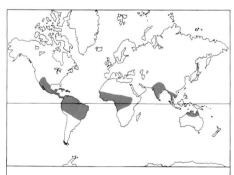

Number of genera: 2
Number of species: about 38
Distribution: tropical, often in drier regions.
Economic uses: tropical ornamental and limited uses as kapok, for cordage and as a medicinal gum.

contain colored sap. Some species of *Cochlospermum* have stout tuberous underground stems. The leaves are alternate, palmately lobed and with stipules. The flowers are regular or slightly irregular, bisexual, often showy and borne in racemes or panicles; there are five free, imbricate, deciduous sepals, five imbricate or contorted petals, and numerous free stamens. The anthers open at the tip by pore-like slits. The ovary is superior, with three to five fused carpels containing a single locule with parietal placentas in *Cochlospermum*, and three locules with axile placentas in *Amoreuxia*. The ovules are numerous. The style is simple, with a minute stigma. The fruit is a three- to five-valved capsule, containing seeds which may be hairy or not, and coiled or straight in shape. The seeds contain oily endosperm; the cotyledons are broad, and the embryo is the same shape as the seed.

Classification. The family comprises two genera, *Cochlospermum* (about 30 species) and *Amoreuxia* (eight species, southern United States of America to Peru). The ovary in *Cochlospermum* has a single locule (although there may be more at the apex or base) and the seeds are covered in woolly hairs, while in *Amoreuxia* the ovary is completely three-locular, and the seeds have no hairs or are slightly hairy.

The Cochlospermaceae was once included in Bixaceae, from which it differs in its palmate leaves, three- to five-valved, not two-valved, fruit and oily endosperm.

Economic uses. The large, often copious flowers of species of *Cochlospermum* make them useful, if sometimes gaunt, ornamentals in dry tropical gardens. The Central American species *Cochlospermum vitifolium*, rose imperial, is cultivated in many parts of the tropics, especially in drier places. It grows to about 33ft (10m) with a slender, open-crowned habit. The plants are leafless when the large yellow flowers appear in January to April at the shoot tips. Flowering may occur sporadically through the year in areas far from tropical America. The five- to seven-lobed leaves appear in June. A double-flowered form does not set fruit, but its spectacular 5.5in (14cm) diameter blossoms are larger than the single flowers. The buttercup tree or yellow cotton tree, *C. religiosum*, is a native of India, and has flowers like the rose imperial but often in greater numbers. In addition, in Queensland a red-flowered form of *C. gillivraei* is reported as being showy, as is *C. heteroneurum* from northern Australia. The former yields a useful kapok, as do some other species. The bark fiber of *C. vitifolium* is used locally to make cordage. The tissues of *C. religiosum* contain a fragrant colorless sap; in older trees an amber-colored gum (karaya or kutira gum) with medicinal value may exude.   B.M.

Cistaceae. 1 *Fumana procumbens* (a) habit showing simple opposite leaves and solitary flowers ($\times\frac{2}{3}$); (b) flower with petals removed showing outer whorl of articulated sterile stamens and inner whorl of fertile stamens surrounding the elongated style with curved base and discoid stigma ($\times 6$); (c) dehiscing capsule showing three valves containing seeds ($\times 2\frac{2}{3}$). 2 *Tuberaria guttata* habit ($\times\frac{2}{3}$). 3 *Cistus ladanifer* var *maculatus* (a) habit ($\times\frac{1}{2}$); (b) dehiscing capsule with ten valves ($\times 2$); (c) cross section of capsule showing seed ($\times 2\frac{2}{3}$). 4 *C. symphytifolius* cross section of ovary showing projecting placentas bearing numerous ovules ($\times 4$). 5 *Lechea mexicana* half flower with ovary containing two ascending ovules ($\times 8$).

CISTACEAE

Rockroses

The Cistaceae is a medium-sized family of shrubs and subshrubs (occasionally herbs) which are characteristic of dry, sunny habitats. They bear large showy, short-lived flowers and many species are grown as ornamentals (rockroses).

Distribution. The family occurs in Old World temperate regions, especially the Mediterranean, with some in North and South America.

Diagnostic features. The leaves are opposite (rarely alternate: *Halimium*, *Hudsonia*, *Crocanthemum*), simple, usually with stipules, and often bear ethereal oil glands or glandular hairs. The flowers are regular, bisexual and are either solitary or borne in cymes. There are five sepals (two of which are often small and then sometimes regarded as bracteoles) and five, three (*Lechea*) or no petals, which are overlapping (contorted in *Hudsonia*) and often crumpled in the bud. The stamens are numerous, hypogynous and have free filaments, which in some species are sensitive to touch. In *Tuberaria* and *Fumana* the outer stamens are sterile. The ovary is superior, of five to ten or three fused carpels,

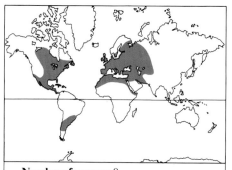

Number of genera: 8
Number of species: about 165
Distribution: chiefly north temperate (especially the Mediterranean region).
Economic uses: ornamentals (notably *Cistus*, rockroses) and fragrant ladanum resin.

with one locule having two or numerous ovules on each parietal placenta. There are three to five styles, which may be free or united. The fruit is a loculicidal capsule with five or ten valves (three in *Helianthemum*) containing numerous seeds with endosperm and a curved embryo.

Classification. *Cistus* includes about 20 species of evergreen shrubs bearing large

white or pink flowers with crumpled petals. They are often abundant in Mediterranean shrub communities. *Halimium* (nine species) comprises smaller shrubs, all but one with yellow flowers, found mainly in the Iberian Peninsula in similar habitats to *Cistus*. *Tuberaria* (11 species) includes small annual and perennial herbs with yellow flowers; the widespread Mediterranean annual *Tuberaria guttata* extends north in exposed coastal heath to Wales and Ireland. *Fumana* (10 species) and *Helianthemum* (about 70 species) are typically dwarf shrubs with yellow flowers, often growing gregariously in dry, base-rich grassland or on open rocky ground in the Mediterranean region and the neighboring mountains. *Helianthemum nummularium* occurs widely north to Britain and Scandinavia; *H. canum* and *H. oelandicum* form a polymorphic group with a broad but disjunct distribution in the mountains of central and southern Europe with outlying sites reaching to the British Isles, Öland in the Baltic, and Russia. *Crocanthemum* includes about 25 species of dwarf shrubs, with both conspicuous yellow flowers and minute cleistogamous flowers, distributed from the Atlantic coast of the United

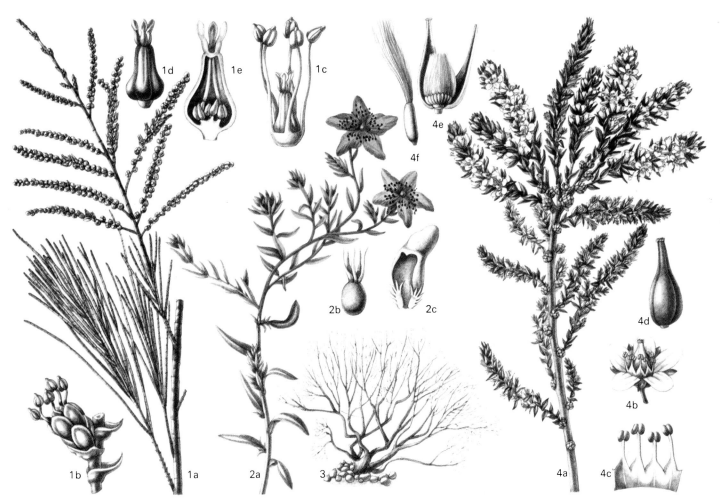

Tamaricaceae. 1 *Tamarix aphylla* (a) shoot with minute leaves and dense raceme of flowers ($\times\frac{2}{3}$); (b) part of inflorescence ($\times 4$); (c) stamens and gynoecium ($\times 6$); (d) four-lobed gynoecium ($\times 8$); (e) vertical section of ovary with basal ovules ($\times 10$). 2 *Reaumuria linifolia* (a) leafy shoot with solitary flowers ($\times\frac{2}{3}$); (b) gynoecium ($\times 2$); (c) petal ($\times 1\frac{1}{2}$). 3 *Tamarix africana* habit ($\times\frac{1}{120}$). 4 *Myricaria germanica* (a) flowering shoot ($\times\frac{2}{3}$); (b) flower ($\times 2$); (c) stamens united at the base ($\times 4$); (d) fruit—a capsule ($\times 2$); (e) dehiscing capsule showing cluster of hairy seeds ($\times 2$); (f) seed which is hairy at the apex only ($\times 4$).

States of America to Chile. *Lechea* has about 17 species and *Hudsonia* three species in eastern North America; all are slender subshrubs or herbs with tiny flowers.

Within the Violales, the Cistaceae is most closely allied to the Bixaceae. It also bears a superficial resemblance to the Papaveraceae.

Economic uses. Several species and hybrids of *Cistus* and *Halimium*, and variously colored cultivars and hybrids of *Helianthemum nummularium*, are often cultivated and make attractive garden plants. The leaves of several species of *Cistus*, especially *Cistus ladanifer* and *C. incanus* subspecies *creticus*, produce the aromatic resin ladanum, formerly used in medicine. *Cistus salviifolius* has been used in Greece as a substitute for tea. M.C.F.P.

TAMARICACEAE
Tamarisks

The Tamaricaceae is a family of small heath-like shrubs or small trees.

Distribution. The family is chiefly temperate and subtropical, growing in maritime or sandy places in Norway and from the Mediterranean, North Africa and south-eastern Europe through central Asia to India

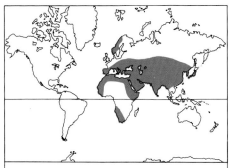

Number of genera: 4
Number of species: about 120
Distribution: mainly temperate and subtropical in maritime and sandy habitats.
Economic uses: some ornamental species and others yielding dyes, medicines and tannins from galls.

and China, and in southwestern Africa.

Diagnostic features. The plants are halophytes or xerophytes with slender branches bearing alternate, small, tapering or scale-like leaves without stipules. The flowers are minute, regular, bisexual, without bracts and either solitary (as in *Reaumuria*) or in dense spikes or racemes (as in *Tam-*

arix). The sepals and petals are both four or five in number and free. The petals and the five to ten or numerous stamens are inserted on a fleshy, nectar-secreting disk. The stamens are free or slightly fused at the base, with bilocular anthers which dehisce longitudinally. The ovary is superior of two, four or five fused carpels and has a single locule, with few to numerous ovules inserted on parietal or basal placentas. There are as many placentas as there are carpels. The styles are usually free and in some species they are absent and the stigmas are sessile (eg *Myricaria*). The fruit is a capsule containing seeds with or without endosperm.

The seeds are sometimes winged but in most species they are covered with long hairs either all over or in a tuft at the apex. The embryo is straight with flat cotyledons.

Classification. The four genera are disposed into two tribes, REAUMURIEAE and TAMARISCEAE. The former contains *Reaumuria* (20 species) and *Hololachna* (two species), both of which have solitary flowers and endospermic seeds. The species of *Reaumuria* are halophytic shrubs or undershrubs native to the eastern Mediterranean and central Asia. The solitary flowers are terminal with showy

Ancistrocladaceae. 1 *Ancistrocladus vahlii* (a) flowering shoot showing hooked tip to twig, simple, alternate leaves and flowers in a loose inflorescence ($\times\frac{2}{3}$); (b) shoot with fruits enclosed in enlarged wing-like sepals ($\times\frac{2}{3}$); (c) flower with petals, stamens and one sepal removed to show thickened style surmounted by three stigmas ($\times 8$); (d) corolla opened out showing stamens with short fleshy filaments ($\times 8$); (e) stamen with basifixed anthers ($\times 12$); (f) half fruit containing single seed ($\times 1$). 2 *A. heyneanus* (a) flowering shoot ($\times\frac{2}{3}$); (b) flower ($\times 2$); (c) flower opened out ($\times 2$); (d) stamen ($\times 6$); (e) fruit (a nut) surrounded by the persistent calyx ($\times\frac{2}{3}$).

petals, each bearing two longitudinal appendages on the inside. The stamens are numerous and either free or more or less fused into five bundles opposite the five petals. The ovary bears five styles and contains few seeds. The two species of *Hololachna* are native to Central Asia and bear axillary solitary flowers whose petals are devoid of appendages. There are only five to ten stamens, free or shortly connate at the base. The ovary has two to four styles and contains few seeds.

The Tamarisceae consists of *Tamarix* (90 species) and *Myricaria* (10 species), both characterized by their numerous flowers in a spike-like or racemose inflorescence and numerous non-endospermic seeds.

Tamarix species are halophytic shrubs and small trees native to Western Europe, the Mediterranean, North Africa, northeast China and India. The inflorescence is borne either on the woody lateral branches or on the terminal young shoots.

Myricaria consists of 10 species of undershrubs distributed in Europe, China and Central Asia. The inflorescence is a long terminal raceme and the flowers possess 10 stamens, fused or connate at the base, and

the ovary is crowned by three sessile stigmas.

The Tamaricaceae is probably most closely related to Frankeniaceae. Both share the heath-like shrubby habit, leaves without stipules, regular flowers, sepals and petals, superior ovary with one locule and parietal or basal placentation and the capsular fruit containing seeds with a straight embryo.

Economic uses. The twigs of the shrub *T. mannifera* (from Egypt to Afghanistan) yield the white sweet gummy substance manna as a result of puncture by the insect *Coccus maniparus*. Insect galls on species of *Tamarix* (*T. articulata* and *T. gallica*) are a source of tannin, dyes and medicinal extracts. The wood of *T. articulata* is used in North Africa for house construction.

Tamarix gallica and *T. africana*, which produce profuse slender branches, are often grown as ornamental shrubs for their rather feathery appearance and their catkin-like inflorescences. *T. pentandra*, a somewhat taller shrub (12ft–15ft, 3.5m–4.5m), produces long spikes of rose-pink flowers ('Rubra' has deep red flowers) and is sometimes grown as a hedge or windbreak, as is *T. gallica* in Mediterranean coastal resorts. S.R.C.

ANCISTROCLADACEAE

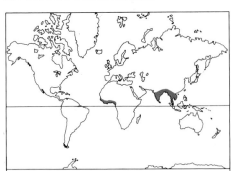

Number of genera: 1
Number of species: 20
Distribution: tropics.
Economic uses: limited local uses.

This tropical family of lianas contains the single genus *Ancistrocladus*.

Distribution. The 20 species grow in tropical Africa, Sri Lanka, Burma, the eastern Himalayas and southern China, extending to western Malaysia.

Diagnostic features. Most are lianas (rarely shrubs), sympodially branched, each branch ending in a coiled hook. The leaves are

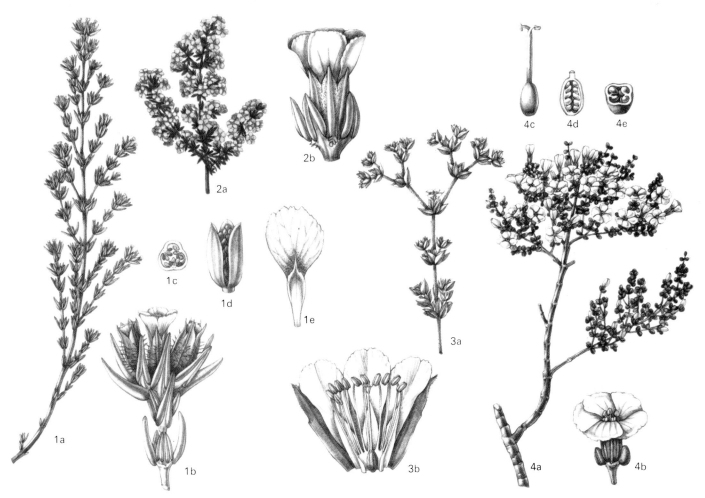

Frankeniaceae. 1 *Frankenia boissieri* (a) flowering shoot showing small heather-like opposite leaves and cymose clusters of flowers ($\times\frac{2}{3}$); (b) inflorescence showing folded leaves and flowers with hairy, tubular calyx and regular perianth with free petals ($\times3$); (c) cross section of ovary with single locule and ovules on three parietal placentas ($\times8$); (d) dehiscing fruit—a capsule ($\times6$); (e) petal showing scale on the claw ($\times6$). 2 *F. laevis* (a) flowering shoot ($\times\frac{2}{3}$); (b) flower ($\times6$). 3 *Hypericopsis persica* (a) flowering shoot ($\times\frac{2}{3}$); (b) half flower ($\times4$). 4 *Beatsonia portulacifolia* (a) flowering shoot ($\times\frac{2}{3}$); (b) flower ($\times3$); (c) gynoecium ($\times6$); (d) vertical section of ovary ($\times6$); (e) cross section of ovary ($\times6$).

simple, alternate and entire, with very small stipules which soon drop; sometimes the stipules are absent. The flowers are small, regular and bisexual with articulated pedicels, arranged in dichotomous cymes with branches curved back. There are five overlapping sepals with a short calyx tube fused to the base of the ovary; in fruit the sepals become unequally enlarged and wing-like. There are five petals which are more or less fleshy, contorted, slightly joined or cohering (joined but apparently free). There are 10 stamens in a single series, rarely five, with short fleshy filaments joined beneath and anthers with two locules dehiscing lengthwise. The ovary comprises three fused carpels and is semi-inferior. It has one locule, containing a single erect, basal ovule. The styles are three, free or joined and with three stigmas. The fruit is dry and woody, surrounded by the wing-like, enlarged and persistent (accrescent) calyx lobes. The seeds have a markedly ruminate endosperm and the cotyledons are deeply folded.

Classification. The affinities of the Ancistrocladaceae are very uncertain. It has previously been included in the Dipterocarpaceae and relationships have been suggested with the Violaceae and Ochnaceae.

Economic uses. The roots of *Ancistrocladus extensus* are reportedly boiled and used to counter dysentery in Malaya and the young leaves used for flavoring in Thailand.

V.H.H.

FRANKENIACEAE

Most members of this small family are salt-tolerant herbs (halophytes) of a characteristic appearance with smallish, somewhat heath-like leaves.

Distribution. The relatively large type-genus *Frankenia* (about 80 species) is distributed throughout the warm temperate and subtropical regions, although richest in the Mediterranean region and others with a similar climate. Because of their salt-loving physiology members of this family are well represented in arid and maritime environments. Two small genera, *Anthobryum* (four species) and *Niederleinia* (three species), are restricted to South America, while the monotypic *Hypericopsis* occurs in southern Iran.

Diagnostic features. The leaves are decussate, simple and entire, without stipules, and often have inrolled margins as an

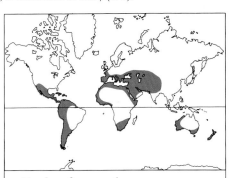

Number of genera: 4
Number of species: about 90
Distribution: warm temperate and subtropical.
Economic uses: limited use as ornamental oddities and local use of *Frankenia* species for fish poison.

adaptation for the desiccating conditions in which they usually grow. The flowers are regular and bisexual, except in the Patagonian *Niederleinia*, where they are unisexual and borne either on the same plant or on separate plants. They are usually arranged in terminal or axillary cymes, although sometimes solitary. The calyx is tubular with four to seven short lobes. The petals, equal in

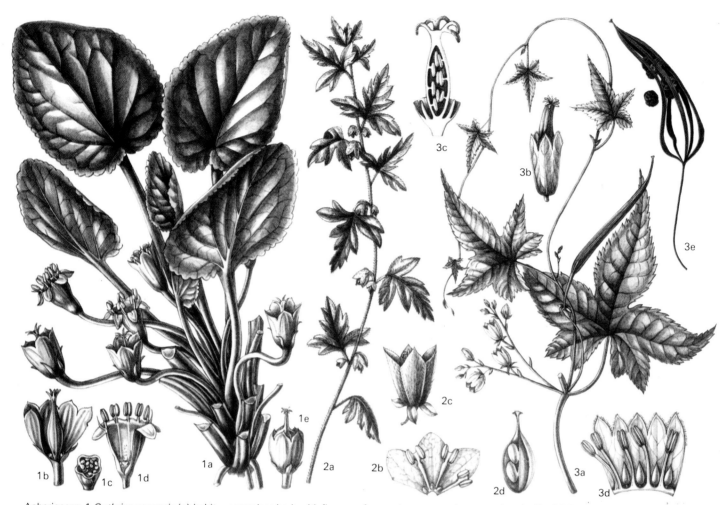

Achariaceae. 1 *Guthriea capensis* (a) habit—a stemless herb with flowers of separate sexes on the same plant ($\times\frac{2}{3}$); (b) female flower opened out showing ovary surmounted by lobed stigma ($\times\frac{2}{3}$); (c) cross section of ovary showing single locule and parietal placentas ($\times 1$); (d) male flower opened out ($\times\frac{2}{3}$); (e) fruit (a capsule) surmounted by the persistent corolla tube ($\times\frac{2}{3}$). 2 *Acharia tragodes* (a) habit—a woody dwarf shrub ($\times\frac{2}{3}$); (b) male flower opened out ($\times 2$); (c) female flower ($\times 2$); (d) capsule with one valve removed ($\times 1$). 3 *Ceratiosicyos ecklonii* (a) habit ($\times\frac{2}{3}$); (b) young female flower ($\times 2$); (c) vertical section of gynoecium ($\times 2$); (d) male flower opened to show fleshy staminodes ($\times 2$); (e) dehiscing capsule ($\times\frac{2}{3}$).

number to the calyx lobes, are free (although with converging claws in *Anthobryum*) and have a long claw in the calyx tube but expanded and spreading outward above. Each petal has a scale at the base of this expanded limb, which is continued down the sides of the claw. There are normally six stamens (about 24 in *Hypericopsis*) in two often unequal whorls, sometimes united at the base of the ovary, sometimes free; the bilocular anthers are turned outward and dehisce by longitudinal slits. The ovary is superior, of two to four united carpels, with a single locule containing several parietal placentas. The few or many ovules are anatropous, ascending or with a long, recurved stalk. The style is simple and has a usually two- or three-lobed stigma. The fruit is a capsule which dehisces lengthwise and remains in the persistent calyx, and the usually numerous endospermic seeds have a straight embryo; *Niederleinia* has a single placenta with one seed.

Classification. The family has strong affinities with the Tamaricaceae, one difference being the presence of opposite (decussate) leaves in members of the Frankeniaceae, not alternate as in the Tamaricaceae.

Economic importance. The family is of little economic importance; some species are occasionally seen as ornamental oddities. The largest member of the family is sometimes separated as a distinct genus *Beatsonia*, and is a relatively spectacular shrub some 2ft (60cm) high, native to St. Helena. Local exploitation of *Frankenia* species includes the use of *Frankenia ericifolia* in the Macaronesian Islands as a fish poison, and *F. berteroana*, a small shrub in Chile, is burnt and the ash used as a source of salt.

I.B.K.R.

ACHARIACEAE

The Achariaceae is a very small family of three genera and three species of small shrubs and stemless or slender-stemmed climbing herbs.

Distribution. Members of this family are exclusive to South Africa.

Diagnostic features. The leaves are alternate or radical, simple, serrated or palmately lobed and without stipules. In *Guthriea* they arise from the crown of the root.

The flowers are borne either singly or in a racemose inflorescence and are regular and unisexual, with both sexes borne on the same

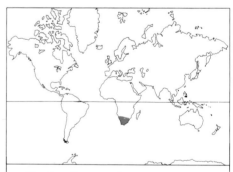

Number of genera: 3
Number of species: 3
Distribution: S Africa.
Economic uses: none.

plant. Both male and female flowers have three to five sepals which are fused at the base. The three to five petals are united into a tube-like structure opening out at the top into as many lobes as there are petals. The stamens equal the petals in number with filaments fused to the corolla tube at different levels according to species. The portion of the stamen connecting filament to anther is broadly expanded. In the female flower the ovary is composed of three to five

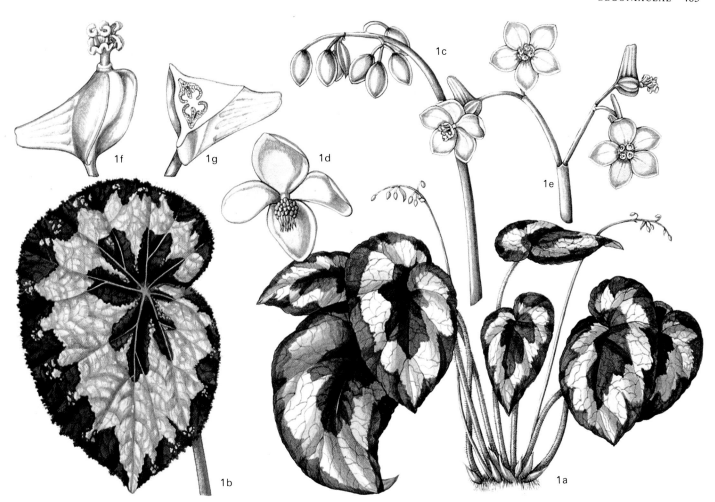

Begoniaceae. 1 *Begonia rex* (a) habit showing leaves with stipules and axillary inflorescences ($\times\frac{1}{3}$); (b) young leaf with one side larger than the other—a characteristic feature ($\times 1$); (c) male flower buds ($\times 1$); (d) male flower showing four perianth segments and cluster of stamens each with an elongated connective ($\times 1$); (e) female flowers showing five perianth segments ($\times\frac{2}{3}$); (f) young winged fruit with persistent styles that are fused at the base and bear twisted, papillose stigmatic surfaces ($\times 2$); (g) cross section of young winged fruit with two chambers and numerous seeds on branched, axile placentas ($\times 2$).

fused carpels and is superior, with one locule containing few to numerous ovules on three to five parietal placentas. There is a single style surmounted by a two-lobed stigma. There is no indication of a rudimentary gynoecium in the male flower or of rudimentary stamens or staminodes in the female flower. The fruit is a globular capsule which on ripening splits into three to five valves releasing the few to numerous seeds. The seeds have an aril and contain a small embryo surrounded by copious endosperm.

Classification. The three genera, *Acharia, Ceratiosicyos* and *Guthriea*, have only one species each. They can readily be distinguished from each other by their habit, the persistence of the petals (which may either fall off early or persist as the fruit ripens), the position of the stamens and the shape of the fruit. Both *Guthriea* (a stemless herb) and *Acharia* (a woody shrublet) have stamens inserted on the corolla tube which is persistent, while *Ceratiosicyos* (a slender-stemmed herb) has stamens inserted at the base of the corolla tube which falls off shortly after the anthers have shed their pollen.

This family has a number of features in common with the passion flower family (Passifloraceae) to which it is considered to be related. The presence of both sepals and petals, stamens equal in number to the petals, a unilocular superior ovary with three to five parietal placentas and numerous ovules developing into endospermic seeds are features of both families, which in turn are thought also to show relationships with the gourd family (Cucurbitaceae).

Economic uses. There are no known economic uses for any of the three species of Achariaceae.

S.R.C.

BEGONIACEAE
Begonias

The Begoniaceae is a family of perennial herbs and shrubs, the great majority being included in the genus *Begonia*, which includes many popular ornamentals grown for their foliage and flowers.

Distribution. *Begonia* itself is widespread in the tropics and subtropics. Two of the four satellite genera are South American: *Semibegoniella* (two species, Ecuador) and *Begoniella* (five species, Colombia). The other two genera are Pacific: the monotypic

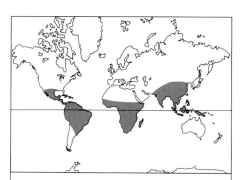

Number of genera: 5
Number of species: over 900
Distribution: tropics and subtropics.
Economic uses: ornamentals species (begonias), and limited local uses.

Hillebrandia in Hawaii and the 13 species of *Symbegonia* in New Guinea.

Diagnostic features. Most species have a characteristic succulent, often jointed, stem, with large membranous stipules. Many also have a thick rhizome or tubers, and some climb with the aid of aerial roots; a few have woody stems and are fibrous-rooted. The leaves, which are usually alternate and arranged in two ranks, are asymmetrical and have large, membranous, deciduous stipules; small axillary bulbs sometimes develop as a form of vegetative reproduction. The cymose, or more rarely racemose, inflorescence bears separate male and female flowers which differ even in the structure of the perianth; the segments are usually free, although united in some of the satellite genera, and they may be regular or irregular. In male flowers there are usually four petal-like segments in two opposite pairs at right angles to one another, the lower, larger ones representing the calyx and the upper the corolla; both pairs are valvate in bud. The female flowers usually have two to five imbricate petal-like segments, although *Hillebrandia* has 10. The stamens in the male flowers are numerous (four in *Begoniella*), free or joined at their bases, and have two-celled anthers often with an elongated connective and opening by longitudinal slits, rarely by pores. The ovary in female flowers is inferior (partly so in *Hillebrandia*), most often winged, usually comprising two or three fused carpels and locules with simple or branched axile placentas bearing numerous anatropous ovules. The styles may be united or joined at their bases, and the stigmas are often twisted and papillose. The fruit is a tough or fleshy, usually winged, loculicidal capsule, and the seeds have a straight embryo and no endosperm.

Classification. The most recent studies of *Symbegonia* and *Begoniella* suggest that these should be included within *Begonia*.

The family is a homogeneous assemblage of no obvious affinities. It is usually placed in the Violales but differs from the majority of families in this order on account of the general flower structure (eg ovary inferior). It is probably most closely related to the Datiscaceae.

Economic uses. *Begonia* species provide many very popular ornamentals. Two groups of species and hybrids are particularly popular, namely those related to *Begonia rex*, rhizomatous pot plants with hairy, warty and decorated leaves, and those related to *B. semperflorens*, fibrous-rooted bedding plants which are totally hairless and bear numerous flowers. Leaves of *B. tuberosa* in the Moluccas are cooked locally as a vegetable, while others have medicinal uses.   I.B.K.R.

LOASACEAE
Blazing Star and Rock Nettle
The Loasaceae is a family comprising mostly herbs with rough, often stinging hairs.
Distribution. The family is native to the American tropics and subtropics, with the two species of *Kissenia* native to southern Arabia and southwest Africa.
Diagnostic features. The plants are herbs or rarely shrubs, sometimes climbers. They are generally covered with rough hairs, which may be barbed (as in *Petalonyx*, the sandpaper plant of southwestern North America)

and frequently are nettle-like, often delivering a severe sting. The leaves are alternate or opposite, entire or variously divided, without stipules. The flowers are bisexual, regular and either solitary or borne in cymes or heads. The calyx is formed of five, or four to seven, sepals joined at their bases into a tube fused with the ovary. The corolla is formed of four or five petals which are free or rarely fused, often concave. There are usually numerous stamens, sometimes two or five, the inner often staminodes united into a large colorful nectary (as in *Blumenbachia, Loasa*). The ovary is inferior of one or normally three to five fused carpels and has one to three locules containing one to many ovules borne on parietal placentas. The style is simple. The fruit is a capsule. The seeds, with or without endosperm, have a straight embryo.

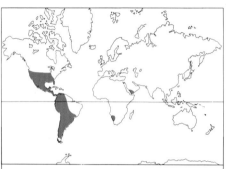

Number of genera: 15
Number of species: 250
Distribution: American tropics and subtropics, Arabia and SW Africa.
Economic uses: garden ornamentals.

Classification. The Loasaceae is usually divided into three subfamilies: MENTZELIOIDEAE, with three to five (rarely six) carpels each with numerous ovules, ten to many stamens, and usually no staminodes; LOASOIDEAE, with three to five carpels each with numerous ovules, 12 to many stamens and episepalous staminodes; and GRONOVIOIDEAE, with one apical ovule and five stamens, some of which are occasionally staminodes.

The Loasaceae is most closely related to the Begoniaceae.

Economic uses. Among genera grown as annuals or perennials for their showy flowers are *Loasa, Mentzelia* (blazing star), *Eucnide* (rock nettle), the usually climbing *Blumenbachia* and the twining *Grammatocarpus volubilis*.   D.M.M.

DATISCACEAE
Datiscas
The Datiscaceae is a small family of tropical and subtropical trees and herbs of little economic value.
Distribution. *Datisca glomerata* occurs in dry southwestern North America, *D. cannabina* from the Mediterranean to central Asia, *Octomeles* chiefly in the East Indies, and *Tetrameles* in Indochina and Malaysia.

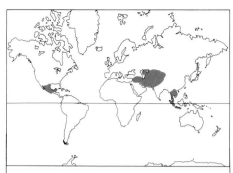

Number of genera: 3
Number of species: 4
Distribution: tropics and subtropics, centered in SW America, W Asia, Indochina, Malaysia and E Indies.
Economic uses: some ornamentals.

Diagnostic features. The family comprises trees (*Octomeles, Tetrameles*) or perennial herbs (*Datisca*). The leaves are alternate, either pinnate (*Datisca*) or simple, and without stipules. The flowers of *Datisca* are either unisexual with the sexes on different plants, or bisexual and crowded in clusters on long leafy branches. The calyx has three to nine unequal lobes; there are no petals. The stamens are eight to many, with short distinct filaments and large bilocular anthers which dehisce longitudinally. The bisexual flowers often bear staminodes. In the female and bisexual flowers the calyx tube is adnate to the ovary which is inferior formed of three to five fused carpels and a single locule with three to five parietal placentas bearing numerous ovules. There are three to five free thread-like styles which are deeply forked at the apex. The fruit is a membranous capsule bearing seeds with a straight embryo and little or no endosperm.

In *Octomeles* and *Tetrameles* the flowers are unisexual and borne on different plants; they have four to eight calyx lobes and six to eight petals in the male flowers (*Octomeles*) or no petals (*Tetrameles*). There are four to eight stamens with long filaments and bilocular anthers dehiscing longitudinally. The ovary is inferior with one locule and four to eight parietal placentas bearing numerous ovules and either eight (*Octomeles*) or four (*Tetrameles*) styles. The fruit is similar to that of *Datisca*.

Classification. Depending on interpretation the family comprises either three genera and four species or one genus (*Datisca*) and two species. It has been suggested that *Octomeles* and *Tetrameles* are related to the Lythraceae, and *Datisca* to the Haloragaceae. There is some dispute about the relationship of *Datisca* to the other two genera, which are sometimes placed in a separate family (Tetramelaceae).

Economic uses. The *Datisca* species are sometimes cultivated as ornamentals. The leaves, roots and stems of *D. cannabina* yield a yellow dye once used for dyeing silk.

                                      S.R.C.

CUCURBITACEAE
The Gourd or Pumpkin Family

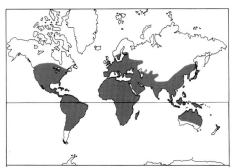

Number of genera: about 90
Number of species: about 700
Distribution: centered in the tropics, with some semidesert species.
Economic uses: major food plants, including cucumbers, marrows and squashes, gourds, melons, chayote, pumpkins, courgette and gherkin and many other uses.

The Cucurbitaceae is a medium-sized and botanically highly specialized family of mainly climbing plants. It is of major importance to Man as a source of food.

Distribution. The Cucurbitaceae is well represented in the moist and moderately dry tropics of both Old and New Worlds, particularly in rain forest areas of South America and wood-, grass- and bushland areas of Africa. Some species occur in semidesert or even desert vegetation. Cucurbits are poorly represented in Australasia and all temperate regions.

Diagnostic features. Members of the family are typically climbing plants with palmately veined leaves, spiraling tendrils, inferior ovaries and unisexual flowers with yellowish petals, as in the familiar cucumber, melon, watermelon, squashes and gourds. The few non-climbing species are probably derivative. Most are perennial herbs with a swollen tuberous rootstock which can be subterranean or wholly or partly superficial. Some are annual, a few are softly woody lianas. The rootstock is formed by swelling of the hypocotyl, which begins early in the seedling stage. The stems of most are characterized by bicollateral vascular bundles with internal as well as external phloem. The leaves are alternate, simple and palmately lobed or palmately compound with three or more leaflets. In most species a solitary, branched or unbranched tendril arises at the side of each leaf base. The tendril tip curls round any suitable nearby object, such as a plant stem; the rest of the tendril then coils in a spring-like manner, drawing the stem in close to its support. The flowers are nearly always unisexual, on the same or different plants. The sepals and petals (usually five of each) are borne at the top of a cup- or tube-like expanded receptacle (hypanthium); the petals are often more or less united at the base. The stamens are distinc-

tive for the union, in various degrees, of filaments and anthers, the reduction of the number of pollen sacs in each anther from four to two, and for the elaboration and convolution of the pollen sacs themselves. Commonly there are three stamens, two double with four pollen sacs each, one single with two pollen sacs, inserted on the lower part of the hypanthium. In other cases, the filaments are more or less completely fused into a single central column. In the female flowers, the ovary is inferior, usually with a single locule with one to three placentas attached to the walls. Ovules and seeds vary from one to many in each fruit; the ovules are anatropous and the seeds, which are without endosperm, usually large. The fruits may be berries, firm-walled berries (such as the melon) known as pepos, fleshy or dry capsules, or leathery and indehiscent.

Classification. There are two subfamilies: the Cucurbitoideae with eight tribes, and the single-tribed Zanonioideae.

SUBFAMILY CUCURBITOIDEAE
Plants with one style, tendrils unbranched or two- to seven-branched from the lower part, spiralling only above the point of branching; the pollen is various and the seeds unwinged.

JOLIFFIEAE. Ovules usually horizontal, hypanthium short; petals fimbriate or with basal scales; pollen reticulate. The tribe includes *Telfairia* (tropical Africa); *Momordica* (Old World tropics).

BENINCASEAE. Ovules horizontal; hypanthium in female flowers short; fruit usually smooth and indehiscent; pollen sacs convoluted and pollen usually reticulate. The tribe includes *Acanthosicyos* (south tropical Africa, with *Acanthosicyos horridus* a spiny shrub of the Namib desert dunes); *Ecballium* (Mediterranean); *Benincasa* (tropical Asia); *Bryonia* (Eurasia); *Coccinia* (Old World tropics); *Citrullus* (Old World tropics and subtropics).

MELOTHRIEAE. Ovules horizontal; hypanthium bell-shaped or cylindrical and alike in both sexes; pollen sacs straight or almost so, and pollen reticulate. Included are the genera *Dendrosicyos* (Socotra, with *Dendrosicyos socotranus* a small succulent-stemmed tree); *Trochomeria* (tropical Africa); *Corallocarpus* (Old World tropics); *Cucumeropsis* (tropical Africa); *Cucumis* (Africa and Asia); *Ibervillea* (southern North America); *Kedrostis* (Old World tropics); *Seyrigia* (Madagascar, leafless succulent lianas); *Zehneria* (Old World tropics); *Gurania* (New World tropics, lianas with a red or orange hypanthium and sepals, pollinated by hummingbirds).

SCHIZOPEPONEAE. Ovules pendulous in a three-locular ovary; three free stamens; fruit dehiscing explosively into three valves; pollen reticuloid. The tribe includes *Schizopepon* (eastern Asia).

CYCLANTHEREAE. One to many ovules, erect or ascending in a unilocular ovary with one to three placentas; stamen filaments united into

a central column; fruit often spiny, usually dehiscent, often explosively; pollen punctate, not spiny. The tribe includes *Apatzingania* (Mexico, fruits geocarpic); *Cyclanthera* (New World); *Elateriopsis* (New World tropics); *Marah* (southwestern United States); *Echinocystis* (North America).

SICYOEAE. Ovule single, pendulous in a unilocular ovary; filaments united into a central column; fruit one-seeded, indehiscent, usually hard or leathery; pollen spiny. Members of the tribe include *Polakowskia* (Central America); *Sechium* (Central America); *Sicyos* (New World, Pacific and Australia).

TRICHOSANTHEAE. Ovules horizontal; hypanthium long and tubular in both sexes; petals fimbriate or entire; fruit fleshy or dry and dehiscent by three valves; pollen striate, smooth or knobbly, not spiny. Members include *Hodgsonia* (tropical Asia); *Peponium* (Africa and Madagascar), *Trichosanthes* (tropical Asia).

CUCURBITEAE. Ovules horizontal or erect; fruit fleshy, indehiscent, and one- to many-seeded; pollen large, spiny, with numerous pores. Included are *Calycophysum* (tropical South America, pollinated by bats); *Cucurbita* (New World, pollinated by specialized solitary bees of the genera *Peponapis* and *Xenoglossa*); *Sicana* (tropical New World).

SUBFAMILY ZANONIOIDEAE
This subfamily comprises a single tribe, ZANONIEAE, with two or three styles, tendrils two-branched from near the apex, spiraling above and below the point of branching; ovules pendulous; pollen small, striate and uniform; seeds often winged. It includes *Fevillea* (tropical South America); *Alsomitra* (tropical Asia, with *Alsomitra macrocarpa*, a liana with large fruits and large, beautifully winged seeds); *Gerrardanthus* (tropical Africa); *Xerosicyos* (Madagascar, leaf-succulents); *Cyclantheropsis* (tropical Africa and Madagascar, fruit a one-seeded samara); *Zanonia* (Indomalaysia).

The relationships of the Cucurbitaceae are completely obscure, a fact recognized by their frequent classification in a single-family order, the Cucurbitales. They are unrelated to the bulk of families amongst which they were once placed, in or near the Campanulales. They resemble only superficially the Passifloraceae, near which they have been placed by some authors, while the Caricaceae, Loasaceae, Begoniaceae and Achariaceae, though similar in some features, differ widely in others. The Cucurbitaceae are highly specialized in habit, floral structure and biochemistry. Of the two subfamilies, the Zanonioideae is in some ways the less specialized.

Economic uses. Major food crops are produced in tropical, subtropical and temperate regions by *Cucurbita* species (pumpkins, squashes, gourds, vegetable marrows, courgettes, vegetable spaghetti), *Cucumis* species (*Cucumis melo*, melon, cantaloupe, honey-

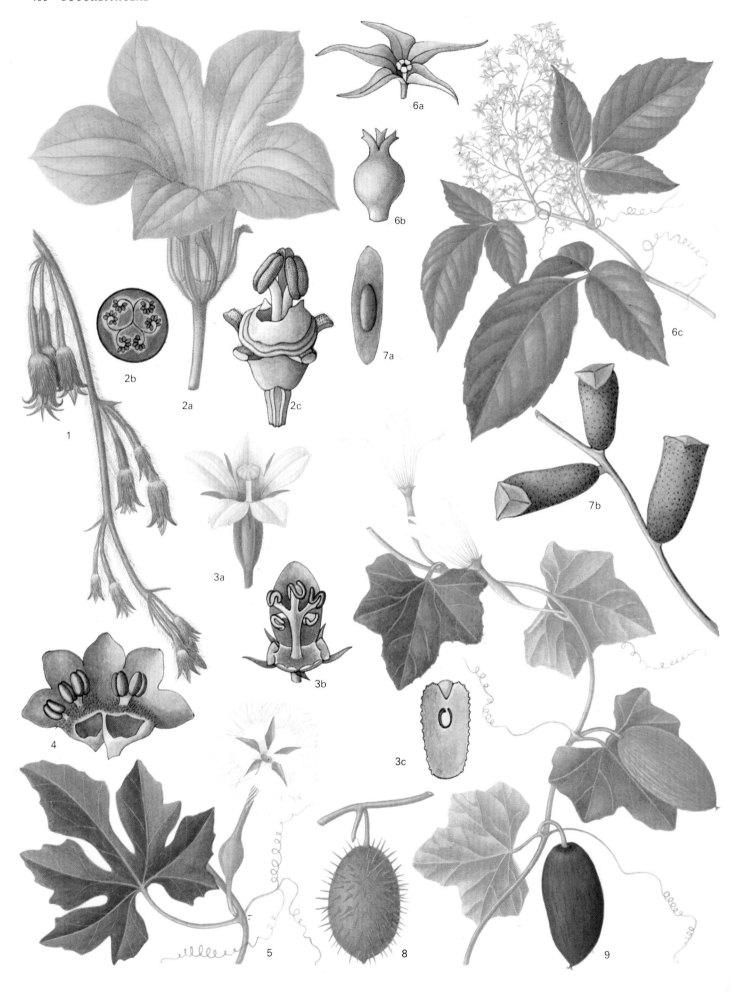

dew, and *C. sativus*, cucumber) and *Citrullus lanatus* (watermelon; citron). Other important food sources are *Cucumis anguria* (West Indian gherkin), *Lagenaria siceraria* (calabash, bottle gourd), *Benincasa hispida* (wax gourd), *Sechium edule* (chayote), *Luffa cylindrica* (loofah) and *L. acutangula*, *Trichosanthes cucumerina* var *anguina* (snake gourd), *Momordica charantia* (bitter melon; balsam apple), *Sicana odorifera* (cassa-

banana), *Cyclanthera pedata* (achocha), *Hodgsonia heteroclita* (lard fruit), *Telfairia occidentalis* (oyster nuts, the seeds yielding an edible oil), *Cucumeropsis mannii* (egussi), and *Praecitrullus fistulosus* (dilpasand, tinda). *Luffa cylindrica* is the source of loofah sponges (dried skeleton of the fruit), while dry fruits of *Lagenaria siceraria* have been used as containers since ancient times. This species is one of the earliest of man's cultivated plants and the only one with an archaeologically documented prehistory in both Old and New Worlds. Fruits of wild *Citrullus lanatus* (tsamma), *Acanthosicyos naudinianus* and *A. horridus* (narras) are important sources of food and water in the desert areas of southern Africa.

Bitter substances, known as cucurbitacins, are widespread in the family. Many of the edible species occur in both bitter (inedible) and non-bitter (edible) variants.

As ornamentals, Cucurbitaceae are of minor importance; *Cucurbita pepo* produces the ornamental gourds and species of *Momordica, Kedrostis, Corallocarpus, Ibervillea, Seyrigia, Gerrardanthus, Xerosicyos* and *Cyclantheropsis* are sometimes cultivated by succulent enthusiasts.   C.J.

SALICALES

SALICACEAE
Aspens, Poplars and Willows
The Salicaceae is a family of mostly north temperate trees and shrubs containing the aspens, the poplars and the willows.
Distribution. The family is common throughout the north temperate zone. Two of the genera, *Salix*, the willows, and *Populus*, the aspens and poplars, are well known, but the other two contain very few species restricted to northeast Asia. There are a few Southern Hemisphere and tropical species.

Most willows are shrubs or small trees; few are forest trees and few are ever ecological dominants. Most are scrub or marginal species, being particularly common in wet places and on mountains. Most poplars, on the other hand, are tall trees and some can dominate the landscape in northern areas.
Diagnostic features. The leaves are simple, usually alternate, have stipules and are almost invariably deciduous. The flowers are unisexual, male and female flowers borne on separate plants.

Cucurbitaceae. 1 *Gurania speciosa* female flowers (×⅔). 2 *Curcurbita moschata* (a) male flower (×⅔); (b) cross section of ovary (×⅔); (c) female flower with petals and sepals removed (×⅔). 3 *Sechium edule* (a) female flower with discoid stigma (×1⅓); (b) stamens partly joined in a single column (×2); (c) vertical section of ovary with single pendulous ovule (×2). 4 *Kedrostis courtallensis* male flower opened out to show two double and one single epipetalous stamens (×4). 5 *Trichosanthes tricuspidata* leaf, tendril and female flower (×⅔). 6 *Gynostemma pentaphyllum* (a) female flower (×6); (b) young fruit with remains of styles (×8); (c) leafy shoot with tendrils and inflorescence (×⅔). 7 *Zanonia indica* (a) winged seed (×¼); (b) fruits (×⅔). 8 *Echinocystis lobata* fruit (×⅔). 9 *Coccinea grandis* leaves, tendrils, female flowers and fruit (×⅔).

Salicaceae. 1 *Populus sieboldii* (a) leafy shoot and pendulous fruiting catkins (×⅔); (b) young female catkin (×⅔); (c) female flower with cup-like disk (×6); (d) ovary (×6); (e) stigmas (×6); (f) shoot with young male catkin (×⅔); (g) male flower (×6); (h) mature male catkins together with remains of one from the previous year (×⅔). 2 *P. nigra* 'Italica' (Lombardy poplar) habit. 3 *Salix caprea* (a) leaves (×⅔); (b) young female catkins (×⅔); (c) female flower and bract (×6); (d) vertical section of female flower (×6); (e) cross section of ovary (×8); (f) mature female catkins (×⅔); (g) male catkin; (h) male flower (×6).

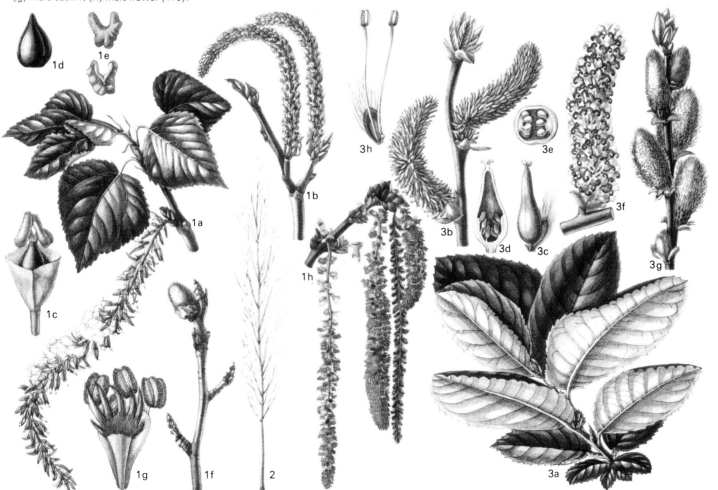

Number of genera: 4
Number of species: about 350
Distribution: temperate with few in tropics and S Hemisphere.
Economic uses: wood used for pulp, matches, and boxes, osiers for basket making and some are popular ornamentals.

The flowers are borne in catkins which usually appear before or at the same time as the leaves, in early spring. The individual flowers occur in the axil of a small bract, and lack petals or sepals. The male flowers usually have two up to 30 free or united stamens. The female flower has a bicarpellate, unilocular, superior ovary with numerous anatropous ovules on parietal or basal placentas. The style may be short or long and is often divided.

The method of pollination is markedly different in the two main genera. In *Populus* the catkins are pendulous and scentless; they dangle in the breeze and pollination is effected by wind. There are no nectaries but there is a disk- or cup-shaped gland of unknown function at the base of each flower. In *Salix* the catkins are rigid and furnished with one or two small knob-like glands at the base of each flower. These glands secrete a sweetly-scented nectar and are very attractive to insects, particularly bees and moths, which effect pollination. Willows can be an important source of food for hive bees in early spring, and are also popular with lepidopterists hunting for early moths. Of the other two small genera, *Chosenia* is wind- and *Toisusu* insect-pollinated.

The fruits of all the species are small capsules bearing numerous seeds, each furnished with a tuft of hairs to aid in dispersal by wind. Many species shed the whole catkin once the seed is ripe, often forming cottony drifts under the trees in late spring. The seeds have no endosperm and a straight embryo.

Hybrids are very common in both the poplars and willows, and there is a hybrid in Japan between a species of *Chosenia* and one of *Toisusu*. A great many artificial hybrids have also been synthesized by plant breeders, and, since these hybrids are often subsequently propagated vegetatively, many of them are known as one sex only.

Classification The Salicaceae is a taxonomically isolated family. Some authorities suggest that it is a florally reduced derivative of the order Violales, and others propose a closer relationship with the Flacourtiaceae and Tamaricaceae.

Economic uses. Although the timber of willows and poplars is not of high quality it is put to a great many uses, and the rapid growth of the plants is an asset. They are important natural resources in some countries and have been extensively planted in others, for example poplars in France. The wood is used principally for pulp, matches and boxes. Willows, particularly the weeping willow, are popular ornamentals, and their supple twigs are used in basket-making. A specialized use of the willow is in the making of cricket bats. Willow bark is used for tanning and some medicines.

C.A.S.

Capparaceae. 1 *Capparis spinosa* (a) leafy shoot with spiny recurved stipules and large, solitary, axillary flowers ($\times\frac{2}{3}$); fruit (b) entire and (c) in cross section ($\times\frac{2}{3}$). 2 *Dipterygium glaucum* winged seed ($\times 6$). 3 *Cleome hirta* (a) leafy shoot with flowers and capsular fruits ($\times\frac{2}{3}$); (b) half flower with toothed sepals, two petals, six curved stamens and ovary with numerous ovules ($\times 2\frac{1}{2}$). 4 *Podandrogyne brachycarpa* fruit—a capsule ($\times 1$). 5 *Buhsia trinervia* dry inflated fruit ($\times 1$).

CAPPARALES

CAPPARACEAE
Capers

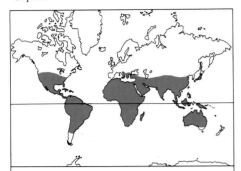

Number of genera: 40–50
Number of species: about 700
Distribution: tropics (particularly Africa) and subtropics.
Economic uses: condiments (capers) and garden flowers.

The Capparaceae is a medium-sized family related to the Cruciferae, containing herbs, trees and shrubs and some lianas. Few of its members are of horticultural or economic importance; the best-known are the capers.

Distribution. The family is found in the warmer parts of the world, mainly in the tropics and subtropics of both hemispheres and in the Mediterranean. It is well represented by about 15 genera in Africa where it forms a conspicuous element of the flora of dry regions.

Diagnostic features. The leaves are alternate, rarely opposite, and simple or palmate or digitate. They have two to seven leaflets and minute or spiny stipules which are persistent or caducous. The inflorescences are terminal or axillary, and may be racemose or corymbose, or the flowers may be solitary or fascicled and often showy. The flowers are bisexual or rarely unisexual (the sexes then on separate plants). They are usually irregular, with four to eight sepals which are free or variously joined, in some cases forming a hood which dehisces and falls off at flowering time. There are four to sixteen petals (sometimes absent), which may be equal, or the two posterior ones larger. The stamens range from four to many: when there are six stamens, four of them may be considered as derived from the splitting of the middle pair during development; higher numbers are similarly derived, and then many of the filaments lack anthers. Often there is a development of the axis between the petals and the stamens producing an internode called an androgynophore, bearing the androecium and gynoecium. The ovary may be sessile, but is more usually borne on an internodal development between the androecium and gynoecium called a gynophore; it is superior, of two fused carpels, and has one locule with parietal placentas, or may be divided by false septa into two or more locules; the ovules are few to numerous. There is a single style and the stigma is bilobed or capitate. The fruit is a capsule dehiscing by valves, sometimes with the appearance of a siliqua, or a round to cylindrical berry, rarely a single-seeded indehiscent nut. The seeds are without endosperm and the embryo is variously folded. A curious feature is the development of the axis in the form of swellings, disks or tubular structures, sometimes inside, sometimes outside the corolla. Pollination is by insects, and possibly by bats in some South American species.

Classification. It is generally agreed that the Capparaceae is allied to the Cruciferae and may have evolved from a common ancestor. Relationships with the Papaveraceae and Resedaceae have also been suggested. The Capparaceae contains many woody members, and the anatomy of the wood shows several advanced features.

Economic uses. Capers of commerce are derived from the flower buds of *Capparis* species. Several species are cultivated as garden plants, especially *Cleome spinosa*, the spider flower, a strongly scented annual with white or pink flowers. Species of *Capparis*, *Gynandropsis* and *Polanisia* are also grown occasionally as garden plants.
V.H.H.

TOVARIACEAE

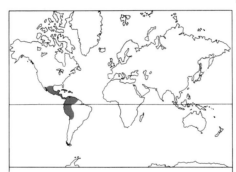

Number of genera: 1
Number of species: 2
Distribution: tropical America and the Caribbean.
Economic uses: none.

The Tovariaceae is a small family consisting of one genus (*Tovaria*) and two species of tropical shrubs or annual herbs.

Distribution. The family is native to tropical America and the Caribbean area.

Diagnostic features. The two species are herbs or shrubs with pungent smelling parts, and alternate, trifoliolate leaves without stipules. The flowers are regular, bisexual, hypogynous in lax terminal racemes, and consist of eight narrow sepals with overlapping edges, eight petals and eight free stamens with hairy filaments, dilated near the base. The ovary is superior and has six to eight fused carpels, with six to eight locules containing numerous ovules borne on axile placentas; the locules are formed by membranous dividing walls. The style is short with a lobed stigma. The fruits are berries, mucilaginous when young, but with a membranous outer coat. They are about 0.4in (1cm) in diameter. The many small, shiny seeds have curved embryos and a sparse endosperm.

Classification. Both species are green-barked shrubs which sometimes behave like annuals. In *Tovaria pendula*, which occurs in Peru, Bolivia and into Venezuela, the flowers and fruits are greenish, the anthers brown or yellow. The other species, *T. diffusa*, grows in dense, wet thickets in the mountains of Central America and the West Indies, and has pale green or yellow flowers and very long sparsely-flowered racemes.

The Tovariaceae is related to the Capparaceae, but has fruits reminiscent of certain members of the Phytolaccaceae.

Economic uses. No economic uses have been recorded for this family.
B.M.

CRUCIFERAE
The Mustard Family

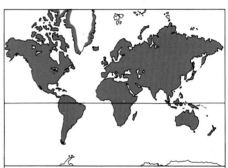

Number of genera: about 380
Number of species: about 3,000
Distribution: cosmopolitan, mostly temperate, with centers in the Mediterranean region, SW and central Asia.
Economic uses: many important vegetable, fodder and oilseed crops and popular garden flowers.

The Cruciferae is a large natural family of major economic importance, containing a wide array of crop plants grown as salads, vegetables, for oilseed, animal feed and condiments, and several well-known garden ornamental plants such as the wallflower, honesty and aubretia.

Distribution. Members of the family are found in most parts of the world but are mainly concentrated in the north temperate region and more especially in the countries surrounding the Mediterranean basin and in southwestern and central Asia, where more genera occur than anywhere else in the world. The family is only sparingly represented in the Southern Hemisphere, and there are very few species in tropical regions. In the Mediterranean area 113 genera occur of which 21 (17%) are endemic, and 625 species of which 284 (45%) are endemic. The Irano-Turanian region has 147 genera of which 62 (42%) are endemic and 874 species of which 524 (60%) are endemic, while in the Saharo-Sindian region there are 65 genera, 19 (30%) being endemic and 180 species, 62 (34%) of which are endemic. Two of the tribes (see below) are confined to South Africa – the Chamireae containing a single species, *Chamira circaeoides*, and the Heliophileae comprising mainly the genus *Heliophila* with about 70 species mostly confined to the winter rainfall area around the Cape. Another tribe, the Pringleeae, contains as its sole member the species *Pringlea antiscorbutica*, the Kerguelen Island cabbage, found only on the remote islands of Kerguelen and Crozet in the Southern Hemisphere.

Diagnostic features. The Cruciferae are mostly annual to perennial herbs, rarely small shrubs such as *Alyssum spinosum* or tall shrubs reaching up to 6.5ft (2m) in height (eg *Heliophila glauca* from South Africa), and very rarely "climbers" such as *H. scandens* which attains a height of 10ft (3m). An unusual aquatic species is *Subularia aquatica*, a usually submerged annual with long narrow leaves, circular in cross-section. The curious hummocks of *Xerodraba pycnophylloides* from the Andes of Argentina are known as vegetable sheep. The stems become spiny in *Vella* and some *Alyssum* species. A very curious habit is shown by *Anastatica hierochuntica*, rose of Jericho, which becomes detached from the soil when the seeds begin to ripen in the dry season; the leaves fall off and the branches inroll so that the whole plant becomes an intricate ball which is blown about, containing the enclosed seed pods, until it reaches a wet area suitable for germination.

The leaves are usually alternate and without stipules. The hairs of the indumentum vary from simple to forked, many-branched, star-like or peltate, features which are useful for identification of genera and species.

The inflorescence is usually a raceme or corymb, usually without bracts or bracteoles. The basic floral structure is highly characteristic and constant: four sepals, four cruciform petals, six stamens, (four long and two short) and an ovary with two parietal placentas. There are, however, some exceptions to this plan. The flowers are usually bisexual, regular and hypogynous. There are four sepals; sometimes the inner ones are convexly swollen at the base and contain nectar secreted by the nectaries at the base of the stamens. The petals are four, arranged in the form of a cross (cruciform, hence the name of the family), rarely absent as in some *Lepidium* and *Coronopus* species, free, often clawed, imbricate or contorted. In a few genera such as *Teesdalia* and *Iberis* (candytuft) the outer petals are radiate and larger than the inner. The stamens are typically six, and tetradynamous, that is one outer pair with short filaments, and two inner pairs, one

posterior, one anterior, with long filaments. There may be only four stamens in some species of *Cardamine* and up to 16 in *Megacarpaea*. The filaments are sometimes winged or with tooth-like appendages. The shape and disposition of the nectaries at the base of the stamens is variable and widely used in the classification of the family. The nectaries appear like swellings or little cushions. The ovary is superior, of two carpels and is syncarpous, with two parietal placentas, usually with two locules through the formation of a membranous false septum or replum by the union of outgrowths from the placentas; sometimes the ovary is transversely plurilocular. The stigma is capitate to bilobed.

As characteristic as the flower is the fruit, which is basically a bilocular capsule with a false septum (replum), usually dehiscent, opening by two valves from below. When it is at least three times as long as wide it is called a siliqua, and when less than three times as long as wide, a silicula. The fruit may sometimes be indehiscent, breaking into single-seeded portions; rarely it is transversely articulate with dehiscent and indehiscent segments, sometimes breaking at maturity into single-seeded portions (lomentum). The fruits range from linear-oblong to ovate to spherical; they may be winged or not and stalked or not; the seeds may be in one or two rows.

The range of variation shown in fruit types is vast and fruit characters are relied upon very extensively in the classification of the family at tribal, generic and specific level. Examples of unusual or anomalous fruits are *Cakile* which has siliquas which divide into two single-seeded joints, the lower sterile and forming a thick stalk, the upper indehiscent, globose and single-seeded; *Lunaria* (honesty) in which the silicula is flattened laterally to give a very broad septum; or the silicula may be compressed anterior-posteriorly to give a very narrow septum as in *Capsella* (shepherd's purse). *Geococcus pusillus* from Australia buries its fruits by sharply reflexing its pedicels at fruiting time, thus forcing the fruit into the soil. Similarly *Morisia hypogea* from Sardinia and Corsica is a stemless species whose peduncles bend downwards after flowering and bury the closed pod in the ground. The seeds are non-endospermous and the testa often contains mucilaginous cells of various types which swell up when wetted and produce a halo of mucilage. The ovules are campylotropous, the embryo being curved with the radicle in one half of the seed and the cotyledons in the other.

Great taxonomic importance is attached to the shape of the embryo and the position of the radicle relative to the cotyledons. The main types recognized are: (1) notorhizal with the radicle incumbent, ie lying on the back of one cotyledon, the cotyledons not being folded on themselves; (2) pleurorhizal,

with the radicle accumbent, against the edges of the cotyledons; (3) orthoplocous, with the cotyledons conduplicate; (4) spirolobous, as in (1) but with the cotyledons once folded; (5) diplecolobous, as in (4) but with the cotyledons folded twice or more.

Classification. Various attempts have been made to produce a natural subdivision of the family into tribes, using fruit characters, embryo features, nectary glands, distribution of myrosine cells in the embryos and other such features, but the most widely used is that proposed by O. E. Schulz in a posthumous classification published in 1936. This classification was based on a wide range of features. Various modifications have been suggested, notably by Janchen, and it has to be admitted that several of the tribes are far from being satisfactory. Only two of the tribes, the Brassiceae and the Lepideae, can be regarded as natural, apart from the monotypic ones (Pringleae and Chamireae) which are confined to South Africa. The tribes usually recognized are:

THELYPODIEAE. *Stanleya, Macropodium*
PRINGLEEAE. *Pringlea.*
SISYMBRIEAE. *Sisymbrium, Braya, Alliaria, Arabidopsis.*
HESPERIDEAE. *Hesperis, Cheiranthus, Matthiola, Anastatica.*
ARABIDEAE. *Arabis, Aubrieta, Barbarea, Cardamine, Armoracia, Nasturtium, Isatis, Rorippa.*
ALYSSEAE. *Alyssum, Lunaria, Lesquerella, Draba, Berteroa.*
LEPIDIEAE. *Lepidium, Cochlearia, Camelina, Capsella, Iberis, Biscutella, Thlaspi.*
BRASSICEAE. *Brassica, Raphanus, Sinapis, Diplotaxis, Crambe, Rapistrum, Cakile, Morisia, Eruca, Moricandia.*
CHAMIREAE. *Chamira.*
SCHIZOPETALEAE. *Schizopetalum.*
STENOPETALEAE. *Stenopetalum.*
HELIOPHILEAE. *Heliophila.*
CREMOLOBEAE. *Cremolobus, Hexaptera.*

The closest ally to the Cruciferae is generally accepted to be the Capparaceae with which it shows close similarity in the androecium, gynoecium and other features. The genus *Cleome* in the Capparaceae is

Cruciferae. 1 *Iberis pinnata* leafy shoot and inflorescence with flowers having outer petals longer than the inner ($\times\frac{2}{3}$). 2 *Heliophila coronopifolia* shoot with leaves, flowers and fruit ($\times\frac{2}{3}$). 3 *Moricandia arvensis* (a) shoot with sessile leaves, flowers and fruit ($\times\frac{2}{3}$); (b) half flower showing stamens with long and short filaments ($\times 3$). 4 *Biscutella didyma* var *leiocarpa* (a) shoot with leaves, flowers and fruit ($\times\frac{2}{3}$); (b) fruit—a silicula ($\times 4$). 5 *Crambe cordifolia* spherical fruit ($\times 4$). 6 *Isatis tinctoria* fruit—a siliqua ($\times 2$). 7 *Lunaria annua* fruit—a flattened silicula ($\times 1$). 8 *Capsella bursa-pastoris* dehiscing fruit—a silicula with a narrow septum ($\times 6$). 9 *Berteroa incana* fruit—a silicula dehiscing from the apex ($\times 4$). 10 *Thlaspi arvense* cross section of bilocular ovary showing false septum ($\times 12$). 11 *Cheiranthus cheiri* fruit—a siliqua ($\times 1$).

especially close to members of the Cruciferae. Chemically the two families also show similarities. On the other hand there is no reason to regard the Cruciferae as having been derived from the Capparaceae, as has been suggested in the past, and the two families are better regarded as both having evolved from a common stock.

Economic uses. While the Cruciferae contains a considerable number and diversity of crop plants, it is not comparable with, say, the Leguminosae or Gramineae, and although the crop species are mainly grown as food plants they do not form a substantial part of staple diets. Many cruciferous species are used as condiments or garnishes, such as mustard and cress, and many are collected from the wild rather than cultivated. Many cruciferous crops have been cultivated since ancient times, such as *Brassica oleracea*; the ancestral cabbage was cultivated about 8,000 years ago in coastal areas of northern Europe whence it was introduced into the Mediterranean and eastern Europe. The first selection of sprouting broccoli was probably made in Greece and Italy in the pre-Christian era. (See also page 64.)

All important cruciferous crops are propagated from seed; only minor crops such as watercress, horseradish and seakale are vegetatively propagated.

The seed crops can be divided into oils and mustard condiments; forage and fodder crops; and vegetables and salads for human consumption. Cruciferous oil seeds now rank fifth in importance behind soybeans, cotton seed, groundnut and sunflower seed. The main crops are derived from *Brassica campestris* (*B. rapa* (oilseed rape)) but *B. juncea* is important in Asia and *B. napus* (oilseed rape, colza) is cultivated in temperate Europe and Asia. Mustard is obtained from the ground seed of *Brassica juncea*, *B. nigra* and *Sinapis alba*.

Animal feeds are supplied by cruciferous crops in the form of silage, seed meal left over after oil extraction, forage crops grazed in the field, and stored root fodder, used for winter feeds. The characteristic glucosinolates produced by Cruciferae affect the use of many species economically. Glucosinolates are the precursors of the mustard oils which are responsible for the pungency of most crucifers. Although desirable in the case of some crops such as mustard, radish and horseradish, they may also be responsible for toxic manifestations when used as animal feed or in human nutrition. Because of this the production of silage from crucifers is limited. Seed meal is obtained from species such as *Brassica napus*, especially races with a low glucosinolate content. Forage and fodder crops of crucifers are restricted mainly to countries such as Britain, the Netherlands and New Zealand which specialize in intensive small-scale farming of ruminants. The range of species used as forage crops includes *Brassica*

oleracea (kale, cabbage), *B. campestris, B. napus* (rapes) and *Raphanus sativus* (fodder radish); fodder crops include those with swollen stems or root storage organs such as *B. oleracea* (kohlrabi), *B. campestris* (turnip) and *B. napus* (swede).

Considerable proportions of the vegetable crop acreage in Europe and Asia are formed by cruciferous species – some European countries have up to 30% of their vegetable acreages devoted to crucifers compared with 6% in the United States of America. There are some curious geographical differences in what is cultivated, reflecting more national taste rather than the geographical origins of the crops. Thus the Brussels sprout is very much a British crop, with the British production equalling that of the rest of Europe and ten times that of the United States. Likewise cauliflowers are mainly a European crop. The most important species are *Brassica oleracea*, cultivars of which produce kales, Brussels sprouts, kohlrabi, cabbage, broccoli, calabrese and cauliflower, and *B. campestris* which produces turnip, Chinese cabbage, etc.

Ornamental genera include wallflower (*Cheiranthus*), honesty (*Lunaria*), candytuft (*Iberis*), sweet alysson (*Lobularia maritima*), golden alyssum (*Alyssum* spp.), stocks (*Matthiola*), rocket (*Hesperis*), rock cress (*Arabis*), *Draba, Aethionema Erysimum* and *Aubrieta*.   V.H.H.

RESEDACEAE
Mignonette

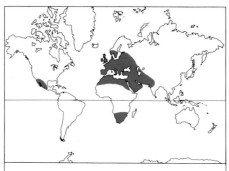

Number of genera: 6
Number of species: about 75
Distribution: centered in the Mediterranean region.
Economic uses: minor uses include sources of a yellow dye, perfume oil and an ornamental (*Reseda odorata*).

The Resedaceae is a small family of herbs and shrubs mostly of dry places, and contains some ornamentals.

Distribution. Centered on the Mediterranean region, the family extends into parts of northern Europe, and eastward to Central Asia and India. *Oligomeris* (nine species) is widely distributed, with outliers in South Africa, the Canary Islands and a single species in the southwestern United States and Mexico. *Caylusea* (three species) spreads from the Cape Verde Islands across northern

Africa to India. *Reseda* (60 species), by far the largest genus, is restricted to Europe and the Mediterranean region to Central Asia.

Diagnostic features. The leaves are alternate and entire or divided; glandular stipules are present. The flowers are irregular, usually bisexual, arranged in a bracteate raceme or spike. There are two to eight sepals which are usually free, sometimes unequal. The petals (occasionally absent) also number two to eight but are not always equal in number to the sepals; they are mostly broadly clawed, with a scale-like appendage at the base and usually a more or less deeply cut lamina. The stamens and ovary are often on a short androgynophore, an upward extension of the receptacle, and there is usually an irregular disk outside the three to 45 stamens. The ovary is superior, of two to seven more or less fused carpels, which are open above, and one locule in which the ovules are usually on parietal placentas. The fruit is usually an indehiscent open capsule, rarely of separate, spreading carpels; *Ochradenus* has a berry. The seeds are kidney-shaped, with a caruncle, curved embryo and very little endosperm.

Classification. The family is divisible into three tribes, based mainly on the placentation. Thus *Sesamoides*, the only genus in the ASTROCARPEAE, has one, rarely two pendulous ovules in the center of the abaxial wall of the almost free carpels. The CAYLUSEEAE, again with a single genus (*Caylusea*), have 10–18 erect ovules on a united basal placenta. The rest of the genera belong to the RESEDEAE, with numerous, pendulous ovules on parietal marginal placentas.

The family is generally considered to be allied to the Cruciferae and Capparaceae.

Economic uses. *Reseda odorata* (mignonette) provides a perfume oil and is grown for ornament and *R. luteola* yields a reddish yellow dye.   I.B.K.R.

MORINGACEAE

The Moringaceae is a family of small, quick-growing deciduous trees. They are gummy, pale-barked and their stems are often thickened with myrosin cells.

Distribution. The family has a distribution from the Mediterranean and North Africa to the Arabian peninsula and India, and is also represented in southwestern Africa and Madagascar.

Diagnostic features. The very graceful leaves are two or three times pinnate and alternate; stipules may be present or replaced by stipitate glands. The numerous flowers are irregular, bisexual, sweet-scented, cream or red, and produced in axillary panicles. The petals are unequal, five in number and slightly longer than the sepals, which have five short, unequal, spreading, reflexed lobes. Five stamens alternate with five staminodes, and all are joined at the base into a cupular disk. The anthers have one locule which

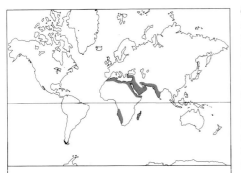

Number of genera: 1
Number of species: 12
Distribution: mainly Mediterranean to India and N Africa.
Economic uses: source of ben oil and some cultivated as ornamentals.

Classification. The family is represented by only one genus, *Moringa*, with 12 species including *Moringa oleifera*, the ben oil or horseradish tree. It forms a link between the Capparaceae and Leguminosae.

Economic uses. The seed of *M. oleifera* is the source of ben oil, formerly used only as a lubricant by watch-makers and others, but now used as a salad oil and in soap manufacture. The young swollen roots are eaten as a vegetable, the similarity of which to horseradish accounts for the common name attributed to the species. All species grow rapidly from seed and are used as boundary markers; some are grown as ornamentals.   S.A.H.

ERICALES

CLETHRACEAE
Lily-of-the-valley Tree

The Clethraceae is a family of tropical and subtropical evergreen or deciduous shrubs, represented by one genus, *Clethra*, with about 120 species. "Clethra" is the Greek name for alder, and is applied to this genus on account of the resemblance of some

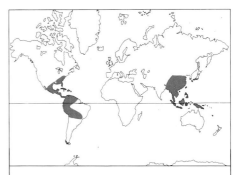

Number of genera: 1
Number of species: about 120
Distribution: tropical and subtropical America and Asia; Madeira.
Economic uses: some ornamentals.

species of *Clethra* to those of alder (*Alnus*).
Distribution. The family is found in tropical and subtropical Asia and America, and also Madeira.
Diagnostic features. The majority of the members of the family, excluding *Clethra arborea*, attain only large shrub-size and bear alternate, simple leaves without stipules. The flowers are bisexual, regular, white and borne in racemes or panicles, without

dehisces by slits. The ovary is superior, of three fused carpels, usually becoming unilocular with parietal placentas bearing numerous biseriate pendulous anatropous ovules. There are two to four slender styles. The fruit is an elongated pod-like capsule with three valves, and contains many black, rounded, winged or wingless seeds without endosperm and a straight embryo.

Resedaceae. 1 *Randonia africana* (a) shoot bearing flowers and fruit ($\times\frac{2}{3}$); (b) flower showing petals with incised margins ($\times 4$); (c) vertical section of flower showing numerous stamens and superior ovary with ovules on axile placentas ($\times 4$); (d) fruit—a capsule ($\times 4$). 2 *Sesamoides canescens* (a) leafy shoot, inflorescences and fruits ($\times\frac{2}{3}$); (b) flower with equal green sepals and both incised and linear petals ($\times 10$); (c) dehiscing fruit ($\times 8$). 3 *Reseda villosa* (a) shoot bearing fruits ($\times\frac{2}{3}$); (b) tip of inflorescence ($\times\frac{2}{3}$); (c) vertical section of flower showing sessile stigma on top of ovary ($\times 3$); (d) flower showing small petals ($\times 2$); (e) dehisced fruit with apical opening ($\times 3$).

bracteoles. There are five sepals, five free petals and two whorls each of five stamens; the anthers are bent outwards in bud and open by pores. The ovary is superior, of three fused carpels and contains three locules and numerous ovules on axile placentas in each locule. The style is three-lobed. The fruit is a loculicidal capsule with many, often winged seeds that have fleshy endosperm and a cylindrical embryo.

Classification. The family is closely related to the Ericaceae and Cyrillaceae.

Economic uses. The best-known ornamental is *C. arborea*, the lily-of-the-valley tree of Madeira, which grows larger than other members of the family and can form a multi-stemmed tree about 25ft (8m) high. In late spring and early summer, the tree is a cascade of fragrant white bell-like flowers, borne in terminal drooping panicles up to 6in (15cm) long. The flowers are similar to those of *Erica*, and borne on delicately spikey stalks, giving the general appearance of a large specimen of the lily of the valley. The leaves are similar to those of *Rhododendron*, about 2in–4in (5cm–10cm) long and half as wide, with serrated edges and woolly beneath. The young shoots are covered with fine hairs and are rust-colored.

Several other species including *C. arborea*, *C. alnifolia* (sweet pepper bush), *C. acuminata* (white alder), *C. monostachya* and *C. tomentosa*, are also known in cultivation as ornamental, fragrant-flowered shrubs.

S.A.H.

GRUBBIACEAE

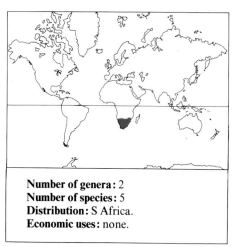

Number of genera: 2
Number of species: 5
Distribution: S Africa.
Economic uses: none.

The Grubbiaceae is a family of two genera and five species of small heath-like shrubs.

Distribution. The family is native to South Africa.

Diagnostic features. The leaves are opposite and in four rows, simple, narrow and without stipules.

The flowers are bisexual, small and sessile. They are arranged in small cone-like inflorescences in the axils of the leaves. The structure of the flower is variously interpreted but is probably as follows: two bract-like sepals and two vestigial sepals,

petals absent or in a 2+2 arrangement surrounding eight stamens. The stamens are in two whorls, sometimes with the filaments laterally compressed. The anthers have two locules and dehisce laterally, by reflexion of the pollen sac wall. The flower has an annular, hairy disk. The ovary is inferior, composed of two fused carpels, and has two locules, each with a single pendulous, anatropous ovule. The style is simple, terminating in a simple bifid stigma. The fruit is a drupe. In some cases the ovaries of several adjacent flowers become coherent or connate, in which case the fruit is a drupe-like or achene-like syncarp. There is only one seed per carpel in the syncarp and it possesses a thin testa and fleshy or oily endosperm surrounding a central linear embryo.

Classification. According to some systems this family is composed of only a single genus, *Grubbia*, with five species, but one, *Grubbia strictus*, is considered sufficiently distinct to warrant a separate generic status as *Strobilocarpus*.

It has been suggested that the Grubbiceae could be related either to the Olacaceae or to the Santalaceae. It shares with both these the features of woody habit, simple leaves, small perianth, nectar-secreting disk and endospermic seeds. However, there is perhaps a stronger affinity with the Empetraceae, which is another family of heath-like shrubs, with linear leaves and no stipules, bracteate flowers, solitary ovule in each locule of the ovary, and an endospermic seed with a straight embryo.

Economic uses. No economic uses for this family have been recorded. S.R.C.

CYRILLACEAE
Leatherwood and Buckwheat Trees

The Cyrillaceae is a small family of three genera of deciduous or evergreen shrubs or small trees.

Distribution. Two of the three genera, *Cyrilla* and *Cliftonia*, each containing one species, are native to southeast North America. The 12 species of *Purdiaea* are found mostly in Cuba, but extend into Central and South America.

Diagnostic features. The leaves are alternate, simple, and without stipules. The flowers are regular, bisexual and arranged in racemose inflorescences. The five sepals are separate or fused at the base, persistent and often enlarged in the fruit. The five petals are equal, free or fused at the base, and may be imbricate.

The stamens are normally ten, in two whorls of five, but the inner whorl may be replaced by sterile staminodes or in some species may be absent altogether. They have free filaments and are inserted on the receptacle, surrounding a superior ovary formed of two to five fused carpels. The ovary has two to four locules with one to numerous pendulous ovules, borne on axile placentas. The ovary is surmounted by a

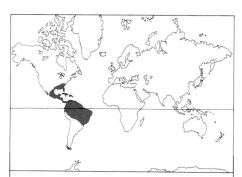

Number of genera: 3
Number of species: 14
Distribution: SE N America, Central and S America.
Economic uses: a few ornamentals.

short style (absent in some species) and there are one to three narrow stigmas. The fruit is a capsule or drupe and has two to four wings in those species where the calyx is enlarged. The seeds have a small straight embryo, enclosed in fleshy endosperm.

Classification. The genera can be separated on the presence or absence of an enlarged calyx at fruiting, and on details of floral structure such as stamen number and nature of the style. Thus *Cliftonia* is characterized by possessing 10 stamens, deciduous calyx (not enlarged after flowering) and very short style divided into three stigmas. *Purdiaea* also possesses 10 stamens, but the calyx becomes enlarged, enveloping the fruit, and the style is slender and undivided. On the other hand *Cyrilla* has only five stamens and a thick, short style ending in a two- or three-lobed stigma.

The family is often regarded as belonging to the Ericales. However, it is distinguished from the rest of the order by the presence of racemose inflorescences, the slight degree of fusion of the petal bases, and by the winged capsular or drupe-like fruit and is sometimes placed in another order, the Celastrales.

Economic uses. There is no economically important species in this family but two shrubs, the leatherwood *(Cyrilla racemosa)* and the buckwheat tree *(Cliftonia monophylla)* possess attractive white flowers and reddish-tinted autumnal foliage, and are grown as ornamentals in gardens.

S.R.C.

ERICACEAE
The Heath Family

The Ericaceae is a large family, mainly of shrubs, containing many well-known genera such as *Rhododendron, Erica* (heath), *Calluna* (heather), *Vaccinium* (blueberries, cranberries etc) and *Gaultheria* (wintergreen).

Distribution. Considered overall, the family is found in almost all parts of the world. It is, however, absent from most of Australia where it is largely replaced by the related family Epacridaceae. The distributions of some of the genera are of more interest than that of the family as a whole. The two largest

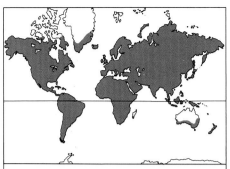

Number of genera: about 100
Number of species: about 3,000
Distribution: cosmopolitan with large concentrations in the Himalayas, New Guinea and southern Africa.
Economic uses: many important horticultural species (rhododendrons, azaleas, heaths and heathers), some edible berries (cranberries and bilberries) and occasional use for timber.

genera are *Rhododendron*, with about 1,200 described species, and *Erica* with over 500 species. Both of these genera show remarkable concentrations of species in relatively small areas. *Rhododendron* has a massing of

more than 700 of its species in the area where China, Tibet, Burma and Assam all meet – the area in which the great rivers of eastern Asia (the Brahmaputra, Irrawaddy, Salween, Mekong and Yangtse) break through the Himalayan chain. The genus also has a secondary center of almost 300 species in New Guinea. The rest of the species are found in the Himalayas and Japan, with a small number occurring in Europe, southern Asia and the United States of America. *Erica* has an even more remarkable concentration of species in southern Africa, where about 450 occur, many of them restricted to the Cape Province. The rest of the species are found in Africa, in the Mediterranean region, and in southern and western Europe. *Gaultheria* also has an interesting distribution, though not one which involves marked concentrations of species, in that it rings the Pacific Ocean almost completely. Such distributions present challenges to plant geographers and students of evolution, and no generally acceptable explanation of them has so far been proposed.

Diagnostic features. As is to be expected with a large family, great morphological variability renders any general description subject to a large number of exceptions. Almost all members of the family are found in acidic habitats, and all that have been examined are dependent to some extent on a fungal mycorrhiza for successful growth. This dependence of the plants on the mycorrhiza varies in extent; most species have developed leaves and photosynthesize normally. But one subfamily, the Monotropoideae (often regarded as a separate family, Monotropaceae) is totally dependent on its symbiont; in this group chlorophyll is absent, the leaves are reduced to small yellowish scales, and the plants live saprophytically among rotting leaf litter, from which, with the help of the fungus, they absorb all their nutrients.

Most of the family are shrubs or climbers, though herbaceous forms are found in the subfamily Monotropoideae. The leaves are always simple and without stipules, usually alternate, and often evergreen. The leaves of several genera show adaptations to dry conditions: such leaves are needle-like or folded, presenting a reduced surface area to the environment, and occur in *Erica, Calluna* and *Cassiope*, among others.

The inflorescences of the Ericaceae are extremely variable, ranging from umbel-like

Cyrillaceae. 1 *Purdiaea nutans* (a) leafy shoot and terminal inflorescence ($\times\frac{2}{3}$); (b) flower partly closed showing unequal sepals ($\times 1\frac{1}{3}$); (c) flower fully open showing ten stamens and slender, undivided style ($\times 1\frac{1}{3}$); (d) young fruit with persistent calyx ($\times 1\frac{1}{3}$); (e) vertical section of gynoecium showing each locule with a single pendulous ovule ($\times 14$); (f) stamen ($\times 2\frac{2}{3}$). 2 *Cyrilla racemosa* (a) shoot with axillary inflorescences ($\times\frac{2}{3}$); (b) flower ($\times 4$); (c) cross section of ovary ($\times 14$); (d) half flower ($\times 6$); (e) gynoecium ($\times 6$); (f) fruit ($\times 6$). 3 *Cliftonia monophylla* (a) shoot with terminal inflorescences ($\times\frac{2}{3}$); (b) winged fruit ($\times 3$).

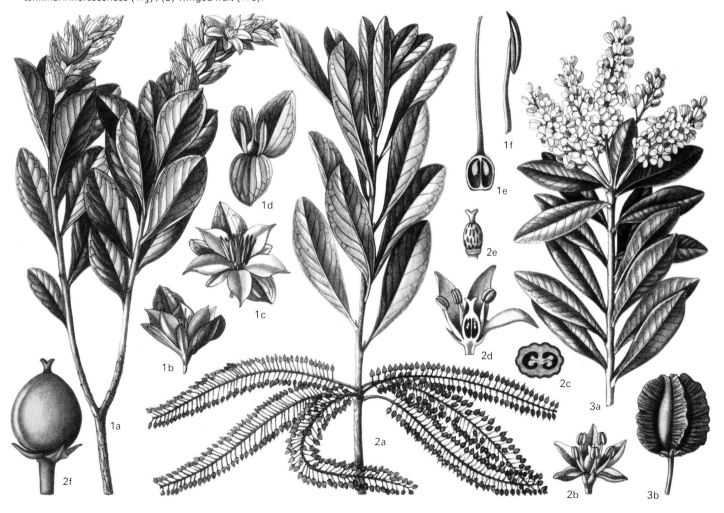

racemes to clusters or to single flowers. The flowers are usually regular and bisexual. The calyx consists of four or five sepals which are fused at the base; in many species of *Rhododendron* the calyx is reduced to an undulate rim. The corolla consists of four or five petals (rarely more, as in some species of *Rhododendron*) which are usually fused to form a tube at the base (the petals are completely free in *Ledum, Leiophyllum* and a few other genera). The stamens are usually twice as many as the petals (ie eight or 10) but are reduced to four or five in some genera and species; they are usually attached directly to the floral receptacle. In *Kalmia* the anthers fit into pockets in the corolla, from which they are released to shed their pollen. The anthers are inverted during growth, and open by means of pores at the apparent apex (which is morphologically the base), and are often ornamented with outgrowths (awns). The pollen is shed mostly in tetrad form, though single grains are found in some genera. The ovary is formed from four or five united carpels (sometimes more in *Rhododendron*) and has one to five (sometimes up to 10) locules with many ovules on usually axile placentas (parietal placentation occurs in the Monotropoideae). It is usually superior, but inferior ovaries are found in many genera of the subfamily Vaccinioideae. The style is simple and the stigma usually capitate. The fruit is usually a capsule opening loculicidally or septicidally, or, in many of the genera with inferior ovaries, a berry. The seeds have fleshy endosperm and a straight embryo.

Classification. The overall classification of the family and some of its allies has been a matter of dispute for many years. Recently, however, Stevens has studied the problem again, and has produced a workable classification. He gives convincing reasons for the inclusion within the Ericaceae of the traditionally recognized families Pyrolaceae and Monotropaceae (as subfamilies Pyroloideae and Monotropoideae). In this work, however, the Pyrolaceae is being considered as a separate family. An outline of Stevens' classification (omitting Pyroloideae) is given below, with five subfamilies:

Ericaceae. 1 *Agapetes macrantha* part of leafy shoot with axillary inflorescence (×⅔). 2 *Arctostaphylos uva-ursi* (a) leafy shoot with terminal inflorescences (×⅔); (b) half flower (×4); (c) stamen with broad hairy filament and anthers crowned by recurved arms and opening by terminal pores (×10); (d) cross section of ovary (×4). 3 *Cassiope selaginoides* stem covered with small clasping leaves (×⅔). 4 *Epigaea repens* (a) leafy stem and inflorescence (×1); (b) gynoecium with lobed ovary and stigma (×4). 5 *Phyllothamnus erectus* flowering shoot (×⅔). 6 *Gaultheria* sp (a) leafy shoot and berries (×⅔); (b) berry (×2⅔). 7 *Erica vallis-aranearum* flowering shoot (×⅔). 8 *E. versicolor* var *costata* flowering shoot. 9 *Rhododendron yunnanense* (a) flowering shoot (×⅔); (b) androecium and gynoecium (×1⅓).

RHODODENDROIDEAE. Shrubs; inflorescences usually terminating the main branches; corolla deciduous; pollen often mixed with a sticky substance (viscin) that causes it to cohere in masses or strings; ovary superior. Divided into seven tribes with 19 genera, of which *Rhododendron, Andromeda, Kalmia, Ledum* and *Daboecia* are the most familiar.
ERICOIDEAE. Shrubs or shrublets; inflorescences not terminating the main branches; corolla persistent in fruit; viscin absent; ovary superior. About 20 genera, most of them found in southern Africa, all heath-like in appearance. *Erica* (heath) and *Calluna* (heather or ling) are the best known.
VACCINIOIDEAE. Shrubs or climbers; inflorescences not usually terminating the main branches, viscin absent; ovary superior or inferior; fruit often a berry. Divided into five tribes with about 50 genera, many of which are found in Andean parts of South America. *Agapetes, Arbutus, Enkianthus, Gaultheria, Cassiope, Lyonia* and *Vaccinium* are well known.
WITTSTEINIOIDEAE. Small shrublet; stamens epipetalous; anthers opening by slits; ovary inferior. One genus (*Wittsteinia*) from Australia, which has sometimes been placed in the Epacridaceae, and whose relationships are still uncertain.
MONOTROPOIDEAE. A variable number of genera is recognized in this subfamily which is in need of considerable study. Attempts to cultivate these plants have usually failed, and many details of their structure and relationships are in doubt. Some authorities place members of this subfamily within its own family Monotropaceae. Chief genus *Monotropa*.

The Ericaceae belongs to a group formerly known as the Bicornes (now Ericales), and is closely related to the Clethraceae, Epacridaceae, Empetraceae and Diapensiaceae.

Economic uses. Many of the Ericaceae are ornamental shrubs, and are widely cultivated in gardens. Possibly the most important is *Rhododendron*, with about 700 of its species in cultivation. Of these, most are Sino-Himalayan species which are hardy in north temperate regions. A wide variety of types is available, ranging from creeping shrublets to moderately sized trees, with shades of white, pink, red, mauve and yellow represented in the flowers. Most are evergreen, but some (azaleas in horticultural terminology) are deciduous. Very many hybrids have been raised by specialists, and plants suitable for various habitats and garden situations can be obtained very easily. A recent development has been the introduction of many New Guinea species into horticulture; they are, however, not generally hardy and cannot be grown in Northern Europe and the United States of America.

Erica is also an important genus in horticulture. Towards the end of the 19th century there was a fashion for the exotic

Cape heaths (South African species), which were grown in cool glasshouses. More recently, however, this fashion has been supplanted by one for the hardy heaths, ie those native to Europe and southwestern Asia. By means of careful selection and propagation, a wide range of small shrublets, with high weed-smothering potential and with the ability to provide color throughout the year, has been developed.

Other genera important in amenity horticulture are *Menziesia, Ledum, Cladothamnus, Elliottia, Kalmia, Phyllodoce, Daboecia, Calluna, Arbutus, Arctostaphylos* (bearberry), *Enkianthus, Cassiope, Pieris, Leucothoe, Zenobia, Gaultheria, Vaccinium, Cavendishia, Macleania, Oxydendrum* and *Pernettya*.

Some species of *Vaccinium* produce edible berries, and these form an important crop in some parts of the world, particularly in the United States of America and to some extent in the Soviet Union. Several species and their hybrids are involved in the overall crop, among them *Vaccinium corymbosum* (highbush blueberry), *V. oxycoccus* (cranberry), *V. angustifolium* (lowbush blueberry) and *V. myrtillus* (bilberry).

Many species of Ericaceae are poisonous to stock and Man. Species of *Kalmia* are very poisonous to sheep, and are known as "lambkill" in various parts of the United States. The wood of some species is of local importance, particularly in the Himalayas.

J.C.

EPACRIDACEAE

The Epacridaceae is a family of heath-like shrubs or small trees. Most members grow in rather open habitats and are distinctly light-demanding.

Distribution. The family is largely confined to Australia, but extends to New Zealand and has a few species in Indomalaysia and one in southern South America. It forms extensive heathlands similar to those dominated by *Erica* (heath) and *Calluna* (heather) in other parts of the world and, indeed, in Malaysia some species grow intermingled with *Erica*.

Diagnostic features. The leaves are usually alternate, simple, narrow, rigid, sessile and without stipules. The flowers are small, regular and usually bisexual; they have bracts and are borne in spikes, racemes or, rarely, panicles; occasionally they are solitary. There are four or five free, persistent sepals. The corolla is tubular, with four or five imbricate or valvate lobes. There are four or five stamens, borne on the corolla or rarely below the ovary, alternating with the corolla lobes, sometimes with glands or tufts of hair between them; the anthers have a single locule and dehisce longitudinally. The ovary is superior of two to five fused carpels, often subtended by a glandular disk, with one to 10 locules (usually five) and one to several ovules per locule, the placentation being

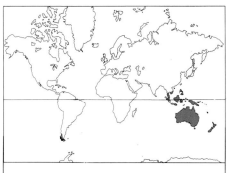

Number of genera: 30
Number of species: about 400
Distribution: mainly Australia with some species in Indomalaysia, New Zealand and S America.
Economic uses: some ornamental shrubs and occasional medicinal use.

axile or apical. The style is simple, the stigma capitate. The fruit is a loculicidal capsule with five valves or a drupe with one to several seeds; the seeds have a straight embryo and fleshy endosperm.

The species are mostly either insect-pollinated, for which the generally fragrant corolla with hairs inside seems to be an adaptation, or pollinated by birds, chiefly honeyeaters and parakeets.

Classification. The family is divided into three tribes:

STYPHELIEAE. Stamens borne at base of corolla; ovary with one ovule per locule; fruit indehiscent, usually fleshy. Eighteen genera, including *Styphelia* and *Trochocarpa*.

EPACRIDEAE. Stamens usually borne at base of corolla; ovary with several ovules per locule; fruit a loculicidal capsule. Ten genera, including *Richea, Dracophyllum* and *Epacris*.

PRIONOTEAE. Stamens borne below ovary, free; ovary with several ovules per locule; fruit a loculicidal capsule. Two monotypic genera (*Prionotes* in Tasmania, *Lebetanthus* in southern South America).

The family is most closely related to the Ericaceae, from which it differs in having palmate, open venation on the leaves and by the anthers which lack appendages and open by a slit rather than pores.

Economic uses. Several genera, notably *Dracophyllum, Epacris, Richea* and *Styphelia*, are grown as ornamental winter-flowering shrubs in the cool greenhouse. The roots and leaves of *Styphelia malayana* are used locally for medicinal purposes while the inner bark of the stems is used for making canoes waterproof.   D.M.M.

EMPETRACEAE
Crowberries

The Empetraceae is a small family of evergreen shrubs of a heath-like habit, with small, close-set leaves, inconspicuous flowers without petals and fleshy or dry fruits.

Distribution. The family is interesting in that two of the genera show major geographical disjunctions. *Empetrum* (the crowberry) is an important member of heathlands in cool temperate regions of the Northern Hemisphere and southern South America, while the two species of *Corema* occur in eastern North America (*Corema conradii*) and southwest Europe (*C. alba*). The third genus, *Ceratiola*, has its only species in southeast N. America. (See also p. 872–874.)

Diagnostic features. The family consists of dwarf shrubs with small, linear, overlapping leaves, without stipules. The flowers are regular, usually unisexual with male and female on separate plants, rarely bisexual, one to three in number in the upper leaf axils

Epacridaceae. 1 *Richea sprengelioides* flowering shoot showing sheathing leaf bases and terminal inflorescences ($\times \frac{2}{3}$). 2 *R. gunnii* (a) cross section of ovary showing five locules ($\times 12$); (b) dehisced fruit—a capsule ($\times 6$). 3 *Epacris longiflora* flowering shoot ($\times \frac{2}{3}$). 4 *Styphelia laeta* (a) flowering shoot with non-sheathing leaves and inflorescences associated with abortive shoots ($\times \frac{2}{3}$); (b) half flower ($\times 2\frac{2}{3}$). 5 *Dracophyllum rosmarinifolium* (a) flowering shoot ($\times 1$); (b) half section of capsule ($\times 4$). 6 *D. capitatum* half flower ($\times 6$). 7 *Trochocarpa laurina* (a) flowering shoot ($\times \frac{2}{3}$); (b) fruit—an indehiscent drupe ($\times 2\frac{2}{3}$); (c) cross section of fruit ($\times 2$). 8 *Styphelia enervia* fruit ($\times 4$).

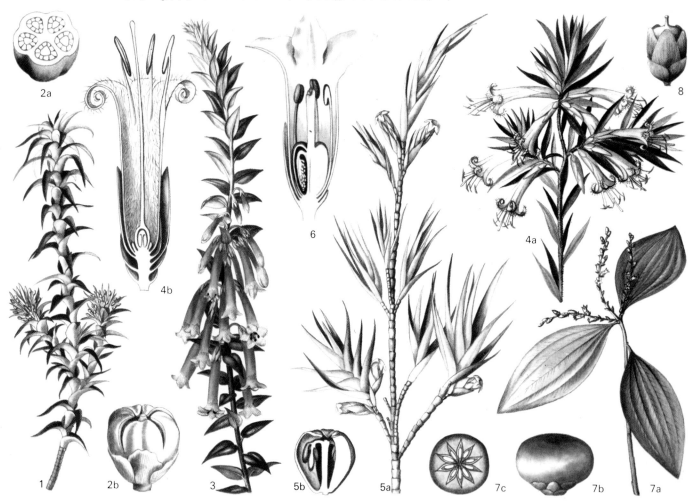

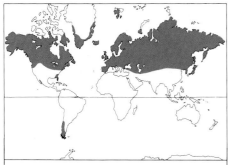

Number of genera: 3
Number of species: 4–6
Distribution: cool-temperate regions, SW Europe, E and SE N America.
Economic uses: limited uses as rock plants and for the edible berries.

or in terminal heads. There are four to six free perianth segments, usually in two similar whorls. The two to four stamens are free and episepalous; the anthers dehisce longitudinally; the disk is absent. The ovary is superior, has two to nine fused carpels and two to nine locules with one anatropous or campylotropous ovule per locule. There is a single short style, with two to nine fringed or lobed stigmatic branches. The fruit is a globose drupe, fleshy or dry with two or more pyrenes, each with one seed; the seeds have copious fleshy endosperm and the embryo is long and erect.

Classification. The three genera may be simply distinguished as follows: *Empetrum*, flowers solitary in leaf axils; three stamens. *Ceratiola*, two to three flowers in leaf axils; two stamens. *Corema*, flowers in terminal head; three or four stamens.

All genera are diploid except for *Empetrum*, which also contains tetraploids. The diploids characteristically have separate male and female plants; unisexual flowers and/or bisexual flowers on the same plant are a derived condition.

The Empetraceae is considered to be close to the Ericaceae, which it resembles both in certain well-marked embryological features and in the possession of several distinctive chemical compounds such as anthocyanidin, galactosides and some rare flavonols, in addition to general habit and morphology.

Economic uses. *Empetrum* and *Corema album* are cultivated for ornament in rock or heath gardens, and crowberry fruits (*Empetrum nigrum*) are used locally for jams and preserves. D.M.M.

PYROLACEAE
Wintergreens

The Pyrolaceae, commonly called the wintergreens, is a family of evergreen perennials with creeping rhizomes.

Distribution. The family is principally cool north temperate and Arctic, with some representatives as far south as Mexico and the West Indics.

Diagnostic features. The leaves are usually alternate, entire or dentate and without stipules. The flowers are terminal, in racemes, cymes or solitary. They are regular and bisexual, with five or four sepals and petals. The sepals are imbricate, the petals free or rarely shortly united. The stamens, eight to 10 in number, are in two whorls, the outer opposite the petals, the inner opposite the sepals. The anthers are free, opening by pores; the pollen is usually in tetrads. The stamens and petals are often situated at the edge of a nectariferous disk. The ovary is superior, of five or four fused carpels, and is incompletely five- or four-locular with thick fleshy axile placentas and numerous small anatropous ovules. The style is simple, and straight or declinate. The embryo is of a few cells without differentiation of the

Empetraceae. 1 *Ceratiola ericoides* (a) leafy shoot with flowers in leaf axils ($\times\frac{2}{3}$); (b) male flower with two anthers dehiscing lengthwise ($\times 8$); (c) ovary crowned by lobed stigma ($\times 12$); (d) cross section of fruit showing two seeds ($\times 6$). 2 *Corema conradii* (a) shoot with flowers in terminal heads ($\times\frac{2}{3}$); (b) head of flowers each with conspicuous stamens ($\times 4$). 3 *Empetrum rubrum* (a) shoot with solitary flowers in leaf axils ($\times 2$); (b) cross section of ovary with nine locules ($\times 10$); (c) male flower showing two whorls each of three perianth segments ($\times 8$); (d) gynoecium showing single, short style with six stigmatic branches ($\times 12$); (e) shoot bearing fruit ($\times\frac{2}{3}$); (f) fruit—a drupe ($\times 2$).

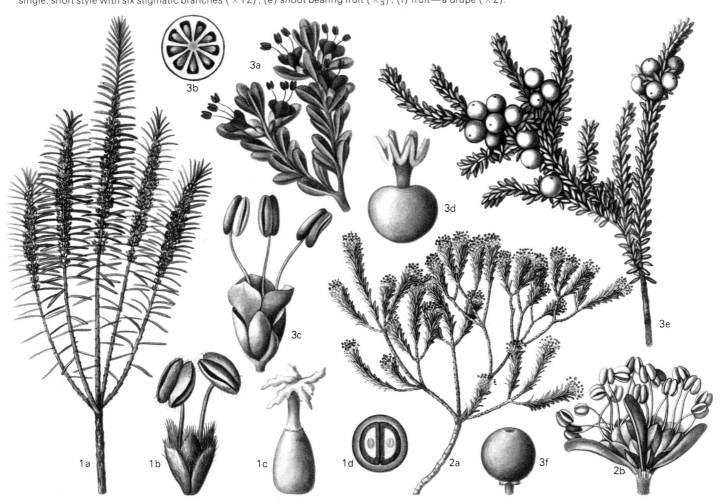

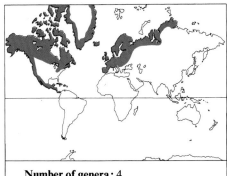

Number of genera: 4
Number of species: about 30
Distribution: temperate and Arctic.
Economic uses: medicinal.

cotyledons. The fruit is a loculicidal capsule with numerous very small wind-dispersed seeds, in a loose testa.

Classification. The family is represented by four genera, *Pyrola, Chimaphila, Moneses* and *Orthilia. Pyrola* contains 20 north temperate species. They are slender creeping plants with short, often distant aerial stems which are frequently reduced to a basal rosette of leaves. The inflorescence is a raceme of pink or white flowers. The characters of the style distinguish the commonest of the 20 species. *Pyrola minor* has a straight, included style, while that of *P. media* is long, straight and exserted, and that of *P. rotundifolia,* long, curved and exserted. The valves of the capsule of *Pyrola* are webbed at the edges. Nectar is secreted by the base of the petals.

The genus *Orthilia* is limited to one (possibly two) species found in circumpolar regions. It is similar to *Pyrola* but the greenish-white flowers of the racemose inflorescence are all arranged on one side. The disk consists of 10 small glands. The petioles are also shorter than those of *Pyrola.*

Moneses is represented by one boreal and Arctic species, and is distinguished from *Pyrola* and *Orthilia* by its opposite leaves, solitary flowers, the absence of webbing on the capsule and the absence of nectar. The disk is distinctly 10-lobed.

Chimaphila, represented by eight species of Eurasia and North and Central America, has strongly toothed, dark green leathery leaves, and pink flowers borne in an umbellate inflorescence.

The genus *Monotropa* is sometimes included in the Pyrolaceae, but in this work is considered to belong to the Ericaceae. The Pyrolaceae is related to the Ericaceae, but is distinguished from it by its herbaceous habit, incompletely septate ovary and undifferentiated embryo.

Economic uses. No economic uses for this family are recorded, except that the leaves of some species have been used to heal wounds.

S.A.H.

DIAPENSIALES

DIAPENSIACEAE
Shortia and Galax

The Diapensiaceae is a small family of herbs and dwarf shrubs.

Distribution. One of the species (*Diapensia lapponica*) is circumpolar, extending through North America, Greenland and northern Eurasia, as far south as South Korea. Three other genera, *Shortia, Pyxidanthera* and *Galax,* have species in North America, the latter two being endemic to the eastern United States. All other members of the family are east Asiatic, particularly in the Himalayan region, but extending east to Japan, where several species of *Shortia* and

Pyrolaceae. 1 *Pyrola rotundifolia* shoot and inflorescence (×⅔). 2 *P. dentata* (a) flower (×2); (b) ovary (×3). 3 *Chimaphila umbellata* (a) shoot and inflorescence (×⅔); (b) flower (×1½); (c) half flower (×2); (d) stamen side (left) and front (right) views (×4); (e) cross section of ovary (×4); (f) fruits (×⅔); (g) dehisced fruit (×3). The following species are sometimes placed in the Pyrolaceae but are here included in the Ericaceae. 4 *Monotropa hypopithys* (a) habit (×⅔); (b) flower (×2); (c) flower (×2); (d) gynoecium and stamens (×3); (e) stamen (×12); (f) vertical section of gynoecium (×3); (g) fruit (×4). 5 *Sarcodes sanguinea* (a) flower (×1); (b) half flower (×2); (c) gynoecium (×2); (d) stamen (×3).

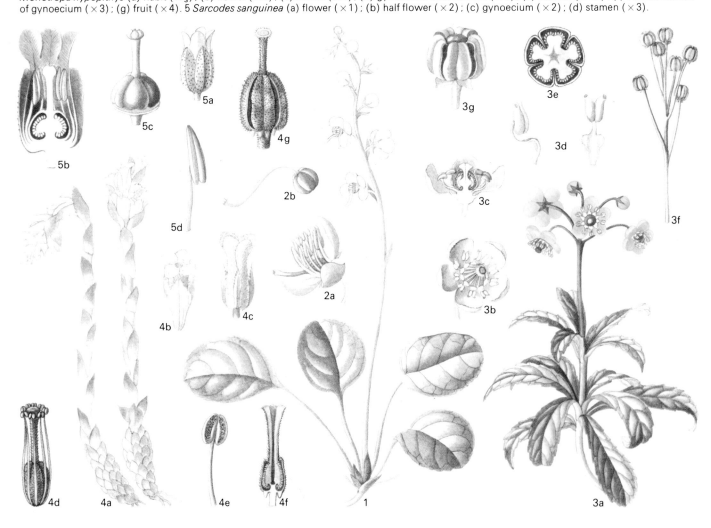

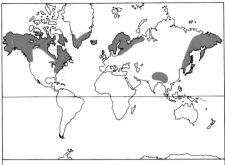

Number of genera: 7
Number of species: 20
Distribution: temperate and cold regions of the N Hemisphere.
Economic uses: cultivated ornamentals (*Shortia, Galax, Schizocodon*).

Schizocodon are found, and Taiwan, which has a number of endemic species of *Shortia*.

Diagnostic features. All members of the family are small shrubs or stemless herbs, usually with rosettes of simple leaves. The flowers are regular, bisexual, either solitary or in racemes, with five sepals, often partly fused, and five partly free petals, the latter forming a corolla tube. There are usually five stamens opposite the sepals and partly fused to the corolla, and sometimes five staminodes opposite the petals. In *Diplarche* there are two whorls, each of five fertile stamens, the inner corresponding to the staminodes of other genera, these being joined to the base of the corolla tube. The ovary is superior, of three (sometimes five) fused carpels, usually with three locules (five in *Diplarche*), and with a simple style. There are few to numerous ovules on axile placentas. The fruit is a loculicidal capsule with many small seeds which have fleshy endosperm and a cylindrical embryo.

Classification. The family is usually considered to contain seven genera, which may be divided into three groups. One comprises *Diplarche*, a genus of two species from the eastern Himalayas, dwarf shrubs with branching racemes of pink flowers. *Galax aphylla*, the only species of its genus, forms a second group. It is a herbaceous perennial growing in woodlands, with creeping rhizomes bearing cordate leaves and producing racemose inflorescences of many small, white flowers on scapes. The other genera form a third group characterized by solitary flowers or few-flowered racemes. Two genera are cushion-like or creeping dwarf shrubs with closely imbricate, linear leaves and solitary flowers: *Diapensia* (Arctic and montane, with several species in the Himalayas) and *Pyxidanthera* (two species on sandy sites in the eastern United States of America). The other three genera, *Shortia*, *Schizocodon* and *Berneuxia* are perennial herbs with stolons, mainly of montane woodlands, with well-developed lanceolate, ovate or cordate leaves and conspicuous white or pink flowers.

The whole family, *Diplarche* in particular, resembles some members of the Ericaceae, but in the latter family the stamens are always free and in a single whorl and the pollen is shed through pores, while the Diapensiaceae has anthers dehiscing by slits.

Economic uses. Several species are used horticulturally. Perhaps the most widely grown is *Galax aphylla*, which provides useful ground cover and decorative foliage. This and species of *Schizocodon* and *Shortia*, also attractive garden plants, are conspicuous in the autumn when their leaves turn bronze or crimson. *Diapensia* and *Pyxidanthera* species are sometimes grown in rock gardens. T.T.E.

Diapensiaceae. 1 *Diapensia himalaica* (a) creeping shoot bearing small, simple overlapping leaves and solitary flowers ($\times \frac{2}{3}$); (b) fruiting shoot ($\times \frac{2}{3}$); (c) five-lobed perianth opened out to reveal five stamens fused to corolla ($\times 2$); (d) cross section of ovary ($\times 6$); (e) dehiscing fruit ($\times 3$); (f) detail of stamens ($\times 8$). 2 *Schizocodon soldanelloides* (a) habit ($\times \frac{2}{3}$); (b) part of corolla opened out to show fertile stamens inserted on corolla tube and linear staminodes at the base ($\times 2$); (c) fruit enclosed in persistent bracts and calyx ($\times 2$); (d) gynoecium ($\times 2$); (e) cross section of ovary ($\times 3$); (f) stamens, dorsal view (left) and ventral view (right) ($\times 6$). 3 *Galax aphylla* habit ($\times \frac{2}{3}$).

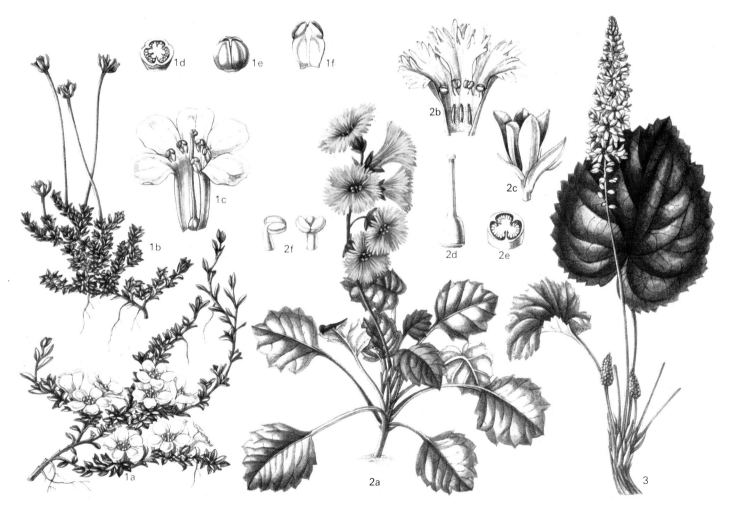

EBENALES

SAPOTACEAE

Chicle, Gutta-percha and Sapodilla

This large family of tropical trees yields timber and latex and edible fruits.

Distribution. The Sapotaceae occurs pantropically, mainly in lowland and lower montane rain forest.

Diagnostic features. White latex is present at least in the twigs, usually also in the bark, and is sometimes copiously produced. The leaves are simple, entire, spirally arranged, often crowded in false whorls and sometimes with stipules which soon drop. The flowers are borne in fascicles, often behind the leaves or on the trunk; they are bisexual, regular or irregular, scented, often white or cream and often nocturnal and bat-pollinated. The sepals are free, in two whorls of two, three or four, or one of five. The petals are usually equal in number to the sepals but usually in one whorl and are fused at the base. The stamens are epipetalous, either equal in number to and opposite the corolla lobes or more numerous, sometimes alternating with staminodes. The ovary is superior, of many

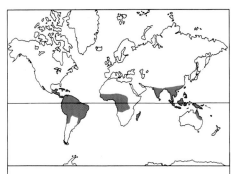

Number of genera: 35–75
Number of species: about 800
Distribution: pantropical in lowland and montane rain forests.
Economic uses: timber, gutta-percha, balata, chicle (chewing gum) and edible fruits (sapodilla plum, star apple, sapote).

fused carpels, with many locules each containing a single axile or basal ovule. The style is simple. The fruit is a berry, not articulated. The one or few seeds have an oily endosperm and bony testa and a large embryo.

Classification. The Sapotaceae is one of the families (another is the Lauraceae) within which generic limits are extremely difficult to perceive and opinions on subdivision vary considerably. From 35 to 75 ill-defined genera can be distinguished; there is no general agreement and new opinions continue to be published. *Sarcosperma*, sometimes considered a monogeneric family (Sarcospermataceae), represents an extreme of evolutionary trends. With this inclusion, the Sapotaceae stands as a close-knit family, the biggest member of the Ebenales.

Economic uses. Timber production is nowadays increasingly significant, for the Sapotaceae are an important component of many tropical rain forests (as in Malaya and Borneo), reaching 100ft (30m) tall and 6.5ft (2m) in girth. Some species have heavy timber, which is hard and naturally durable, but often siliceous; others have lighter timber, some without silica. Gutta-percha, obtained from the latex of *Palaquium* species (especially *Palaquium gutta* of Sumatra, Malaya, Java and Borneo) was once the premier product of the family. It is a polymer of isoprene, differing from rubber by having trans- instead of cis-isomerization, is almost non-elastic, a better insulator of heat and

Sapotaceae. 1 *Madhuca parkii* (a) tip of leafy flowering shoot with flowers in fascicles (×⅔); (b) cross section of ovary showing eight locules each with an ovule on an axile placenta (×3). 2 *Mimusops zeyheri* var *laurifolia* (a) leafy shoot with axillary fascicles of flowers (×⅔); (b) perianth opened out (×3); (c) petal with appendages (×3); (d) stamen (×4); (e) staminode (×4); (f) vertical section of ovary (×3). 3 *Sideroxylon costatum* (a) flowering shoot (×⅔); (b) flower (×3); (c) corolla opened out (×3); (d) gynoecium (×4); (e) vertical section of ovary (×4). 4 *Achras sapota* (a) fruit—the sapodilla plum (×⅓); (b) cross section of fruit (×⅓).

electricity, becomes plastic on heating, and on cooling retains any shape given while hot. It was developed in the 19th century from a minor curiosity to a major industrial product, principally as an insulant for submarine telephone cables, but also used in golf balls and for temporary dental stoppings (only the last use still persists). The latex was mostly obtained by tapping trunks in a herringbone pattern. Early destructive tapping was followed by efforts for conservation and some plantations were established, as in Java and Singapore.

Mimusops balata (*Manilkara bidentata*) of northern South America also yields a latex, balata, formerly of considerable importance. Chicle, the elastic component of earlier chewing gum, is produced from the latex of *Achras zapota* (*Manilkara zapota*).

Achras zapota also yields the popular edible fruit chiku or sapodilla plum, and *Chrysophyllum cainito* the star apple; both are of American origin but now planted elsewhere in the humid tropics. Some of the fruits termed sapote are the product of *Calocarpum* species, notably *Calocarpum sapota*. The seeds of the north tropical African *Butyrospermum paradoxum*, the shea butter tree, yield an edible oil.

EBENACEAE
Persimmons and Ebonies

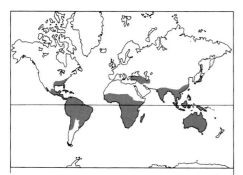

Number of genera: 2
Number of species: 400–500
Distribution: tropical, centered in Indomalesian rain forests; a few N temperate.
Economic uses: timber (ebony) and fruits (persimmon, date plum and Japanese date plum or kaki).

The Ebenaceae is a medium-sized family mainly of tropical trees, the source of ebony and persimmons.

Distribution. The greatest concentration is in the lowland rain forests of the Malay archipelago, with about 200 species, followed in abundance by tropical Africa, then Latin America. There are a few outlying species in the north temperate zone.

Diagnostic features. Members of the family are mostly small trees with a monopodial crown (ie with a single leading shoot) and flattened foliage sprays. Some are shrubs. The outer bark is usually black, gritty and charcoal-like. There is no latex. The leaves are alternate (rarely opposite), simple, entire and without stipules.

The flowers are usually unisexual (with male and female on separate plants), rarely structurally bisexual. Inflorescences are short and determinate, in the leaf axils, sometimes reduced to a single flower, especially in the female. The flowers are jointed at the base and regular, with parts mostly in threes or fives (sometimes sixes or sevens). The sepals are fused, with lobes valvate or imbricate. The petals are fused into a tube with as many lobes as there are sepals, the lobes contorted, white, cream or suffused pink. The stamens are usually epipetalous, in two whorls, two to four times the number of the corolla lobes and fused in radial pairs. The female flowers usually bear staminodes. The ovary is superior (rarely inferior) and sessile, with as many locules as there are petals and sepals. Each locule has two pendent ovules attached at the apex, but is usually divided by a false septum with one ovule in each half, the halves being connate at the apex. The styles are fused at least at the base; there are as many stigmas as locules. The male flowers usually have a pistillode. The fruit is a berry, the pericarp pulpy to fibrous, with a stony inner part, only rarely dehiscent, seated on the persistent, often enlarged, calyx. The seeds are several, with endosperm, which is sometimes ruminate.

Classification. Nowadays nearly all species are put into the genus *Diospyros* (including *Lissocarpa* and *Maba*) with 400–500 species. *Diospyros* is pantropical with some outlying members. The only other genus, *Euclea* (14 species), is confined to eastern and southern Africa. *Diospyros* itself is closely knit and only a few small distinctive sections can be segregated from the main core.

Together with the Sapotaceae, the family comprises the bulk of the order Ebenales.

Economic uses. The family is best known for the black, hard heartwood, ebony of commerce, produced by most but not all species of *Diospyros*. *Diospyros reticulata* (Mauritius) and *D. ebenum* (Sri Lanka) are among the finest producers of ebony. The fruits of several species are eaten, throughout the range. A few have been brought into cultivation. Best known are the persimmons, a group of outlying warm north temperate species; *Diospyros kaki* of eastern Asia (kaki, Chinese or Japanese date plum, or persimmon), extensively cultivated in China and Japan, and known through to the Mediterranean; *D. lotus* of Eurasia (date plum) and *D. virginiana* of North America. Crushed seeds of certain Malesian species are used as fish poison. In all species the fruit is extremely astringent until it is very ripe.

STYRACACEAE
Silverbell and Snowbell Trees

The Styracaceae is a family of shrubs and trees best known as the source of benzoin

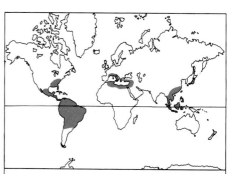

Number of genera: 12
Number of species: 180
Distribution: centered in E Asia, W Malesia, SE N, C and S America.
Economic uses: gum resins used medicinally and in perfumes, ornamentals (*Halesia* and *Styrax*).

(gum benjamin) and storax; it is also noted for several beautiful ornamentals.

Distribution. There are three centers of distribution: eastern Asia to western Malesia; southeastern North America to central and South America; and, with one species (*Styrax officinale*), in the Mediterranean.

Diagnostic features. The leaves are alternate, simple, without stipules and usually entire. The flowers are regular, usually bisexual and usually borne in racemes or panicles. The calyx is tubular with four or five persistent lobes, the corolla tubular at the base but often only very shortly so, with four to seven valvate lobes. The stamens are equal in number to and alternate with the corolla lobes, or double the number, usually adnate to the corolla tube or united as a tube. The ovary is superior or inferior, of three to five fused carpels with three to five locules each containing one to many anatropous ovules on axile placentas. The style is simple with a capitate or lobed stigma. The fruit is a drupe or capsule, with the calyx persistent. The one to few seeds with copious endosperm are eaten and dispersed by animals. The embryo is straight or slightly curved.

Classification. *Styrax* itself (130 species) is the most important genus. Most probably related to the Ebenaceae and Sapotaceae, the family is very heterogeneous in nature, unlike its relatives, and is perhaps not natural. *Afrostyrax*, a tree native to west tropical Africa, was formerly placed in this family but is now believed to be totally unconnected and is often placed together with *Hua* (another genus of tropical African trees) in the segregate family Huaceae. The affinities of the latter family are, however, entirely obscure.

Economic uses. The wood is mostly soft and of little use. Resin is the chief product. The tropical resins (chiefly from *Styrax benzoin*) are traded as benzoin (corrupted as gum benjamin), and used medicinally (in friar's balsam) and in incense. The resin is obtained by wounding the bark. Produced chiefly in Thailand, Sumatra and Bolivia, it consists principally of two alcohols combined with cinnamic acid and free cinnamomic and benzoic acids. The trees are scattered and uncommon in lowland tropical rain forest, and production depends on continual and careful wounding. *Styrax officinale* (Mediterranean) yields the resin storax, used as an antiseptic, inhalant and expectorant. *Halesia* includes the silverbell or snowdrop trees, *Styrax* the snowbell trees; both groups are beautiful, distinctive ornamentals.

T.C.W.

PRIMULALES

PRIMULACEAE
The Primrose Family

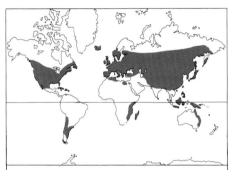

Number of genera: about 28
Number of species: nearly 1,000
Distribution: cosmopolitan, but chiefly in the N temperate zone with some alpine species.
Economic uses: many popular garden and house ornamentals (eg primroses, auriculas, cyclamens).

The Primulaceae is a family of perennial or annual herbs, including a number of popular garden ornamentals, such as primulas and cyclamens, and the familiar wild primrose, *Primula veris*.

Distribution. The family is cosmopolitan in distribution but with most members indigenous to the north temperate zone.

Diagnostic features. Most species perennate by means of sympodial rhizomes (as in *Primula*) or tubers (as in *Cyclamen*) and bear simple leaves without stipules (except in *Coris*). The leaves are opposite or alternate or in the form of a rosette arising from the stem base, and are usually entire (the submerged leaves of the aquatic genus *Hottonia* are pinnately dissected). Often the leaves and stems bear simple or compound glandular hairs.

The flowers are often borne on leafless scapes (as in *Primula veitchii*, *Soldanella alpina*), either solitary or in umbellate, racemose or paniculate inflorescences. The flowers have bracts and are usually regular (irregular in *Coris*), bisexual and often heterostylous. There are normally five sepals (occasionally six in *Lysimachia*) fused into a calyx tube which is persistent with four or five pointed segments. With the exception of

Glaux, which has no petals, the corolla consists of five (or occasionally four) petals usually fused into a tube but with the lobes reflexed in some genera (eg *Dodecatheon* and *Cyclamen*). There are five stamens fused to the corolla tube opposite the petals. In a few instances (including *Samolus* and *Soldanella*) there are also five staminodes alternating with the petals. This suggests that the antipetalous position of the stamens has resulted during the course of evolution from the loss of an ancestral outer whorl. The anthers are bilocular and dehisce longitudinally. The ovary is composed of five carpels fused to form a unilocular, superior or semi-inferior ovary with free central placentation and few to numerous ovules. There is a single style terminating in a head-like stigma. The fruit is a five-valved capsule or occasionally a pyxidium (as in *Anagallis*, where it opens by a cap-like cover). The fruit usually contains numerous small seeds with a small straight embryo surrounded by fleshy or hard endosperm.

Classification. The genera may be separated into a number of tribes on the basis of floral symmetry, position of the ovary and aestivation of the corolla:

PRIMULEAE. Ovary superior, corolla lobes imbricate in the bud, capsule with valvate dehiscence; includes *Primula* (primroses, about 500 species), *Androsace* (100 species), *Soldanella* (11 species), *Hottonia* (two species), *Dodecatheon* (about 50 species).

CYCLAMINEAE. Ovary superior, capsule with valvate dehiscence, flowers with reflexed petals, plants with tubers; only *Cyclamen* (15 species).

LYSIMACHIEAE. Ovary superior, capsule with valvate dehiscence or pyxidium, corolla lobes contorted in bud; includes *Lysimachia* (about 200 species), *Trientalis* (four species), *Glaux* (one species), *Anagallis* (28 species).

SAMOLEAE. Ovary semi-inferior; only *Samolus* (10–15 species, chiefly in the Southern Hemisphere).

CORIDEAE. Spiny calyx, flowers irregular; only *Coris* (two species, mainly Mediterranean). This is a curious genus of small thyme-like woody herbs, sometimes treated as a separate family, the Coridaceae.

The Primulaceae was once considered to be related to the Caryophyllaceae. The relationship was based on the nature of the gynoecium, and the vascularization and other anatomical features suggested the evolution of the primulaceous form from the caryophyllaceous type. However, the Primulaceae is more advanced in such features as the fusing of the corolla segments and the reduction of the androecium usually to five stamens. Here it is placed with the Myrsinaceae in a separate order, the Primulales, related to the Ebenales.

Economic uses. Although economically the Primulaceae is mainly of ornamental importance, it is worth noting that *Cyclamen purpurascens* (*C. europaeum*) (common cyc-

lamen) contains the poisonous glycoside cyclamin, while *Anagallis arvensis* was once an important medicinal plant and contains a poisonous glycoside similar to saponin. *Lysimachia vulgaris* yields a yellow dye and also has reputed uses as a febrifuge or fever-reducing agent. Flowers of *Primula veris* are used for home-made wine.

Many species of *Primula* are cultivated for their attractive flowers either as house pot plants (eg *Primula × kewensis* and *P. obconica*), in rock gardens (*P. auricula* and *P. allionii*) or in garden borders (*P. denticulata* and *P. bulleyana*).

A number of cyclamen species including *Cyclamen hederifolium* are grown in the open, but the progenitor of the popular winter flowering pot cyclamens is *C. persicum*, of which there are innumerable cultivars including 'Butterfly' with salmon-pink frilled petals; 'Cardinal' with scarlet petals, 'Silberstrahl' with red petals each with a narrow silvery-white margin and 'White Swan' with pure white petals.

Some species of *Anagallis* (eg *A. arvensis* and *A. linifolia*) have provided the source of garden varieties suitable for edging borders or for rock gardens.

Lysimachia nummularia is useful for ground cover and species of *Dodecatheon*, with their rose-purple flowers, are useful perennial border plants.

S.R.C.

MYRSINACEAE

The Myrsinaceae is a medium-sized family of trees and shrubs, of little economic importance except for a few species grown as ornamentals.

Distribution. The family is mainly warm temperate, subtropical and tropical in distribution with representatives from New Zealand and South Africa in the south to Japan, Mexico and Florida in the north.

Diagnostic features. The leaves are alternate, simple, leathery, and without stipules and are usually dotted with glands or conspicuous resin ducts. The flowers are small, regular, bisexual or unisexual (then with the sexes on separate plants) and are normally borne in fascicles, either on scaly short shoots or on spurs in the leaf axils, but they may also be in terminal panicles, corymbs or cymes. There are four to six free or basally connate, small

Primulaceae. 1 *Dodecatheon meadia* habit showing basal rosette of leaves and flowers, with reflexed petals, borne on leafless stalks ($\times \frac{2}{3}$). 2 *Primula veitchii* (a) habit ($\times \frac{2}{3}$); (b) half flower showing epipetalous stamens and ovules on a free central placenta ($\times 4$); (c) cross section of unilocular ovary ($\times 6$). 3 *Samolus valerandi* half flower with staminodes and stamens ($\times 8$). 4 *Soldanella alpina* habit showing flowers with deeply divided petals ($\times \frac{2}{3}$). 5 *Primula veris* dehisced fruit (a capsule) with part of persistent calyx removed ($\times 3$). 6 *Cyclamen hederifolium* (a) habit showing basal tuber ($\times \frac{2}{3}$); (b) dehisced fruit ($\times 4$). 7 *Lysimachia punctata* leafy terminal inflorescence with yellow flowers ($\times \frac{2}{3}$).

2c

2b

3

5

6b

7

2a

6a

1

4

Number of genera: 32
Number of species: 1,000
Distribution: widely distributed from warm temperate to tropical regions.
Economic uses: several ornamentals and limited local uses as medicines.

sepals and the same number of petals which are connate, valvate or contorted into a four- to six-lobed corolla. The stamens are equal in number to, and usually opposite, the corolla lobes. The anthers have two locules which open by inwardly-facing longitudinal slits and are generally longer than the filaments which are often fused to the corolla. The ovary is either superior or semi-inferior, with one (sometimes four to six) locules and few to numerous ovules on axile or free central placentas. The fruit is a fleshy drupe. The seeds have a straight or slightly curved embryo and fleshy endosperm.

Classification. The Myrsinaceae is divided into two subfamilies: the MAESOIDEAE containing the genus *Maesa* characterized by its half-inferior ovary and many-seeded fruits; and the MYRSINOIDEAE with a superior ovary and a single-seeded fruit. The Myrsinoideae is further divided into two tribes: the MYRSINEAE with few ovules in one row (eg *Oncostemon*, *Embelia*, *Rapanea*) and ARDISIEAE with numerous ovules in many rows (eg *Aegiceras* and *Ardisia*).

The five genera *Theophrasta*, *Neomezia*, *Deherainia*, *Clavija* and *Jacquinia* with about 110 species of tropical American and West Indian trees and shrubs are sometimes placed in the Myrsinaceae, but are normally separated as the family Theophrastaceae. It differs from the Myrsinaceae in having anthers extrorse, five staminodes that are alternate with the corolla lobes and leaves that do not have large glands or resin ducts.

The Myrsinaceae is usually included in the order Primulales near to the Primulaceae but this classification is refuted by some authorities who consider the similarity between Myrsinaceae and the rest of the predominantly herbaceous Primulales to be superficial and place it in an order Myrsinales together with the Theophrastaceae, its most closely related family.

Economic uses. The Myrsinaceae is a family of little economic value. Species of the genera *Ardisia*, *Maesa*, *Myrsine* and *Suttonia* are sometimes grown as ornamentals. *Myrsine africana*, from Africa, China and India is cultivated in gardens of warmer areas for its attractive purple-blue fruits. Several species of *Maesa* from India, the Himalayas and Sikkim and about 16 species of *Ardisia*, especially *A. crispa*, with very persistent red fruits, are also used as garden or warm greenhouse subjects. The leaves of *Ardisia colorata* are used as an infusion in Malaya to treat stomach complaints and in the same area the fruits of *A. crispa* are eaten. In Java the sap of *A. fulginosa* is boiled with coconut oil and used to treat scurvy and in the Philippines the flowers and fruits of *A. squamulosa* are used to flavor fish dishes.

D.B.

Myrsinaceae. 1 *Ardisia humulis* (a) leafy shoot with flowers in axillary inflorescences ($\times\frac{2}{3}$); (b) half flower bud ($\times 4$); (c) corolla opened out ($\times 2$); (d) dehiscing stamen ($\times 3$); (e) fruit ($\times\frac{1}{3}$). 2 *Myrsine africana* (a) leafy shoot with fruits ($\times\frac{2}{3}$); (b) female flower ($\times 5$); (c) male flower ($\times 4$); (d) male flower opened out to show vestigial gynoecium ($\times 4$); (e) female flower opened out to show staminodes ($\times 6$). 3 *Embelia kraussii* (a) leafy shoot and axillary inflorescences ($\times\frac{2}{3}$); (b) flower ($\times 6$). 4 *Aegiceras corniculatum* (a) flower ($\times 1\frac{1}{3}$); (b) flower opened out ($\times 1\frac{2}{3}$); (c) dehisced anther showing transverse septa within the locules ($\times 6$); (d) leafy shoot and fruits ($\times\frac{2}{3}$). 5 *Maesa alnifolia* vertical section of ovary with calyx ($\times 6$).

ROSIDAE

ROSALES

CUNONIACEAE

The Cunoniaceae is a family of trees and shrubs native to the Southern Hemisphere, which is important for its light timber.

Distribution. The main centers of distribution are Oceania and Australasia, but there are a few genera in South Africa and tropical America. The most important genus is *Weinmannia* which has 160 species distributed through Madagascar, Malaysia, the Pacific, New Zealand, Chile, Mexico and the West Indies. *Pancheria* has 25 species in New Caledonia. *Geissois* has 20 species in Australasia, New Caledonia and Fiji. The 20 species of *Spiraeanthemum* are native to New Guinea and Polynesia. *Cunonia* and *Lamanonia* are smaller genera, consisting of 15 and 10 species, respectively. The former has a discontinuous distribution in South Africa and New Caledonia, while *Lamanonia* is native to Brazil and Paraguay.

Diagnostic features. The leaves are leathery,

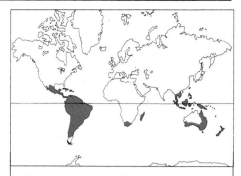

Number of genera: 26
Number of species: about 250
Distribution: S Hemisphere, chiefly Australasia and the Pacific.
Economic uses: timber.

often glandular, opposite or rarely in whorls, occasionally simple, but more often compound, trifoliolate or pinnate. Stipules are present and may be large and united in pairs.

The small flowers are regular, bisexual, but unisexual in a few species, with male and female on different plants. They are either solitary or borne in branched racemes or compact heads. The sepals are three to six in number and either free or fused together at the base. There may be four or five petals, free or united at the base. They are generally smaller than the sepals, and are absent in some species. Most species have numerous stamens, but some have four or five alternating with the petals and others have eight or ten. They are usually inserted by their free filaments on a ring-like, nectar-secreting disk, surrounding the ovary, which is superior, comprising two to five free or fused carpels. There are usually two (sometimes five) locules, each locule or free carpel containing numerous ovules set in two rows on recurved, axile or apical placentas. The styles are distinct, even in those species with fused carpels. The fruit is a capsule or nut and the seed has a small embryo surrounded by abundant endosperm.

Classification. This family has clear affinities with the Saxifragaceae, but differs in having a predominantly tree-like habit, opposite or whorled leaves and recurved placentas. A

Cunoniaceae. 1 *Pancheria elegans* (a) shoot with whorls of simple leaves and flowers in compact heads ($\times\frac{2}{3}$); (b) female flower showing three free sepals and petals and two free styles ($\times 12$); (c) male flower with six stamens ($\times 12$); (d) male flower opened out to show stamens with filaments of two lengths ($\times 12$); (e) bilobed fruit ($\times 12$). 2 *Cunonia capensis* shoot with pinnate leaf and flowers in a panicle ($\times\frac{2}{3}$). 3 *Weinmannia hildebrandtii* (a) shoot with trifoliolate leaves and flowers in panicles ($\times\frac{2}{3}$); (b) flower ($\times 8$); (c) half flower ($\times 8$). 4 *Geissois imthurnii* flower with four sepals, no petals and numerous stamens inserted on a nectar secreting disk ($\times 2$). 5 *Davidsonia prunens*, fruit ($\times\frac{2}{3}$).

Pittosporaceae. 1 *Pittosporum crassifolium* (a) leafy shoot and inflorescences of male flowers ($\times\frac{2}{3}$); (b) male flower ($\times 1$); (c) male flower with perianth removed showing large stamens and vestigial ovary ($\times 1\frac{1}{3}$); (d) gynoecium from female flower with vestigial stamens ($\times 1\frac{1}{3}$); (e) cross section of ovary ($\times 1\frac{1}{3}$); (f) dehiscing fruit—a capsule ($\times 1\frac{1}{3}$). 2 *Billiardiera mutabilis* (a) flowering and fruiting shoot ($\times\frac{2}{3}$); (b) fruit—a berry ($\times 1\frac{1}{3}$). 3 *Sollya heterophylla* flowering shoot ($\times\frac{2}{3}$). 4 *Marianthus ringens* (a) twining, leafy stem and inflorescence ($\times\frac{2}{3}$); (b) flower ($\times 1\frac{1}{3}$); (c) androecium ($\times 2$); (d) stamen with flattened filament ($\times 2\frac{2}{3}$); (e) gynoecium ($\times 2\frac{2}{3}$).

further difference is that most species have flowers with numerous stamens.

Economic uses. The only member of the Cunoniaceae that is economically important is *Ceratopetalum apetalum*, a tall tree native to New South Wales. The timber (known as lightwood) is light brown to pinkish brown in color and is used in carpentry and cabinetmaking. It is also used extensively as flooring, paneling and skirting, and provides a plywood veneer as well as aircraft veneers.

S.R.C.

PITTOSPORACEAE
Parchment-bark

The Pittosporaceae is a medium-sized family of evergreen shrubs and trees. *Pittosporum*, the type genus, contains a number of attractive ornamentals.

Distribution. The family is native mostly to the Old World tropics, eight of the nine genera being endemic to Australasia.

Diagnostic features. The plants are shrubs or small trees, sometimes climbers. The leaves are evergreen and leathery, typically entire, and without stipules. The flowers are bisexual, rarely tending towards unisexuality and polygamy (male, female and bisexual on

the same plant), regular, but weakly irregular in one genus (*Cheiranthera*). There are five free sepals. There are five petals which are mostly united below and often clawed. The stamens are five, attached to the sepals. The ovary is superior, of two fused carpels (sometimes three to five) and one or many locules with placentas in two ranks, axillary or parietal. The style is simple, the fruit a loculicidal capsule or berry; the seeds are mostly numerous, sometimes winged, often (eg *Pittosporum*) smeared with a brownish resin-like mucilage (whence the name, the Greek word *pittos* meaning pitch); there is abundant endosperm. The bark is traversed by resin-containing canals.

Classification. Two tribes are recognized in the family, based on type of fruit:

PITTOSPOREAE. Fruit a capsule. *Pittosporum* (140–200 species, Canaries through West and East Africa and eastern Asia to Hawaii, Polynesia and, chiefly, Australasia); *Cheiranthera* (four species, Australia); *Hymenosporum* (one species, *H. flavum*, Australia and New Guinea); *Bursaria* (three species, Australia).

BILLARDIEREAE. Fruit a berry. *Sollya* (two species, Australia); *Citriobatus* (four species,

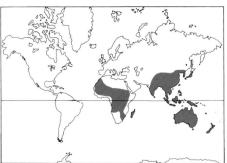

Number of genera: 9
Number of species: 200–240
Distribution: Australasia and Old World tropics.
Economic uses: ornamentals (*Pittosporum* and *Billardiera* species) and *Pittosporum* timber used locally.

Australia, one extending to Malaysia).

The genera may be divided by other characters:

Small trees, or shrubs without thorns; flowers not blue: seeds winged (*Hymenosporum*); seeds not winged (*Pittosporum*).

Shrubs with thorns: flowers in dense terminal panicles (*Bursaria*); flowers axillary (*Citriobatus*).

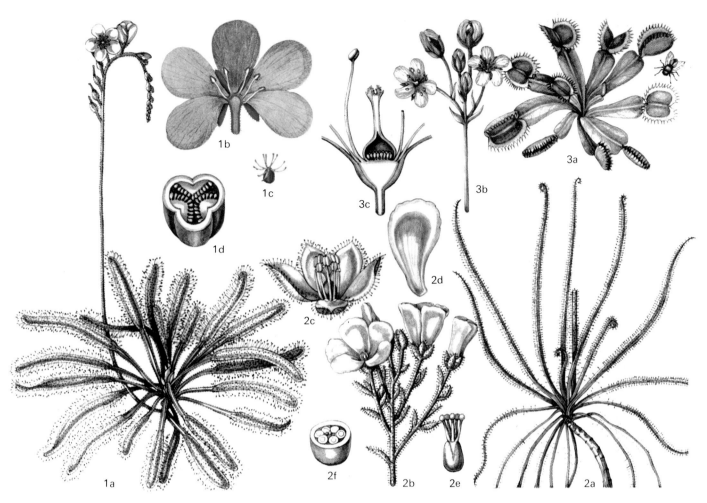

Droseraceae. 1 *Drosera capensis* (a) habit showing basal rosette of leaves covered in stalked glands ($\times\frac{2}{3}$); (b) perianth opened out to reveal stamens ($\times 2$); (c) gynoecium ($\times 2$); (d) half section of ovary ($\times 10$). 2 *Drosophyllum lusitanicum* (a) habit ($\times\frac{2}{3}$); (b) inflorescence ($\times\frac{2}{3}$); (c) flower with petals removed ($\times 2$); (d) petal ($\times 2$); (e) gynoecium with free styles and rounded stigmas ($\times 3$); (f) half section of ovary ($\times 4$). 3 *Dionaea muscipula* (a) habit showing leaves modified to form a trap ($\times\frac{2}{3}$); (b) inflorescence ($\times\frac{2}{3}$); (c) vertical section of base of flower showing ovary with basal ovules ($\times 4$).

Subshrubs with climbing stems and slightly irregular flowers (*Cheiranthera*).

Subshrubs with climbing stems, flowers regular and often blue; anthers oblong, fruit a capsule (*Marianthus*), anthers oblong, fruit a berry (*Billardiera*); anthers linear and tapering, forming a closed cone around the style (*Sollya*); anthers linear, finally recurved from style (*Pronaya*).

The family is closely related to the Escallonioideae subfamily of the Saxifragaceae (sometimes regarded as a segregate family, the Escalloniaceae) but is distinguished by the presence of resin canals.

Economic uses. These are few and essentially confined to *Pittosporum*, whose wood is used locally and for inlay work. The chief use of *Pittosporum* (parchment-bark, Australian laurel) is ornamental. The following shrub and small tree species are grown for their flowers (purple, white or greenish yellow, sometimes very fragrant) and attractive foliage; they are hardy in warm temperate sheltered and "Riviera" sites: *Pittosporum crassifolium*, *P. ralphii*, *P. tenuifolium*, *P. eugenioides* (all from New Zealand), *P. tobira* (Japan and China) and *P. undulatum* (Victoria box, Australia). The Tasmanian

evergreen climber *Billardiera longiflora* (apple berry) is grown for its creamy white to purple flowers and blue edible berries.

F.B.H.

DROSERACEAE
Sundews and Venus' Fly Trap

The Droseraceae is a family of carnivorous annual or perennial herbs, sometimes with woody stems, comprising the genera *Drosera* (sundew), *Drosophyllum*, *Aldrovanda* and *Dionaea* (Venus' fly trap).

Distribution. *Drosera* is cosmopolitan, with concentrations in Australia and New Zealand. *Drosophyllum* is found in the Iberian peninsula, *Aldrovanda* throughout much of Eurasia southwards to Australia and tropical Africa, and *Dionaea* in southeastern United States of America. They commonly grow in bogs and other waterlogged soils, indeed *Aldrovanda* is aquatic, and the carnivorous habit may be an evolutionary response to their growth in habitats containing little or no available nitrogen.

Diagnostic features. The leaves are alternate, rarely in whorls, often in basal rosettes and may or may not have stipules. They are covered with sessile or stalked glands on the

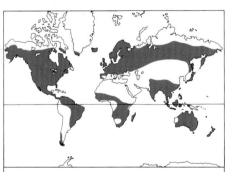

Number of genera: 4
Number of species: about 83
Distribution: cosmopolitan, with centers in Australia and New Zealand.
Economic uses: ornamental curiosities.

upper surface, and sometimes have median joints forming a trap. The flowers are regular, bisexual and are often in coil-like (circinnate) racemes, but sometimes solitary. There are five (sometimes four) sepals, more or less connate at the base, five (four) free petals and four up to 20 free stamens. The pollen is in tetrads. The ovary is superior, of two, three or five fused carpels with one locule, and three to numerous ovules on a basal placenta; the two to five styles are free or rarely connate. The fruit is a capsule which dehisces loculicidally into two to five valves; the seeds are usually numerous, containing endosperm and a small basal embryo.

Drosophyllum and *Drosera* have their leaves covered with long, red, gland-tipped hairs, motile in the latter genus, which entrap and digest insects by means of the proteolytic enzymes and ribonucleases which they secrete. This process is usually aided by bacterial activity, although this has not been detected in *Drosophyllum*, perhaps because of the antiseptic properties of the formic acid which is also secreted.

In *Dionaea* the leaves are divided longitudinally into two kidney-shaped halves which can come together like a trap. Each half-leaf has long marginal cilia (hair-like growths) and about three long sensitive slender hairs on the upper surface. When the sensitive hairs are touched, the halves of the leaf quickly swing on their common axis and the finger-like cilia intercross to form a barred cage. After subsequent movement the surfaces of the halves come into contact and any insect thus trapped is digested and absorbed by the secretory glands which cover the leaf surface. The trap opens and is active again in about 24 hours, but repeated stimulation greatly reduces the quickness of the motion.

In the aquatic *Aldrovanda* the leaves have a wedge-shaped basal part from which arise four to six long, narrow terminal segments and an orbicular lobe which is hinged along the midrib. This lobe can close rapidly (in about 1/50 second) to trap small aquatic animals, which are subsequently digested and absorbed by secretory glands on the leaf-surface.

Classification. The Droseraceae was formerly grouped with the other carnivorous families, Nepenthaceae and Sarraceniaceae, into a single order, Sarraceniales, but each family is now assigned to a different order on the basis of their individual affinities.

The carnivorous genera *Byblis* and *Roridula* bear considerable superficial resemblance to the Droseraceae and are sometimes placed in this family; other authorities recognize either two segregate families (Byblidaceae and Roridulaceae) or a single segregate family (Byblidaceae).

Economic uses. *Dionaea, Drosophyllum* and several species of *Drosera* are grown, usually in greenhouses, for ornament and interest.

D.M.M.

BRUNELLIACEAE

The Brunelliaceae is a small family of tropical New World trees. There are about 45 species in *Brunellia*, the only genus in the family (not to be confused with *Brunella*, a synonym for the labiate generic name *Prunella*). *Brunellia* commemorates Gabriel

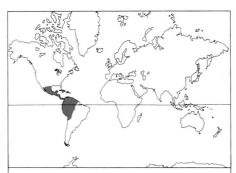

Number of genera: 1
Number of species: about 45
Distribution: New World tropics.
Economic uses: none.

Brunelli, onetime Professor of Botany and keeper of the Public Garden in Bologna, Italy. The family is restricted to the tropics of the New World from Mexico through the Caribbean into Peru. The leaves are simple opposite or in whorls, trifoliolate or compound and often densely hairy, with small caducous stipules. The flowers are regular, unisexual (sexes on separate plants) and borne in axillary or terminal panicles. They have no petals, but the calyx is divided into four to seven parts. There are eight to fourteen stamens in the male flowers. The female flowers have a superior ovary of two to five free carpels narrowing into elongate styles. These mature into dehiscent beaked fruits (follicles) which contain one or two seeds each. The seeds are black and shiny, containing flat cotyledons and a fleshy endosperm.

The family appears to be related to the Cunoniaceae and Simaroubaceae. The species have neither economic nor decorative value.

B.M.

EUCRYPHIACEAE
Eucryphias

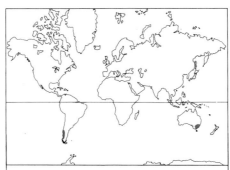

Number of genera: 1
Number of species: 5
Distribution: Chile, Tasmania, New South Wales.
Economic uses: hard timber and ornamental trees and shrubs.

The Eucryphiaceae is a family of evergreen (rarely half-evergreen or deciduous) trees or shrubs, consisting of a single Southern Hemisphere genus, *Eucryphia*.

Distribution. Of the five species in the genus, two are native to Chile, one to New South Wales in Australia, and two to Tasmania.

Diagnostic features. The leaves are opposite, simple or pinnately compound, sometimes trifoliolate, with odd terminal leaflets; the stipules are minute and connate. The flowers are bisexual and regular, large, white, axillary and usually borne singly. There are four imbricate sepals, cohering above, soon separating at the base and falling as one piece; the four (rarely five) petals are imbricate or convolute. The stamens are numerous and the filaments have basal tubular excrescences, inserted on an elongated axis below the (superior) ovary, which is formed of five to 12 fused carpels, with five to 12 (rarely 18) locules and as many styles. There are several pendulous ovules on axile placentas in each locule. The fruit is a woody or leathery capsule, dehiscing along the ventral sutures. The seeds are winged and the embryo embedded in endosperm.

Classification. In spite of its very disjunctive distribution, the family with its single genus is a very natural one. Phytochemical investigation of the flavanoids shows a close correlation with this distribution, the pattern in the three Australasian species being significantly very much simpler. Unfortunately, the flavanoid picture gives no direct information on the puzzling taxonomic position of the family, but indirectly supports a place in the order Rosales near the family Cunoniaceae.

Economic uses. In its native Chile, *Eucryphia cordifolia* makes a fine tree to some 80ft (24m), and the timber has been used for railway sleepers, telegraph poles, canoes, oars and cattle yokes. Indoor uses include furniture and flooring. The bark is a source of tannin. The timber of the Tasmanian species, *E. lucida*, is pinkish and used for general building as well as for cabinetmaking. *Eucryphia moorei* from New South Wales has similar applications.

F.B.H.

BRUNIACEAE

The Bruniaceae is a small family of heath-like shrubby plants, some of which make attractive ornamentals.

Distribution. The family is almost confined to the Table Mountain sandstone areas of the Cape region of South Africa.

Diagnostic features. The slender twigs of the plants are densely covered in small, alternate leaves which are entire, needle-like, oblong and rigid, often with a black tip which is secretory on young leaves. There are no stipules. The more ornamental species have terminal spikes, panicles or heads of bisexual, regular flowers; others have small, solitary axillary ones. There are four or five sepals, free or sometimes joined forming a calyx tube which is more or less fused to the ovary. There are four or five petals, which may or may not be clawed, free or rarely

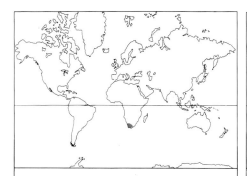

Number of genera: 12
Number of species: about 70
Distribution: Cape region of S Africa.
Economic uses: a few ornamentals.

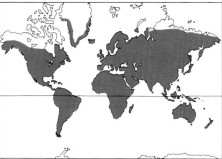

Number of genera: 122
Number of species: 3,370
Distribution: worldwide, centered in N temperate regions.
Economic uses: major bush and tree fruits of temperate regions (apples, pears, cherries, plums etc) and many valued ornamentals (roses, *Spiraea*, *Filipendula*, *Sorbus*, *Cotoneaster* etc).

fused at the base. There are four or five stamens alternating with the petals which are generally free, or rarely partly fused to the corolla; the anthers have two locules opening by long slits. The ovary is semi-inferior, rarely inferior, of one to three fused carpels and is crowned with two or three more or less cohering styles. There are one to three locules containing one to four pendulous anatropous ovules. The fruits are either capsules, splitting into two pieces containing one to four seeds, or sometimes they are indehiscent. The fruits are often decorated with the remains of the sepals or petals. The tiny oblong seeds contain copious fleshy endosperm and a straight embryo.

Classification. The most important genera are *Thamnea* (seven species), *Raspalia* (nine species), *Staavia* (10 species) *Pseudobaeckea* (10 species), *Berzelia* (seven species) and *Brunia* (seven species). This is an isolated family and is perhaps related to the Hamamelidaceae, but in this work is placed in the Rosales.

Economic uses. Some species have been grown for ornament both as cut flowers and living plants and others are used for kindling.   B.M.

ROSACEAE
The Rose Family

The Rosaceae is a large and important family of woody and herbaceous plants. It is valued both for its genera of bush and tree fruits of temperate regions, including apples, cherries, plums, peaches, raspberries and strawberries, and for many popular horticultural ornamentals.

Distribution. The family is worldwide, but with maximum development in the north temperate area.

Diagnostic features. The Rosaceae includes deciduous or evergreen trees, shrubs, shrublets or herbs (the last mostly perennial, but a few annuals occur). There are few climbers and no aquatics. The wood anatomy is unspecialized and the vessels have simple perforations. Branch thorns occur in *Crataegus*, *Prunus* and other genera, with surface prickles in *Rosa* and *Rubus*. The leaves are alternate (rarely opposite), simple or compound, and typically bear a pair of stipules at the base, although these may be difficult to detect or even absent in a few genera (*Exochorda*, *Spiraea* and allies). Glands are commonly present, and are often paired at the top of the petiole.

The flowers are characteristically insect-pollinated and frequently large and showy: a high percentage of all species are actual or potential garden ornamentals. Usually the flowers are regular and bisexual, showing a series from hypogyny through perigyny to epigyny, in which the carpels appear as if swallowed up by the receptacle. *Rosa* is unique in retaining free carpels although the flower is epigynous. A common feature of rosaceous flowers is the presence of an epicalyx, that is, a second, smaller whorl of five sepal-like organs below and alternating with the regular calyx. These have been interpreted as derived by the fusion of stipules of adjacent sepals. The sepals and petals are commonly five, although flower doubling is common in cultivars developed for ornament (*Kerria*, *Prunus*, *Rosa*, etc). It arises by replacement of the numerous stamens and sometimes also styles by petaloid organs. In extreme cases (some Japanese cherries and old-fashioned roses) the center of the bloom may be green where the carpels have been transformed into leaf-like appendages. In such cases the flower is usually completely sterile. The color range is wide, but blue is almost completely absent. The stamens are typically numerous and whorled, not spirally arranged, and two, three or more times the basic number of petals. The anthers have two locules and produce abundant pollen from longitudinal splits. The carpels are normally numerous and free, although varying degrees of fusion occur, and in Prunoideae the number is reduced to one. Each carpel contains usually two anatropous ovules.

The fruits of Rosaceae are very diverse, fleshy or dry, and provide important charac-

ters for dividing up the family. The fleshy-fruited types, so important to European horticulture, belong mainly to the Maloideae (Pomoideae – the pome fruits), the Prunoideae (*Prunus* in the wide sense) and Rosoideae (*Rubus* and *Fragaria*). The seeds contain no endosperm, or only a trace.

Woody members of Rosaceae may propagate vegetatively by suckers, as in *Rubus*, which also tip-roots in the brambles. Runners (stolons) are a characteristic of some herbaceous genera (*Fragaria*).

The flowers of the Rosaceae are mostly among the simplest and least specialized for pollination, relying on a large and wasteful production of pollen which attracts a wide range of insects, large and small. Some genera, like *Rosa*, produce pollen only, but most also secrete nectar from a disk surrounding the carpels. This disk may be freely exposed (*Rubus*) or more or less screened by the filaments (*Geum*). The latter flowers are regarded as more highly evolved, eliminating short-tongued visitors and attracting only the longer-tongued flies and bees. Protandry is the general rule, and self-compatibility is exceptional. Several genera show a breakdown of the normal sexual cycle and may be regarded as "evolutionary dead-ends." The dog roses (*Rosa* section *Caninae*) are said to be "subsexual" because half or more of the chromosomes remain unpaired and are lost prior to gamete formation. *Alchemilla*, *Sorbus* and the brambles (*Rubus*) are more or less completely apomictic.

A marked departure from insect pollination is found in the Sanguisorbeae, notably in the genera *Acaena* and *Poterium*. These rely on wind-pollination. The flowers are much reduced, in part unisexual, lacking petals and nectar, and are massed together in capitate or spicate heads.

Classification. The family can be divided into groups, subfamilies and tribes as follows:

GROUP I: BASIC CHROMOSOME NUMBER 7, 8 OR 9
SUBFAMILY SPIRAEOIDEAE

Two to five carpels (rarely one, or up to twelve), whorled, not usually immersed in the receptacle or elevated on a gynophore, with two to many ovules; fruit usually dehiscent.

SPIRAEEAE. Follicles with wingless seeds; stipules almost or quite absent (*Aruncus*, *Gillenia*, *Neillia*, *Physocarpus*, *Sibiraea*, *Sorbaria*, *Spiraea*, *Stephanandra*).

EXOCHORDEAE. Capsules with winged seeds (*Exochorda*).

HOLODISCEAE. Fruit indehiscent (*Holodiscus*).

SUBFAMILY ROSOIDEAE

Carpels many (rarely few), on a usually convex or conical gynophore, exposed or enclosed in a hollow, persistent receptacle; each carpel with one to two ovules; fruit always indehiscent.

ULMARIEAE. Receptacle flat or weakly concave; filaments almost club-shaped, soon

10b

10a

10c

10d

15

11a

11b

14

16

13

12

Rosaceae. 1 *Rubus ulmifolius* (a) flowering shoot ($\times\frac{2}{3}$); (b) fleshy fruits ($\times\frac{2}{3}$). 2 *Rubus occidentalis* half flower showing hypogynous arrangement of parts ($\times 2$). 3 *Fragaria* sp vertical section of false fruit—a fleshy receptacle with the true fruits embedded in it ($\times 1$). 4 *Sanguisorba minor* leafy shoot and fruit ($\times\frac{2}{3}$). 5 *Agrimonia odorata* fruit comprising a receptacle covered with hooks enclosing the achenes (not visible) ($\times 4$). 6 *Rosa* sp, vertical section of hep showing urn-shaped receptacle enclosing the achenes ($\times 1\frac{1}{2}$). 7 *Potentilla agyrophylla* var *atrosanguinea* flowering shoot ($\times\frac{2}{3}$). 8 *Kerria japonica* flowering shoot ($\times\frac{2}{3}$). 9 *Rosa pendulina* flowering shoot clearly showing the stipules at the base of the leaf stalks ($\times\frac{2}{3}$). 10 *Chaenomeles speciosa* (a) flowering shoot ($\times\frac{2}{3}$); (b) vertical section of fruit comprising swollen receptacle and calyx enclosing the true fruits ($\times\frac{2}{3}$); (c) cross section of ovary ($\times 6$); (d) vertical section of flower showing epigynous arrangement of parts ($\times 2$). 11 *Cotoneaster salicifolius* (a) leafy shoot with fruit ($\times\frac{2}{3}$); (b) vertical section of fruit ($\times 2\frac{2}{3}$). 12 *Sorbus aria* flowering shoot ($\times\frac{2}{3}$). 13 *Prunus insititia* leafy shoot and fruits—drupes ($\times\frac{2}{3}$). 14 *Prunus* sp vertical section of fruit ($\times 1\frac{1}{3}$). 15 *Prunus avium* vertical section of flower with petals removed showing perigynous arrangement of parts ($\times 2\frac{2}{3}$). 16 *Spiraea cantoniensis* vertical section of flower ($\times 4$).

becoming deciduous (*Filipendula, Ulmaria*).
KERRIEAE. Receptacle flat or convex; carpels few, whorled; stamens many, narrowed above from a broad base (*Kerria, Rhodotypos*).
POTENTILLEAE. As Kerrieae, but carpels usually many, on a convex gynophore (*Dryas, Fragaria, Geum, Potentilla, Rubus*).
CERCOCARPEAE. Receptacle cylindrical, enclosing one carpel (*Cercocarpus*).
SANGUISORBEAE. Receptacle urn-shaped, usually hard, enclosing two or more achenes (*Acaena, Agrimonia, Alchemilla, Poterium, Sanguisorba*).
ROSEAE. Receptacle urn-shaped or cylindrical, soft in fruit, enclosing many free carpels (*Hulthemia, Rosa*).

SUBFAMILY NEURADOIDEAE
Carpels five–10, united with one another and with the inner wall of the concave receptacle which is dry at maturity (*Neurada*).

SUBFAMILY PRUNOIDEAE
Carpels one (rarely up to five), free, with terminal styles and pendulous ovules; fruit a drupe (*Prunus*, including *Amygdalus, Armeniaca, Cerasus, Laurocerasus, Padus, Persica*).

GROUP II: BASIC CHROMOSOME NUMBER 17.
SUBFAMILY MALOIDEAE
Carpels two to five, usually fused with the inner wall of the concave receptacle which together with the calyx enlarges to enclose the fruits as a pome (*Amelanchier, Aronia, Chaenomeles, Cotoneaster, Crataegus, Cydonia, Eriobotrya, Malus, Mespilus, Photinia, Pyracantha, Pyrus, Quillaja, Raphiolepis, Sorbus, Stranvaesia*).
The Rosaceae constitute the type family

of the order Rosales, taken by some botanists in a narrow sense to include only two other minor families; by others in the broadest sense to include Leguminosae, Saxifragaceae and several other major families. This great discrepancy reflects perhaps no more than the artificiality of the order as a group in the taxonomic hierarchy.

Perhaps the closest ally of Rosaceae is the Saxifragaceae; it also has many common features with the Ranunculaceae, and the three large overlapping families can be separated only by taking a number of characters together – not by single absolute features. The Ranunculaceae differs in never having stipules and in having flowers almost entirely hypogynous, spirally arranged stamens, more carpels (usually) and endosperm in their seeds. The Saxifragaceae, on the other hand, is distinguished by being predominantly herbaceous, usually lacking stipules, and having a small number of whorled stamens and more or less united carpels. It, too, has endosperm in its seeds.

The fossil record shows the Rosaceae to be among the most ancient of dicotyledons, and its general structure and anthecology suggest that it is among the more primitive. Hutchinson regards it as an offshoot of the woody magnolian line of descent, and as being on a common line of evolution leading up to more specialized orders such as Leguminales (Fabales), Araliales (Umbellales) and the anemophilous tree orders Fagales and Juglandales. He points to the catkin-like, wind-pollinated inflorescences of *Poterium*, mentioned above, as giving a hint of how this last transformation might have occurred.

Taxonomic problems arise at all hierarchic levels in the Rosaceae: many of the controversies are of long standing. The tropical genera show far greater diversity in flower and fruit structure than the temperate, and include advanced features like irregular flowers, synandry, monoecy, apetaly and so on. Not surprisingly the subfamilies and most of the tribes have at one time or another been split off from the Rosaceae as separate families: Hutchinson lists the names of 26 segregate families. Of the subfamilies, the Spiraeoideae seems to be the least specialized in morphology, and has also contributed least to our gardens. By contrast, the well-defined subfamily Maloideae (Pomoideae) stands apart from all the rest not only by its unique fruit structure (pome) but by a basic chromosome number of 17, presumably derived from ancient amphidiploid hybrids between species with 8 and 9. Some botanists regard it as worthy of family status by itself: the Malaceae.

At the generic level controversy especially surrounds those of maximal economic interest, no doubt because their more intensive study has led to the discovery of more and finer taxonomic characters. Even the issue over whether or not the apple and pear should occupy the same genus or not is no

nearer solution than it was two centuries ago! The subgenera within *Prunus* are raised to generic level by some botanists as *Amygdalus* (for the almonds), *Cerasus* (cherries), *Padus* (bird cherries) and *Laurocerasus* (Portugal and cherry laurels), etc.

As regards species, greatest problems concern those genera in which subsexual or asexual reproduction is the norm. These do not display the normal patterns of disjunct populations in the wild, and taxonomists are of two minds (or more!) on how to treat them. The single species *Rubus fruticosus* of Linnaeus has thus been split up into many hundreds of self-perpetuating microspecies by some.

Economic uses. Most of the important bush and tree fruits of temperate regions fall within the Rosaceae. Economically by far the most important is the apple (*Malus*), now grown in numerous hybrid cultivars of complex origin, with over 2,000 named varieties. Apples are grown mainly for dessert, but are also used for making cider. Annual world production is over 20 million tonnes. The next most important genus is *Prunus*, which produces almonds, apricots, cherries, damsons, nectarines, peaches and plums, all of which are grown extensively for consumption as fresh fruit and for canning and making into jams, conserves and liqueurs. Other major rosaceous fruits are blackberries, loganberries and raspberries (*Rubus*), loquats (*Eriobotrya*), medlars (*Mespilus*), pears (*Pyrus*), quinces (*Cydonia*) and strawberries (*Fragaria*).

Many *Prunus* species are also cultivated as ornamentals, notably the Japanese flowering cherries. However, it is the rose, the "queen of flowers," that overshadows all the other ornamentals, being probably the most popular and widely cultivated garden flower in the world, valued since ancient times for its beauty and fragrance. Modern roses are complex hybrids descended from about nine of the wild species. Rose-growing is now a large industry, with some 5,000 named cultivars estimated to be in cultivation.

Among other popular cultivated genera are herbaceous perennials such as *Alchemilla* (lady's mantle), *Geum* (avens), *Filipendula* (meadowsweet), and *Potentilla* (cinquefoil); and trees and shrubs such as *Amelanchier*, *Chaenomeles* (flowering quinces, including *C. lagenaria*, better known as the japonica), *Cotoneaster*, *Exochorda* (pearl bush), *Sorbus* (rowan, mountain ash), *Photinia* and *Pyracantha* (fire thorn).

Attar of roses is extracted from flowers of *Rosa damascena* and its production is a major industry in parts of western Asia and Bulgaria. The bark of *Moquila utilis*, the pottery tree of the Amazon, is used in making heat-resistant pots, and that of *Quillaja* species, the soap-bark tree, contains saponin, which is used as a substitute for soap in cleaning textiles; tannin is also extracted from the bark.   G.D.R.

CRASSULACEAE
Stonecrops and Houseleeks

The Crassulaceae is a family of succulent herbs and small shrubs.

Distribution. The Crassulaceae are distributed throughout the world, mainly in warm dry regions, but are centered in South Africa. Like the other two great families of succulents, Aizoaceae and Cactaceae, they are characteristic of hot, exposed, rocky habitats subjected to long periods of drought, but Crassulaceae have a wider range of adaptability: species of *Sempervivum* and some of *Sedum* are frost-hardy, and some species of *Crassula* and *Sedum* live in a plentiful supply of water, one *Crassula* being an aquatic.

Diagnostic features. The plants are perennial (rarely annual or biennial), soft-wooded and rarely larger than small shrublets. The leaves are always more or less fleshy and mostly entire, without stipules and commonly packed tightly in rosettes which may reach the extreme of surface reduction in a sphere (*Crassula columnaris*). A full range of xerophytic specializations is found, including surfaces covered in papillae, hairs, bristles or wax. Vegetative reproduction from offsets, adventitious buds and fallen leaves is common. The flowers are small but

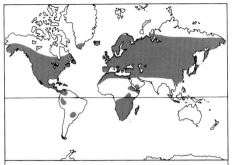

Number of genera: about 35
Number of species: about 1,500
Distribution: cosmopolitan, through the weedy species of *Crassula*, but centered in S Africa.
Economic uses: valued ornamentals for the rock garden and cool greenhouse, eg *Sedum* (stonecrops) and *Sempervivum* (houseleeks).

massed in showy corymbs or panicles. They are structurally simple, with equal numbers (normally five, but as few as three or as many as 30) of mostly perigynous free sepals, petals and carpels, and one (*Crassula*) or two whorls of stamens. The ovary is superior and the carpels (the same number as the petals) may be slightly joined at the base. The ovules

are numerous (rarely few) and inserted on the adaxial suture. The style is short or elongated. The fruit is a group of follicles, each with minute seeds, with little or no endosperm.

Classification. In general terms the family can be divided into two groups: those in which the stamens are as many as the petals and leaves are opposite, for example *Crassula* and *Rochea*; and those in which the stamens are twice as many as the petals and the leaves are alternate or opposite, for example *Kalanchoe* (flower parts in fours), *Umbilicus*, *Cotyledon* (corolla gamopetalous), *Sedum*, *Pachyphytum*, *Echeveria* (flower parts in fives) and *Monanthes*, *Sempervivum* and *Greenovia* (flower parts in sixes or more).

The Crassulaceae is closely related to the non-succulent Saxifragaceae.

Economic uses. The family is valued mainly as ornamentals: the hardy stonecrops (*Sedum* species) and houseleeks (*Sempervivum* species) for the rock garden or alpine house, the tender species for the succulent collection, *Echeveria* for summer bedding, and *Kalanchoe*, *Rochea* and a few others as house plants and florists' flowers. *Aeonium* is cultivated in warm regions.   G.D.R.

Crassulaceae. 1 *Echeveria nodulosa* (a) habit (×⅔); (b) half flower showing fleshy petals and carpels joined at base (×4½). 2 *Pachyphytum longifolium* (a) shoot tip showing clusters of fleshy leaves and lateral inflorescence (×⅔); (b) fruit (×3). 3 *Kalanchöe crenata* (a) habit showing opposite succulent leaves arranged on a fleshy stem (×⅔); (b) tip of inflorescence bearing clusters of tubular flowers (×1).

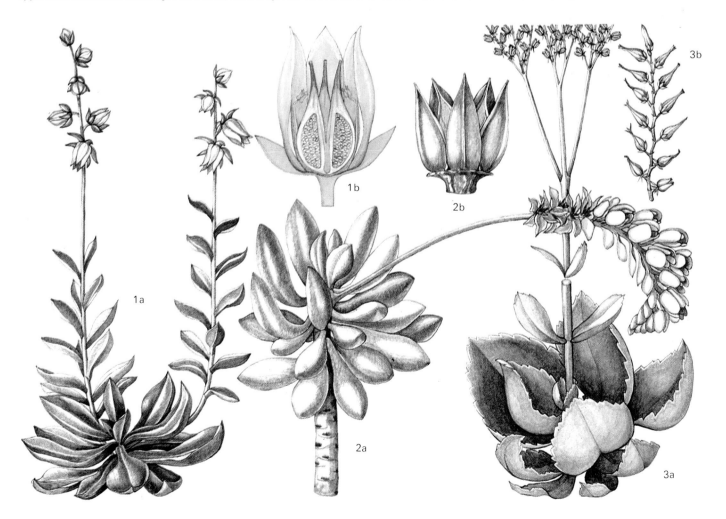

CEPHALOTACEAE
Flycatcher Plant

The Cephalotaceae is a family represented by a single species of pitcher plants, *Cephalotus follicularis*, the Australian flycatcher plant.

Distribution. The species is native to Western Australia, where it grows in the drier parts of peaty swamps.

Diagnostic features. It is a perennial herb with short rhizomes. There are normal entire leaves and others consisting of a stalk which is broadened at the leaf base into a lid, and a blade which is modified into a pitcher decorated with fringed ribs up the sides. The mouth of the pitcher has a corrugated rim. Intermediate leaf forms also occur. The inflorescence, like the leaves, arises from soil level and is a leafless raceme of little cymes. The flowers are regular, bisexual and have a colorful calyx with six hooded lobes, but no petals. The 12 stamens are perigynous, six being longer than the others, and the filaments are free. The connective of the anther is swollen and glandular. The ovary is superior and consists of six free carpels in one whorl, each containing a single locule with one or rarely two basal, erect ovules,

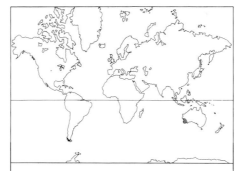

Number of genera: 1
Number of species: 1
Distribution: W Australia.
Economic uses: ornamental.

and crowned by a recurved style. The fruits are follicles, surrounded by the persistent calyx and contain a single seed with fleshy endosperm and a small, straight embryo.

The leaves start growth in July or August, are fully developed by October and are about 5in (13cm) long. The pitchers are mature by January and measure about 2in (5cm) long. It seems that a combination of partial digestion by pitcher-juices and bacterial decay provides nitrogenous materials from

trapped insects, but the plants can thrive without this supplement and are thus not obligate carnivores.

The inside of the pitcher consists of two recognizable zones. The upper is a smooth, glistening, opaque area with an overhang along its lower edge, the surface consisting of epidermis with downward-pointing hairs; this is contiguous with the lid. The lower smooth area is rich in secretory glands which have a digestive function, and has two lateral reddish-colored lumps of tissue endowed with large glands. The bottom lining of the pitcher is free of glands.

Classification. The curious evolutionary parallel between the pitcher-like leaves of *Nepenthes, Sarracenia* and *Cephalotus*, each of which occurs in a different geographical area, and family, has long been debated. Floral morphology has led botanists to think this family is related to the Saxifragaceae.

Economic uses. The plants are occasionally seen in glasshouse collections. B.M.

SAXIFRAGACEAE
Currants, Hydrangeas and Saxifrages

The Saxifragaceae is a large and widespread family consisting mainly of perennial herbs

Cephalotaceae. 1 *Cephalotus follicularis* (a) habit showing foliage leaves, pitchers and the leafless stalk to the inflorescence (×⅔); (b) inflorescence—a raceme of small cymes (×⅔); (c) pitcher and lid (×1⅓); (d) half section of pitcher showing downcurved spikes at rim (×1⅓); (e) section of flower showing hooded sepals, stamens of two lengths, a broad papillose disk and the gynoecium consisting of six free carpels (×8); (f) long stamen with swollen glandular connective at apex (×24); (g) short stamen (×24); (h) vertical section of a carpel with single basal ovule (×24); (i) flower from above (×4); (j) flower (×6); (k) fruit with part of wall removed to show single seed (×24); (l) seed (×32).

and shrubs, with a few annuals and a very few small trees. It contains the currants and gooseberries (both species of *Ribes*), as well as many popular garden flowers such as the hydrangeas and saxifrages. The family is here given a wide interpretation; some authors treat it much more narrowly and give family status to most of the subfamilies detailed below.

Distribution. On its wide interpretation the family is almost cosmopolitan. Its representation in the tropics, South Africa, Australia and New Zealand is, however, very scanty, and the great majority of the species are found in the north temperate zone, especially in eastern Asia and the Himalayas and in North America.

Diagnostic features. The uncertainty as to the limits of the family is due partly to its unspecialized nature and its "central" position, and consequently to the absence of any striking distinctive characters. The leaves are without stipules, and usually simple and alternate, but opposite or compound leaves are found in some genera. There are usually five valvate or imbricate sepals. The petals are always free, valvate or imbricate, and are usually four or five in number (occasionally

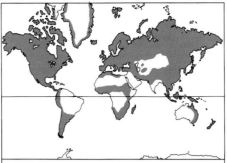

Number of genera: 80
Number of species: about 1,250
Distribution: almost cosmopolitan.
Economic uses: fruits (currants, gooseberries) and cultivated plants (eg saxifrages and hydrangeas).

absent); the stamens are typically twice as many as the petals, but may be more numerous. The ovary is superior or inferior with usually two or four carpels, united at least at the base, forming one to three locules, each with several rows of anatropous ovules on axile placentas. There are as many styles as carpels. The fruit is usually a small capsule, but in the Ribesoideae it is a berry with numerous seeds. The seeds contain much endosperm and a small embryo.

Classification. The principal subfamilies into which the Saxifragaceae may be divided are as follows (some smaller ones are omitted):

ASTILBOIDEAE. Herbs with compound leaves; petals often reduced; carpels sometimes free. *Astilbe*; *Rodgersia*, with creeping rhizome and handsome, digitately compound leaves.

SAXIFRAGOIDEAE. Herbs; leaves usually simple; carpels usually two. *Saxifraga*; *Bergenia*, similar in flower, but with coarse, cabbage-like foliage; *Heuchera*, *Tellima*, *Tolmeia*, *Tiarella*, *Mitella*, all similar in habit to *Heuchera* but with less showy flowers, mostly woodland and damp meadow plants; *Chrysosplenium* (golden saxifrage), without petals.

FRANCOOIDEAE. Herbs; leaves simple but deeply lobed; four carpels. *Francoa*.

PARNASSIOIDEAE. Herbs; leaves entire; four carpels. *Parnassia* (grass of Parnassus), with curious staminodes, each bearing numerous shining yellow glands.

RIBESOIDEAE. Shrubs; ovary inferior; fruit a berry; leaves simple, alternate. *Ribes* (*Grossularia*).

HYDRANGEOIDEAE. Mostly shrubs; leaves simple, usually opposite; fruit a capsule.

Saxifragaceae. 1 *Parnassia palustris* (a) habit ($\times\frac{2}{3}$); (b) flower (viewed from above) showing fan-like staminodes alternating with the stamens ($\times 1\frac{1}{2}$); (c) fruit—a capsule with persistent staminodes at base ($\times 2$). 2 *Peltiphyllum peltatum* (a) leaf ($\times\frac{2}{3}$); (b) inflorescence ($\times\frac{2}{3}$); (c) flower with two petals removed to show stamens ($\times 2$); (d) fruits ($\times 2$). 3 *Bergenia crassifolia* (a) tip of shoot and inflorescence ($\times\frac{2}{3}$); (b) flower opened out showing central bicarpellate ovary ($\times 2$); (c) vertical section of ovary ($\times 2$). 4 *Itea virginica* (a) shoot and inflorescence ($\times\frac{2}{3}$); (b) fruit—a capsule ($\times 3$).

Hydrangea, Philadelphus, Deutzia, Kirengeshoma.

ESCALLONIOIDEAE. Shrubs; leaves simple, alternate; fruit a capsule. *Escallonia*; *Itea*, with evergreen, holly-like leaves and pendulous catkins of small, greenish flowers.

At various times some of these subfamilies and even groups within them have been separated from the Saxifragaceae and raised to the rank of family, eg Francoaceae, Parnassiaceae, Grossulariaceae, Hydrangaceae, Philadelphaceae, Escalloniaceae, Iteaceae.

The family is obviously closely related to the Rosaceae, and indeed *Astilbe* has been repeatedly confused with *Aruncus, Filipendula* and other members of the Rosaceae.

Economic uses. Gooseberries, black, red and white currants, all from the genus *Ribes*, are widely grown for their edible fruits. The most popular garden plants of the family are the hydrangeas and saxifrages. All the genera listed above are also widely cultivated garden ornamentals. D.A.W.

CHRYSOBALANACEAE
Coco Plum

The Chrysobalanaceae is a family of trees

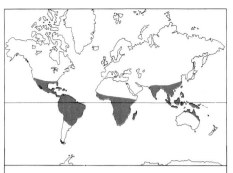

Number of genera: 17
Number of species: about 400
Distribution: tropical and subtropical lowlands.
Economic uses: fruits (coco plum), seed oil and local uses for timber.

and shrubs, some of which are locally important in the tropics as fruit trees.

Distribution. Most of the species are restricted to the lowlands of the tropics and subtropics. Large genera include *Parinari* (pantropical, 43 species), *Hirtella* (89 species in tropical America, one in Africa and Madagascar), *Couepia* (58 species, tropical and subtropical South America), *Licania* (151 species in tropical America, one in Malaysia and New Caledonia), *Magnistipula* (10 species in tropical Africa) and *Maranthes* (10 species in Africa, one in Malaysia, one in Central America). There are some curious intercontinental distributions, for *Parinari excelsa* and *Chrysobalanus icaco* are said to occur in both tropical America and Africa, and the Asian *Maranthes corymbosa* is closely allied to the American species.

Diagnostic features. The leaves are simple, alternate and with stipules. The flowers are bisexual, less commonly unisexual, more or less irregular and markedly perigynous, with five sepals, up to five petals and two to 300 (*Couepia*) stamens. The anthers, borne on filiform filaments, dehisce introrsely. The ovary is superior and has three carpels, but only one develops, usually with two erect basal ovules. The style is simple, with a simple stigma. The fruit is a dry or fleshy drupe with a bony endocarp (stone). The seeds have no endosperm.

Classification. Although many of the genera seem superficially very similar, they are readily separable and characterized.

The family is closely allied to the Rosaceae and was formerly included in it, but differs,

Chrysobalanaceae. 1 *Moquilea canomensis* (a) shoot with axillary inflorescences ($\times \frac{2}{3}$); (b) flower with five free sepals and petals and numerous stamens ($\times 3$); (c) vertical section of ovary with two erect ovules ($\times 3$). 2 *Licania incana* half flower showing epipetalous stamens and ovary with single basal ovule ($\times 8$). 3 *Acioa pallescens* (a) flower with bundle of stamens and filamentous style ($\times 2$); (b) fruit ($\times \frac{2}{3}$). 4 *Hirtella zanzibarica* (a) flower opened out showing numerous epipetalous stamens with long filaments and globose anthers and lateral ovary ($\times 3$); (b) vertical section of ovary with single basal ovule and base of feathery style ($\times 6$); fruit (c) entire and (d) in vertical section ($\times 1$).

among other things, in its erect ovules. The Australian shrubby genus *Stylobasium*, with two species, is sometimes made into a family of its own, Stylobasiaceae, perhaps allied to the Anacardiaceae.

Economic uses. The wood of *Licania ternatensis* is hard and is used in construction under water and underground, as well as for charcoal. In the Solomon Islands, *Maranthes* and *Parinari* are two important genera of timber trees.

Several species are cultivated for their fruit. The most important is the coco plum, *Chrysobalanus icaco. Licania pyrifolia* (merecure) is grown in Venezuela. *Parinari excelsa* is the Guinea plum, which is rather dry and mealy, *P. macrophylla* is the gingerbread plum, and *P. curatellifolia* is the strawberry-flavored mobola plum, all eaten in Africa. The fruit of the last is used in beermaking and a red dye is extracted from the young leaves in West Africa. The fruits of the African *P. capensis* and *Magnistipula butayei* are edible and the latter tree is of importance in rain-making ceremonies. Oil may be extracted from the seeds of many species; *Licania rigida* (oiticica) is grown for this purpose in Brazil, the oil being used as a substitute for tung oil, while the oil of *L. arborea* is used in candle- and soap-making.

D.J.M.

FABALES

LEGUMINOSAE
The Pea Family

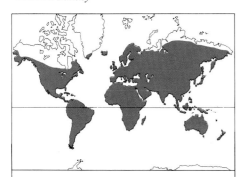

Number of genera: 700
Number of species: 17,000
Distribution: cosmopolitan.
Economic uses: important food crops (peas, beans, groundnut, soybean etc) forage crops (clover, lucerne) or ornamentals (broom, *Acacia*, sweet pea etc) and many other uses such as sources of dyes and timber.

The Leguminosae or Fabaceae is a very large family of herbs, shrubs and trees with a great variety of habit, including aquatics, xerophytes and climbers. Many species are of enormous importance to Man.

Distribution. The approximately 700 genera and 17,000 species have a cosmopolitan distribution in tropical, subtropical and temperate zones. Papilionoideae is the only

one of the three subgroups which is extensive in temperate regions.

Diagnostic features. The leaves are usually alternate, pinnately compound and with stipules. However, there are many exceptions: in gorse (*Ulex*) they are simple and small while in many species of *Acacia* the pinnate leaves are not developed in the young seedlings and the petioles become flattened into phyllodes. The stipules of some species of *Acacia* and *Robinia* develop into spines, while those of the garden pea (*Pisum*) are large and leaf-like. The number of leaflets on pinnate leaves varies greatly and can be of diagnostic value. For example, clover (*Trifolium*) and medick (*Medicago*) have leaves composed of only three leaflets while those of most species of vetch (*Vicia*) are composed of three to twelve pairs. Many species of Leguminosae have leaves which can alter their position at night; this usually involves the folding up of the leaflets. In some species of *Mimosa* (as in *Mimosa pudica*) the leaflets can be made to open merely by a shock stimulus, such as touch. The members of the family that can climb have twining stems (as in *Wisteria*) or tendrils or hooks which represent modified branches, leaves or leaflets.

A feature common to most Leguminosae is the presence of root nodules containing bacteria (*Rhizobium* species) which are capable of taking up atmospheric nitrogen and converting it into other nitrogenous compounds. Thus the leguminous plant can benefit from an augmented nitrogen supply and can grow well on relatively poor soils.

The inflorescence is usually an erect or pendulous raceme and sometimes, as in *Mimosa*, the flowers are arranged in tight clusters. The flowers are regular and unisexual or bisexual in Mimosoideae, and irregular and bisexual in Caesalpinioideae and Papilionoideae. There are five sepals which are more or less fused and and in some irregular flowers the calyx may be organized into two or four lobes. In Mimosoideae the five petals are small and equal, while in the Caesalpinioideae there is a range of irregularity in the corolla extending from the flowers of *Cassia* in which the five petals are nearly the same size, to those of the Judas tree (*Cercis siliquastrum*) which has flowers similar to those of the Papilionoideae. The five petals of the flowers of the Papilionoideae are organized into a butterfly shape with one upstanding dorsal petal (the standard), two lateral petals (the wings) and two lower ventral petals more or less fused along their contiguous margins to form a keel.

The stamens are usually numerous showing partial fusion of the filaments in Mimosoideae, while they are usually 10 or fewer in number, and free, in Caesalpinioideae. The 10 stamens in flowers of the Papilionoideae may be free as in *Sophora* but many have all the filaments fused together (monadelphous) as in *Ulex* or the filaments

of nine only may be fused with the dorsal stamen free (diadelphous) as in *Vicia*. The stamens are enclosed by the keel and the fused filaments form a tube around the ovary.

All the Leguminosae characteristically have a single carpel, the single ovary being superior, and surmounted by style and stigma. The ovules vary in number from two to many and are inserted in two alternating rows on a single placenta. Typically the fruit is a one-chambered pod (legume) which may be constricted between the seeds (lomentum). It is sometimes indehiscent as in the groundnut (*Arachis*) or it may open explosively as in broom (*Cytisus*), gorse (*Ulex*) and lupin (*Lupinus*), as the two walls of the pod twist up violently to throw out the seeds. The legumes may be dry or fleshy, inflated or compressed, winged or not, greenish or brightly colored and range in size from $\frac{1}{10}$ of an inch to 1ft (30cm) or more. The seeds vary in number from one to many and often possess a tough coat. They contain a large embryo with little or no endosperm and in some genera they possess a colored appendage called a caruncle.

Classification. The chief characteristics of the three subfamilies (or families) are:

MIMOSOIDEAE (Mimosaceae). Mainly tropical and subtropical trees and shrubs (approximately 56 genera and 500–3,000 species). The leaves are often bipinnate and the flowers are regular with the petals valvate in bud, and with 10 or more stamens.

CAESALPINIOIDEAE (Caesalpiniaceae). Mainly tropical and subtropical trees and shrubs (approximately 180 genera and 2,500–3,000 species). The leaves are usually pinnate but sometimes bipinnate and the flowers are usually more or less irregular with the lateral petals (wings) covering the standard in the bud. There are 10 or fewer stamens, free or monadelphous.

PAPILIONOIDEAE (Papilionaceae). Temperate, tropical and sub-tropical in distribution, mostly herbs but some trees and shrubs amongst its 400–500 or so genera and upwards of 10,000 species. The leaves are usually pinnate but sometimes simple. The flowers are irregular with the lateral petals enclosed by the standard in the bud. There are 10 stamens, usually diadelphous but sometimes monadelphous or free.

The genera of Mimosoideae can be separated into five or six tribes on the basis primarily of the nature of the leaves and the number and degree of fusion of the stamens. Thus *Inga* (pinnate leaves), *Pithecellobium*, *Calliandra* (bipinnate leaves) and *Acacia* all have flowers with numerous stamens which are fused into a tube in the first three genera but free in the latter. Stamens are five to 10 in number in *Mimosa*, *Neptunia* and *Prosopsis*, the anthers being crowned with a gland in the latter two genera. An alternative classification divides the Mimosoideae into five groups based on their pollen types.

Leguminosae. 1 *Spartium junceum* inflorescence – a raceme ($\times\frac{2}{3}$). 2 *Piptanthus nepalensis* shooting bearing trifoliolate leaves with stipules, flowers and fruit ($\times\frac{2}{3}$). 3 *Onobrychis radiata* inflorescence and pinnate leaf ($\times\frac{2}{3}$). 4 *Erythrina humeana* inflorescence ($\times\frac{2}{3}$). 5 *Erythrina abyssinica* dehiscing fruit (a pod or legume) and seeds ($\times\frac{2}{3}$). 6 *Phaseolus vulgaris* (a) shoot bearing flowers and immature fruit ($\times\frac{2}{3}$); (b) mature fruit with half of pod removed to show seeds ($\times\frac{2}{3}$). 7 *Lathyrus sylvestris* shoot bearing leaves, tendrils and inflorescence ($\times\frac{2}{3}$). 8 *Ulex europaeus*, half flower showing hairy sepals, upstanding standard petal, lateral wing petal and within it the keel petal which surrounds the stamens that have their filaments fused and ovary with numerous ovules ($\times 2\frac{2}{3}$). 9 *Caesalpinia gilliesii* shoot with bipinnate leaf and terminal inflorescence ($\times\frac{2}{3}$). 10 *Mimosa pudica* (a) shoot with sensitive, bipinnate leaves with four secondary stalks and axillary tight clusters of flowers ($\times\frac{2}{3}$); (b) clusters of mature fruit – compressed follicles ($\times\frac{2}{3}$). 11 *Bauhinia galpinii* (a) shoot with simple, bilobed leaves and terminal inflorescence ($\times\frac{2}{3}$); (b) mature fruit ($\times\frac{2}{3}$). 12 *Acacia podalyriifolia* (a) shoot with simple leaves and globose inflorescences ($\times\frac{2}{3}$); (b) mature fruit ($\times\frac{2}{3}$); (c) flower which is regular and has numerous stamens. 13 *Dichrostachys cinerea* cluster of twisted follicles ($\times\frac{2}{3}$).

The Caesalpinioideae can be divided into seven, eight or nine tribes or groups of genera on the basis of a number of characters, including the nature of the leaves, the irregularity of the flower, the degree of fusion of the sepals, and the mode of dehiscence of the anthers, but many of the groups are unsatisfactorily delimited or unnatural. Both *Poinciana* (calyx of five unequal lobes) and *Caesalpinia* (sepals free) have bipinnate leaves while *Cassia* (anthers dehiscing by pores) and *Cynometra* (anthers dehiscing by slits) have once-pinnate or simple leaves and free sepals. On the other hand both *Bauhinia* and *Cercis* possess a short-toothed calyx and simple entire or lobed leaves.

The position of the tribe Swartzieae is debatable. It is a small tropical African and South American group of 10 genera and is unusual in that the calyx is enclosed and entire in bud, becoming divided into lobes or slits as the flower opens. It is usually placed in the Caesalpinioideae as the last tribe, but other authorities place it in the Papilionoideae, or even recognize it as a separate subfamily.

The Papilionoideae is considered to consist of 10 or 11 tribes into which the genera can be grouped on features of habit, leaf form, and degree of fusion of the stamens.

SOPHOREAE. Mainly trees or shrubs with leaves pinnate or simple; stamens free.

PODALYRIEAE. Mostly shrubs (a few herbs) with simple or palmate leaves; stamens free.

GENISTEAE. Mainly shrubs (a few herbs) with simple, palmate or pinnate leaves; stamens usually monadelphous; anthers some large and some small.

TRIFOLIEAE. Mainly herbs (a few shrubs) with pinnate or palmate trifoliolate leaves; stamens usually diadelphous but occasionally monadelphous; anthers all alike.

LOTEAE. Herbs or undershrubs with pinnate leaves or three or more entire leaflets; stamens monadelphous or diadelphous; anthers all alike.

GALEGEAE. Herbs, shrubs (a few trees and climbing shrubs), with pinnate leaves, usually with five or more leaflets.

HEDYSAREAE. Herbs, shrubs or woody climbers with usually diadelphous stamens and fruit a lomentum.

VICIEAE. Herbs with pinnate leaves ending in a point or tendril; stamens usually diadelphous.

PHASEOLEAE. Usually climbing herbs (a few shrubs and trees eg *Erythrina*) with pinnate (usually trifoliolate) leaves; stamens usually diadelphous.

DALBERGIEAE. Trees or shrubs (a few climbers) with pinnate leaves of five to numerous pairs of leaflets; stamens monadelphous or diadelphous and fruit indehiscent.

There is little doubt of the close relationship to each other of the three subfamilies of the Leguminosae. The group as a whole has probably been derived from rosaceous ancestors, with perhaps the closest relationship with the Rosaceae (especially the segregate family Chrysobalanaceae) being shown by the Caesalpinioideae.

Economic uses. The family is of major economic importance. In the Mimosoideae, *Acacia* yields a number of valuable products. The Australian black wattle (*Acacia decurrens*) and golden wattle (*A. pycnantha*) are the source of wattle bark, which is used in tanning. A number of species, including the Australian blackwood (*A. melanoxylon*) and *A. visco*, are the source of useful timbers. Species including *A. stenocarpa* and *A. senegal* yield gum arabic while the pods and beans of the Mexican mesquite tree (*Prosopis juliflora*) are ground up and used as an animal stock feed. A number of *Albizia* species are valuable timber trees.

Caesalpinioideae also contains a number of useful species, including *Cassia acutifolia* and *C. angustifolia* native to the Middle East, whose dried leaves are the source of the purgative senna. Several *Caesalpinia* species are sources of dyes and timber. The pods of the tamarind (*Tamarindus indica*) are used as a fresh fruit and for medicinal purposes in India, while a number of species, such as the flamboyant tree, *Delonix regia* (*Poinciana regia*) and species of *Caesalpinia* (eg *Caesalpinia pulcherrima*, pride of Barbados), are grown as ornamentals in the tropics and in greenhouses in temperate zones.

The Papilionoideae is especially important because the seeds and pods of many of the herbaceous species are sources of human and animal food. They are of particular value in the protein-deficient areas of the world because they are rich in protein as well as mineral content. Certain species such as

clover (*Trifolium repens*) and lucerne (*Medicago sativa*) either can be used for feeding livestock or can be ploughed into the soil, functioning as excellent fertilizer and greatly increasing the nitrogen levels of the soil. Among the better-known species used as human food are the garden pea (*Pisum sativum*), chick pea (*Cicer arietinum*), French, haricot, snap, string, green or kidney bean (*Phaseolus vulgaris*), broad bean (*Vicia faba*), pigeon pea (*Cajanus cajan*), grass pea (*Lathyrus sativus*), lablab (*Dolichos lablab*), jack bean (*Canavalia ensiformis*), lima bean (*P. lunatus*), mung bean (*P. aureus*), scarlet runner (*P. coccineus*), lentil (*Lens culinaris*), soybean (*Glycine max*), and groundnut (*Arachis hypogea*). The cowpea (*Vigna sinensis*) clover and lucerne are widely used as forage plants.

Many genera contain species highly prized as ornamentals in both temperate and tropical countries. Some of the better-known in this category are lupin (*Lupinus*), broom (*Cytisus*), *Laburnum*, sweet pea (*Lathyrus*), *Baptisia*, *Wisteria* and *Genista*.

The twigs, leaves and flowers of *Genista tinctoria* were the source of a yellow dye used for coloring fabrics. Species of *Indigofera* yield the dye indigo. S.R.C.

PODOSTEMALES

PODOSTEMACEAE

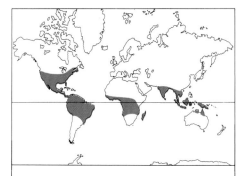

Number of genera: 45
Number of species: about 130
Distribution: mainly tropical, in streams and waterfalls.
Economic uses: none.

The Podostemaceae is a family of aquatic herbs resembling mosses.

Distribution. The plants are found widely in the tropics growing in rapidly flowing water, attached to rocks and stones.

Diagnostic features. These submerged freshwater herbs have a highly modified and varied vegetative structure, comprising a thallus and usually root-like organs (haptera) that anchor the plants. The flowers are regular, bisexual, either solitary or in a cymose inflorescence and when young are often enclosed in a spathe of enlarged, partially united bracts. The perianth comprises two to three sepals, united at the

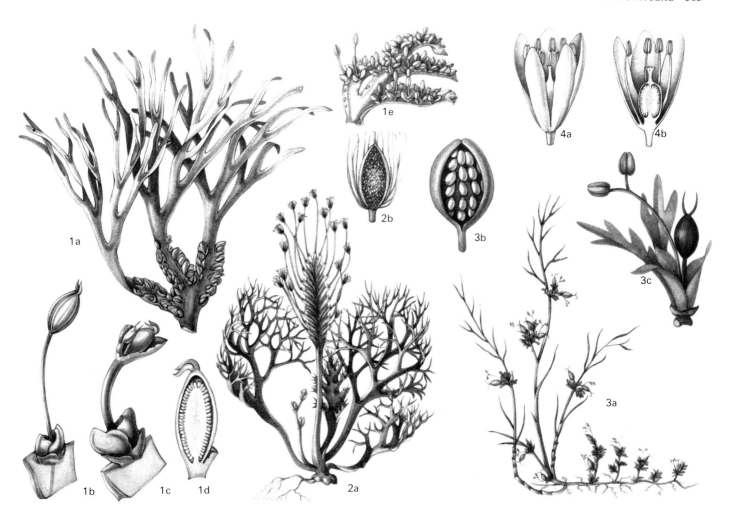

Podostemaceae. 1 *Dicraeia algiformis* (a) ribbon-like thallus (shoot) bearing flowers ($\times\frac{2}{3}$); (b) fruit—a capsule ($\times 3$); (c) expanded flower with basal involucre ($\times 3$); (d) vertical section of ovary showing numerous ovules on axile placentas ($\times 6$); (e) portion of thallus bearing flowers and fruit ($\times\frac{2}{3}$). 2 *Mourera weddelliana* (a) habit showing basal rhizoids and erect inflorescence ($\times\frac{2}{3}$); (b) vertical section of ovary surrounded by persistent stamens ($\times 4$). 3 *Podostemum ceratophyllum* (a) habit ($\times\frac{2}{3}$); (b) fruit with wall cut away ($\times 6$); (c) flower with two divided bracts, three green sepals, stalked ovary and two stamens with filaments fused at base ($\times 3$). 4 *Weddellina squamulosa* entire (a) and half (b) flower ($\times 9$).

base; petals are absent. There are one to four (sometimes numerous) hypogynous stamens; the filaments are either free or partially united and the anthers have two locules, dehiscing lengthwise. The ovary is superior, of two united carpels, forming two locules each with a large axile placenta bearing numerous ovules. The styles are free and slender. The fruit is a capsule containing numerous minute seeds without endosperm.

The seeds are dispersed during the dry season and do not germinate until they are submerged in the rainy season. A thallus grows from the seed and from it the haptera are produced. Flowers are not produced until the end of the rainy season and after fruiting the thallus usually dies.

Classification. The most common genera are *Apinagia* (50 species, South America), *Rhyncholacis* (25 species, South America), *Marathrum* (25 species, tropical America), *Podostemum* (17 species, pantropical), *Castelnavia* (nine species, Brazil), *Mourera* (six species, tropical America), *Dicraeia* (five species, Madagascar). *Weddellina* (one species tropical South America).

The peculiar structure of the family suggests no obvious close alliance with any other group, and the family is placed in its own order, Podostemales. It is generally felt that this is allied to Rosales and perhaps approaches Saxifragaceae or Crassulaceae (particularly the semiaquatic *Crassula* species) of that order. It may have affinities with the Hydrostachydaceae, another group of aquatics, which has sometimes been placed in the Podostemales but is nowadays referred to the Scrophulariales.

Economic uses. None are known.

D.J.M.

HALORAGALES

THELIGONACEAE

The Theligonaceae is a small family of annual and perennial herbs.

Distribution. The family occurs in the Mediterranean region, in China and Japan.

Diagnostic features. Members of the family have entire, ovate, fleshy leaves; the lower are opposite and the upper alternate, by the suppression of one leaf of each pair. There are peculiar united membranous stipules. Large club-shaped glands are present at the

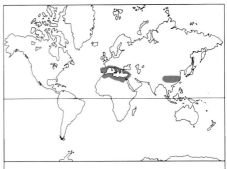

Number of genera: 1
Number of species: 2 or 3
Distribution: temperate N Hemisphere.
Economic uses: young shoots used as vegetable.

apex of the leaves. The flowers are unisexual (with both sexes on the same plant), in one- to three-flowered clusters. The male flowers have a valvate to globose perianth, splitting into two to five lobes when the flower opens. There are seven up to 12 (sometimes as few as two and as many as 30) stamens with filiform filaments and anthers that are erect in the bud, but pendulous later. The female flowers have a tubular, shortly toothed

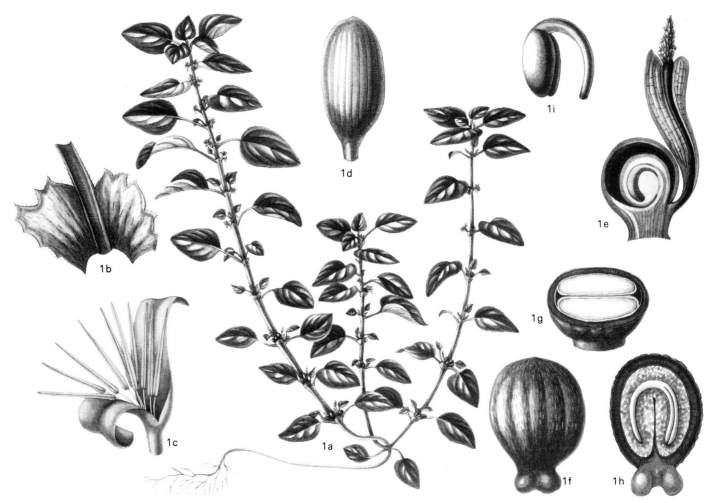

Theligonaceae. 1 *Theligonum cynocrambe* (a) habit showing leaves opposite at base of stem and alternate at the apex ($\times\frac{2}{3}$); (b) united membranous stipules ($\times 6$); (c) male flower with bilobed perianth and numerous stamens with short, filiform filaments and long anthers ($\times 10$); (d) male flower bud ($\times 10$); (e) half female flower with lateral tubular perianth and style that arises from the base of the ovary ($\times 10$); (f) fruit—a nut-like drupe ($\times 10$); (g) cross section fruit ($\times 10$); (h) vertical section of fruit showing single seed with a curved embryo embedded in fleshy endosperm ($\times 10$); (i) embryo with two large, globose cotyledons ($\times 12$).

perianth and an ovary of a single carpel containing a single basal ovule. The style is simple and arises from the base of the ovary. The ovary enlarges irregularly on one side and the style becomes lateral at fruiting time. The fruit is a subglobose nut-like drupe containing one seed with fleshy endosperm.

The genus *Theligonum* exhibits myrmecochory (dispersal of seeds by the agency of ants). Ants feed on the oil body or elaiosome of various seeds and frequently carry the seed some distance from the parent plant. The oil body of the seeds is formed of a portion of the pericarp which remains attached to the base of the seed. The ants eat the oil body and then leave the seed undamaged.

Classification. The family is represented by one genus, *Theligonum*, with two or possibly three species. *Theligonum cynocrambe* grows in damp shady rock habitats in the Mediterranean region, as a glabrous somewhat succulent annual. *Theligonum japonicum* grows in the mountains and woods of western China and Japan, as a creeping, branched perennial herb with a line of short recurved hairs on the stems.

The relationship of the family Theligo-

naceae (sometimes called the Cynocrambaceae) with other families is much disputed. Morphological observations have suggested a relationship with the Haloragaceae, Hippuridaceae or Portulacaceae, but there seems little anatomical evidence to support this. The Theligonaceae have also been regarded as part of the Urticaceae but this relationship is also doubtful.

Economic uses. Young shoots of *T. cynocrambe* are sometimes eaten as a vegetable.

S.A.H.

HALORAGACEAE
Gunneras, Water Milfoil, Haloragis

This family of aquatic or moist terrestrial herbs ranges from delicate aquatics, as in *Myriophyllum* (the water milfoil), to large robust species of *Gunnera* growing in forest margins, with leaves up to 20ft (6m) in circumference and stout inflorescences up to 5ft (1.5m) high.

Distribution. The family occurs in temperate and subtropical regions, chiefly in the Southern Hemisphere.

Diagnostic features. The aquatic representatives, like many of those of comparable habit in other families, show heterophylly,

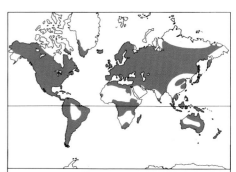

Number of genera: 7
Number of species: about 180
Distribution: temperate and subtropical, chiefly S Hemisphere.
Economic uses: garden ornamentals and ground cover (*Gunnera*) and limited use in tanning (*G. chilensis*).

with the submerged leaves pinnately divided into unbranched capillary segments and the aerial leaves normally simple, and toothed or entire.

The plants are annual or perennial herbs, aquatic or terrestrial, sometimes with a persistent woody base. The leaves are opposite to alternate or in whorls, entire to

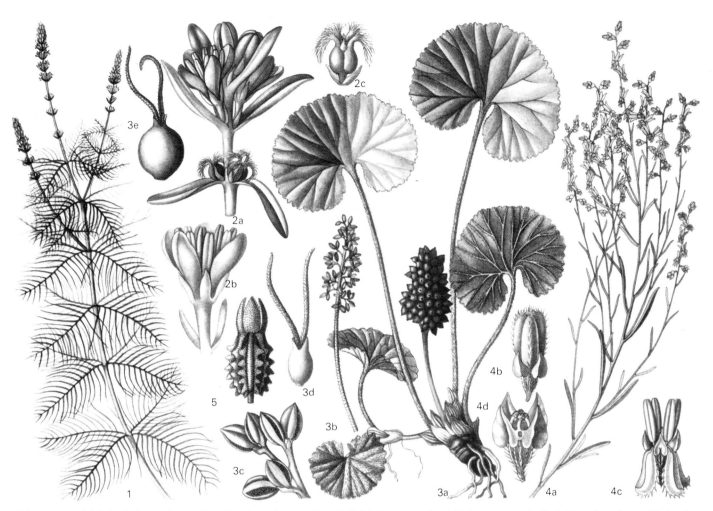

Haloragaceae. 1 *Myriophyllum spicatum* shoot bearing submerged much divided leaves and aerial inflorescences ($\times\frac{2}{3}$). 2 *M. pedunculatum* (a) tip of inflorescence with separate male and female flowers ($\times 6$); (b) male flower ($\times 8$); (c) female flower with plumed stigmas ($\times 8$). 3 *Gunnera magellanica* (a) habit ($\times\frac{2}{3}$); (b) female inflorescence ($\times\frac{2}{3}$); (c) tip of male inflorescence each flower comprising only two stamens ($\times 4$); (d) female flower ($\times 4$); (e) fruit ($\times 4$). 4 *Haloragis cordigera* (a) flowering shoot ($\times\frac{2}{3}$); (b) flower ($\times 6$); (c) flower showing heart-shaped sepals, down-curved petals and large anthers ($\times 4$); (d) flower with petals and stamens removed to show styles and stigmas ($\times 8$). 5 *H. acanthocarpus* fruit ($\times 8$).

lobed, usually finely pinnate when submerged; stipules are present or absent. The flowers are bisexual or unisexual, regular, usually very small, solitary and axillary or in spikes or panicles. The calyx tube is adnate to the ovary, with two to four lobes, sometimes none. The petals are free, two, four or rarely three in number, or absent, concave, often hood-shaped. The stamens are eight or two to six in number, or absent, with filaments usually long and slender and basifixed anthers, dehiscing laterally. The ovary is inferior, of two to four fused carpels, with one, two or four locules and as many pendulous ovules as styles; there are one to four free styles with feathery or papillose stigmas. The fruit is usually very small, dry or succulent, indehiscent or separating into one-seeded nutlets; the seed has copious endosperm and an erect embryo.

Classification. The Haloragaceae is usually subdivided as follows (*Gunnera* is sometimes placed in a separate family, Gunneraceae):

SUBFAMILY HALORAGOIDEAE
Ovary two- to four-loculed; leaves without stipules; inflorescence small; fruit dry; petals present or absent.

HALORAGEAE. Fruit indehiscent. *Loudonia* (Australia), *Haloragis* (Australasia north to Himalayas), *Meziella* (Australia), *Laurembergia* (tropical Africa and Asia), *Proserpinaca* (North America).

MYRIOPHYLLEAE. Fruit separating into two or four nutlets. *Myriophyllum* (cosmopolitan in fresh waters).

SUBFAMILY GUNNEROIDEAE
Ovary unilocular; leaves stipulate; inflorescence large; fruit succulent; petals absent. *Gunnera*.

The family is most closely related to the Hippuridaceae (mare's tails), which has sometimes been included with it, and in floral features it resembles the Onagraceae, but the affinity is obscure.

Economic uses. Some species of *Gunnera* are used for ornament or ground cover in gardens. The stem of the Chilean *Gunnera chilensis* has been used on a small scale for tanning and dyeing. D.M.M.

HIPPURIDACEAE
Mare's Tail
The Hippuridaceae comprises the single species of aquatic herbs, *Hippuris vulgaris*, with a number of specialized races.

Distribution. *Hippuris* is found in wetlands

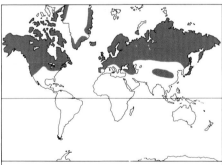

Number of genera: 1
Number of species: 1
Distribution: temperate and cold wetlands of the N Hemisphere.
Economic uses: young shoots eaten.

throughout the temperate and cold regions of the Northern Hemisphere.

Diagnostic features. *Hippuris* or mare's tail is a perennial herb that usually grows in shallow water. The stem is a perennial, creeping rhizome from which arise erect leafy shoots. The erect shoots bear flowers when they emerge above the surface of the water but after flowering they die down to the rhizome; the non-flowering submerged shoots usually remain green throughout the winter. The leaves are borne in whorls of four up to 12. The submerged leaves are linear, pale green and flaccid; the emergent leaves are shorter, obovate to linear, dark green and rigid. The flowers are inconspicuous and borne solitary in the axils of emergent leaves. Although the flowers are small and very reduced they are variable within a single plant and may be bisexual, unisexual or rudimentary and apparently sterile. The perianth is reduced to a small rim around the top of the ovary. There is one, relatively massive stamen: its size can probably be considered an adaptation to wind-pollination. The ovary is inferior formed of one carpel containing a single, pendulous ovule. The style is long and slender with stigmatic papillae throughout its length. The fruit is a small, ovoid, smooth one-seeded nutlet.

Classification. There are some ecologically specialized races of *Hippuris* found in the Arctic and the Baltic Sea, but as there is no clear-cut morphological differentiation it is usual to recognize only one species (*Hippuris vulgaris*). As with so many other reduced dicotyledonous aquatics, the relationships of the Hippuridaceae are disputed. It is generally considered to be related to the Haloragaceae, and is here placed in the Haloragales. Embryological and recent phytochemical investigations, however, suggest a relationship with the Tubiflorae (a large group including the Convolvulaceae, Labiatae, Scrophulariaceae, Solanaceae, Acanthaceae). However, no other Tubiflorae have a single, inferior carpel, and some recent workers have suggested that the family should be placed near the Cornaceae.

Economic uses. The submerged shoots of *Hippuris* remain green in winter and form an important winter food for many animals. The Eskimos also gather and eat the young shoots of *Hippuris*.   C.D.C.

MYRTALES

SONNERATIACEAE

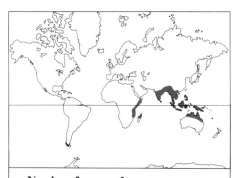

Number of genera: 2
Number of species: 8
Distribution: tropical.
Economic uses: wood used locally and fruit and leaves eaten locally.

This tropical family of trees and shrubs has two genera, *Sonneratia* and *Duabanga*.

Distribution. The family occurs from East Africa through Asia into Australasia and the western Pacific.

Diagnostic features. The leaves are opposite, simple, entire, and without stipules. The flowers are regular, bisexual or unisexual (sexes on the same plant), solitary or borne in threes and are conspicuous, having a bell-shaped, leathery calyx tube with four to eight lobes, four to eight free petals (sometimes absent), and many free stamens which are inflexed in bud and inserted on the calyx. The anthers are kidney-shaped and open lengthwise. The ovary is superior, of numerous fused carpels, sometimes partly fused to the base of the calyx tube; it contains four to many locules each with numerous ovules on axile placentas. There is a single long style with a head-like stigma. The fruits are capsules in *Duabanga*, berries in *Sonneratia*, and contain many seeds which lack endosperm and have short, leafy cotyledons.

Classification. The five *Sonneratia* species grow in tidal mudflats and possess erect conical breathing roots which project from the mud like those of certain species of mangrove. *Duabanga* contains three species of lowland and mountain forest trees growing to 100ft (30m). Their large flowers, which last only one night, are up to 3in (7cm) across, green outside, white inside, and in size resemble those of *Sonneratia*.

In many respects the flowers of both genera are morphologically close to those of *Lagerstroemia* in the family Lythraceae, to which the Sonneratiaceae is related, as it is to the Punicaceae (the pomegranates).

Economic uses. The wood of most species is used locally, and the fruit or leaves of some *Sonneratia* species may be eaten.   B.M.

TRAPACEAE
Water Chestnut

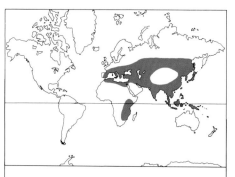

Number of genera: 1
Number of species: 1, 3 or about 30
Distribution: throughout Old World, naturalized in N America and Australia.
Economic uses: fruits (water chestnuts) a staple food in parts of Asia.

This family of floating aquatics has a single genus. *Trapa*, whose fruits, the water chestnut, are an important food in parts of Asia.

Distribution. Excepting the arctic regions, *Trapa* occurs almost throughout the Old World. It has become naturalized in North America and Australia.

Diagnostic features. *Trapa* is an aquatic annual or short-lived perennial. The stems are rooted in mud and float in water. Submerged leaves are opposite and linear, very short-lived and soon replaced by green, pinnately-branched roots, frequently mistaken for leaves. The floating leaves are alternate and form a rosette; the petiole often bears an ellipsoidal, spongy swelling which acts as a float; the leaf blades are rhombic with a toothed margin. The flowers are regular, bisexual, inconspicuous, solitary, axillary and short-stalked. The sepals are four, triangular, adnate to the ovary and develop into two, three or four hard horns or spines in fruit. The petals are four, white or lilac. The stamens are four. The ovary, of two fused carpels, is half-inferior, forming two locules, each with a single pendulous anatropous ovule on an axile placenta. The fruit is a large, woody, variously sculptured, spinose nut. The seeds have no endosperm and the cotyledons are very unequal in size and shape.

Classification. The sculpturing of the fruit is very variable and there is little agreement as to which variants should be recognized as species, the number of species being given variously as one, three or up to about 30. The Trapaceae is allied to the Onagraceae.

Economic uses. The fruits of *Trapa*, water chestnuts, contain much starch and fat and are a staple food in eastern Asia, Malaysia and India. Most tinned "water chestnut" is in fact *Cyperus esculentus*, *Trapa* grows very quickly and forms stable surface-floating mats which may hinder navigation in various parts of the world. The sturgeon breeding grounds in the Caspian Sea are threatened by *Trapa*.   C.D.C.

LYTHRACEAE
Cupheas, Lythrums and Henna

The Lythraceae is a small family of herbs, shrubs and trees including several ornamentals and species producing dyes, including henna (*Lawsonia inermis*).

Distribution. The family is distributed mainly in the tropics, but also in temperate regions. The temperate representatives are mostly annual and perennial herbs, often growing in damp habitats.

Diagnostic features. The leaves are opposite, whorled or spiral, simple and entire, with very small or no stipules. A constant anatomical feature is the presence of bicollateral vascular bundles (ie with phloem on both the inside and outside of the xylem). The flowers, borne in racemes, panicles or cymes, are usually regular and bisexual. They have four (or six) sepals and petals and twice as many stamens, although there is wide variation in number of parts. There is sometimes another whorl of appendages

Lythraceae. 1 *Lawsonia inermis* (a) leafy shoot with axillary and terminal inflorescences ($\times\frac{2}{3}$); (b) fruit ($\times 3$); (c) cross section of fruit ($\times 3$). 2 *Peplis portula* (a) habit showing adventitious roots ($\times\frac{2}{3}$); (b) vertical section of fruit ($\times 4$). 3 *Cuphea ignea* (a) leafy shoot with solitary axillary flower ($\times\frac{2}{3}$); (b) vertical section of flower ($\times 1\frac{1}{2}$). 4 *Lythrum salicaria* produces three types of flower (only one type on each individual) with the style and the two whorls of stamens at three levels in the floral tube (tristyly); seed-set is far higher when the stigma receives pollen from stamens of the same length as itself (shown as arrows) than when it is pollinated from longer or shorter stamens.

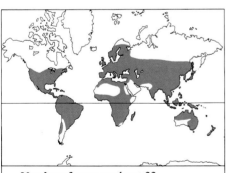

Number of genera: about 22
Number of species: about 450
Distribution: mainly tropical, sometimes temperate.
Economic uses: dyes, commercial timbers and ornamentals.

outside the sepals, forming an epicalyx. The petals, usually crumpled in bud, are free and borne on the rim of a deep calyx tube, alternating with the sepals. The stamens are inserted at different levels within the calyx tube, but rarely close to the petals. Heterostyly is quite a common family characteristic. The ovary is superior, sometimes stalked, and has two to six locules, each with two to many ovules on axile placentas; rarely there

is one locule with parietal placentas. The style is simple and the stigma usually capitate. The fruit is a dry, dehiscent or indehiscent capsule. The seeds are numerous, with a straight embryo and no endosperm.

Classification. The main division of the Lythraceae is into two tribes, the Lythreae and Nesaeae, distinguished by a technical character: in the former the cross-walls (dissepiments) of the ovary are only partial so that the top of the fruit is unilocular, whereas in the latter the dissepiments are complete. The largest genera of the Lythreae are *Cuphea*, *Diplusodon*, *Rotala* and *Lythrum*, and of the Nesaeae, *Nesaea* and *Lagerstroemia*.

The Lythraceae, with their typically four-petaled flowers and internal phloem, belong to the Myrtales. The family has affinities with the Myrtaceae, Onagraceae, Punicaceae, Sonneratiaceae and Combretaceae, but it is a distinct group not linked with any other by intermediates. The families just mentioned differ from the Lythraceae in having inferior ovaries, fleshy fruits, and stamens which are generally inserted on the rim of the calyx tube with the petals.

Economic uses. The Lythraceae are known

chiefly as the source of certain dyes. The most famous is henna, produced from *Lawsonia inermis*. The leaves of *Woodfordia fruticosa* yield a red color and the bark and wood of some *Lafoensia* species, including *Lafoensia pacari*, give a yellow dye. Several species have valuable timber, notably *Physocalymma scaberrima*, which has rose-pink wood, *Lafoensia speciosa*, and various members of *Lagerstroemia*. *Lagerstroemia indica* (crepe myrtle), *Lawsonia inermis* (mignonette tree) and *Woodfordia fruticosa* are grown as ornamental trees and shrubs in warm climates, and several *Cuphea* species are grown as pot-plants. *Lythrum salicaria* (purple loosestrife) and other *Lythrum* species are grown as perennials in temperate regions.　　　　　　　　　　F.K.K.

RHIZOPHORACEAE

Mangroves

The Rhizophoraceae is a tropical family of shrubs, climbers and trees, four genera of which are mangroves, half of the world's main mangrove genera.

Distribution. The family is found throughout, and is virtually confined to, the tropics. One of the genera, *Cassipourea* (not man-

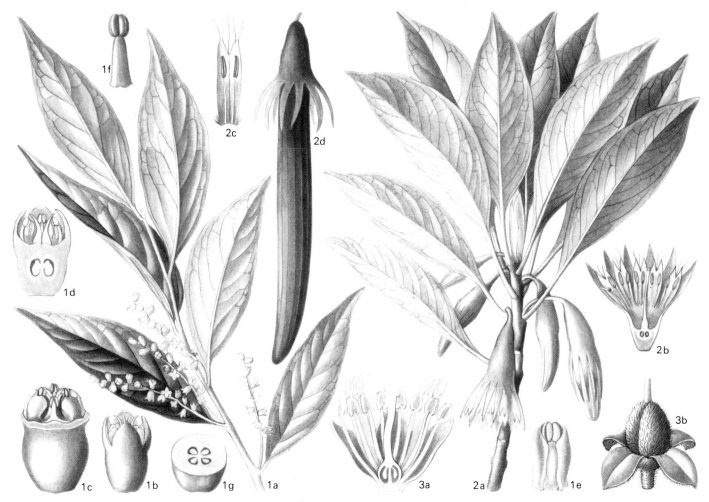

Rhizophoraceae. 1 *Anisophylla griffithii* (a) shoot with alternate leaves and axillary inflorescences ($\times\frac{2}{3}$); (b) flower with four sepals ($\times4$); (c) flower with sepals removed ($\times6$); (d) half flower showing inferior ovary with free styles ($\times4$); (e) petal and stamen ($\times14$); (f) stamen ($\times14$); (g) cross section of ovary ($\times5$). 2 *Bruguiera gymnorhiza* (a) shoot with alternate leaves and solitary axillary flowers ($\times\frac{2}{3}$); (b) half flower showing notched petals and inferior ovary ($\times\frac{2}{3}$); (c) petal and stamens ($\times1\frac{1}{3}$); (d) fruit ($\times\frac{2}{3}$). 3 *Cassipourea rowensorensis* (a) half flower with superior ovary and single style ($\times4$); (b) fruit ($\times2\frac{2}{3}$).

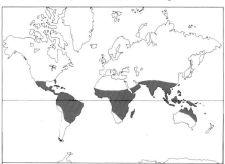

Number of genera: 16
Number of species: about 120
Distribution: tropical rain forests, and mangroves.
Economic uses: tannin (mangrove bark), timber for charcoal and fuel and local uses for food and medicine.

groves), contains well over half the species in the family, and is one of only four genera in the Americas. (See also pp. 890–891.)

Diagnostic features. Although so well known, the four genera of rhizophoraceous mangroves comprise only 16 species. The majority of species are shrubs or climbers (less often trees) of tropical rain forests. The leaves are simple and entire, usually opposite and with conspicuous, caducous stipules, rarely alternate and without stipules. The flowers are bisexual (rarely unisexual), regular, and hypogynous to epigynous, borne in cymes or racemes, rarely solitary, in the leaf axils. There are three up to 16 persistent, valvate sepals and the same number of petals, usually with a claw and jagged at the tip. There are eight to many stamens inserted on the edge of a disk, the anthers with four, rarely many, locules dehiscing by a valve. The female flowers bear staminodes sometimes adnate to the petals. The ovary is inferior or superior, of two to 12 fused carpels, and has two to 12 locules, each usually with two anatropous, pendulous ovules. There is usually a simple style. The fruit is a berry or drupe, or dry and indehiscent, rarely a dehiscent capsule or winged; the seeds, sometimes with an aril, and germinating on the plant in mangrove species, are with or without fleshy endosperm.

Classification. There are three tribes in the family, by far the best-known comprising four genera of mangroves: *Rhizophora*, which is pantropical; *Bruguiera* and *Ceriops*,

found throughout tropical Asia and in Africa; and *Kandelia*, confined to Southeast Asia. These four genera, together with three genera of the Combretaceae and the genus *Avicennia*, are the most important mangroves throughout the world, and share many characteristics of ecology, growth-form and reproductive biology.

The Rhizophoraceae is quite closely related to the Combretaceae, and shares with it the woody habit and simple, usually entire leaves. It also has a similar range in ecology and associated growth-habit, but it has usually stipulate leaves and shows a greater range of basic floral construction.

Economic uses. Apart from many native uses in food and medicine, several species are valuable sources of timber. This is particularly true of the mangrove species, whose wood, hard and dense but not very durable, is used mainly for charcoal production and fuel. Mangrove bark is also widely used in the preparation of leather in the tanning industry.   C.A.S.

PENAEACEAE

The Penaeaceae is a small family of heath-like shrubs which include some ornamentals.

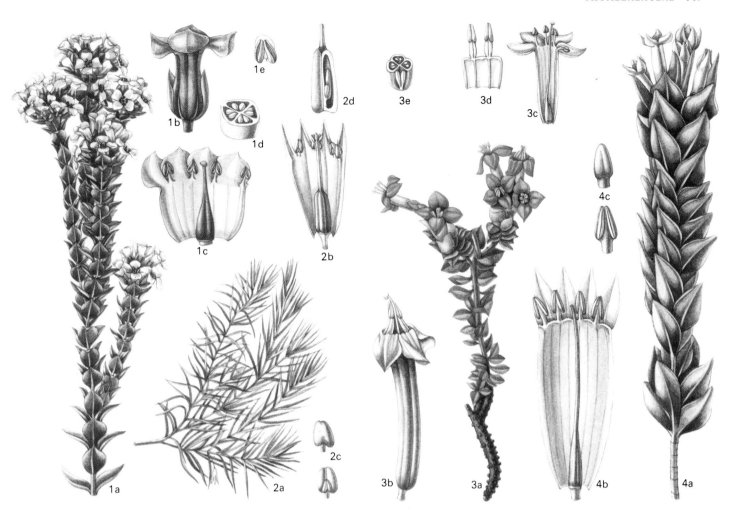

Penaeaceae. 1 *Brachysiphon fucatus* (a) leafy shoot and flowers ($\times\frac{2}{3}$); (b) flower ($\times 3$); (c) flower opened out showing stamens attached to the calyx ($\times 3$); (d) cross section of ovary ($\times 6$); (e) anthers ($\times 6$). 2 *Penaea ericifolia* (a) shoot ($\times\frac{2}{3}$); (b) flower opened out ($\times 4$); (c) stamens front (lower) and rear (upper) views ($\times 8$); (d) ovary with part of wall removed ($\times 6$). 3 *P. squamosa* (a) flowering shoot ($\times\frac{2}{3}$); (b) flower ($\times 2\frac{1}{2}$); (c) flower opened out ($\times 1\frac{1}{2}$); (d) stamens ($\times 3$); (e) cross section of ovary with part of vertical wall cut away to show basal ovules ($\times 4$). 4 *Glischrocolla formosa* (a) flowering shoot ($\times\frac{2}{3}$); (b) flower opened out ($\times 2$); (c) stamens back (upper) and front (lower) views ($\times 3$).

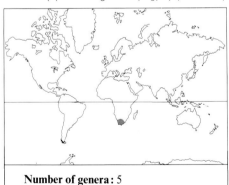

Number of genera: 5
Number of species: 27
Distribution: southern Africa.
Economic uses: some ornamentals.

Distribution. The family occurs only in southern Africa.

Diagnostic features. All the members of the family are shrubby and have a heath-like habit with small, opposite, sessile, entire leaves with or without minute stipules. The flowers are regular, bisexual and borne singly but often crowded in the upper leaf axils, and are subtended by two to four leafy and colored bracts. The tubular calyx has four lobes. There are no petals and the four

stamens are inserted on the throat of the calyx, alternating with the lobes. The anthers have only short filaments, two pollen sacs each, and open facing into the flower by long slits. The ovary is superior, with four locules, each opposite a calyx lobe, and has a terminal style with a four-lobed stigma. There are two to four basally inserted, or four axile, ovules in each locule. The fruit is capsular, four-valved on opening, with the calyx persistent. There are usually only one or two mature seeds in each locule of the fruit following abortion of the others, the seed having no endosperm and a thick embryo with small cotyledons. The seed coat is often smooth and glossy.

Classification. The largest genera are *Penaea* (12 species) and *Brachysiphon* (11 species), which together with *Saltera* (one species) are placed in the tribe PENAEEAE, characterized by basal placentation. In *Penaea* the style is four-angled, cross-shaped at the top with the four stigmatic surfaces in the angles. In *Brachysiphon* the style is cylindrical and the stigma capitate. *Saltera* has a calyx tube about three times as long as the free lobes, not twice as long as in *Penaea* and *Brachysiphon*. The genera with axile placentation,

the monotypic *Glischrocolla* and *Endonema* (two species), are placed in the tribe ENDONEMEAE. *Endonema* has a calyx tube about four times as long as the free lobes, and flowers borne laterally on branches, while *Glischrocolla* has a tube about three times as long as the free lobes, and flowers borne on branch tips.

The family is related to the Lythraceae by some botanists and to the Thymelaeaceae by others.

Economic uses. Certain species in the family are ornamental, eg *Brachysiphon fucatus* and *Endonema retzioides*. The gum (sarcocolla) yielded by *Penaea mucronata* and *Saltera sarcocolla* has been used locally in medicine. B.M.

THYMELAEACEAE
Daphne
The Thymelaeaceae is a medium-sized family, mainly of shrubs. *Daphne* includes attractive ornamentals.

Distribution. Although found in both temperate and tropical regions, the family is more diverse in the Southern Hemisphere than in the Northern Hemisphere, and is especially well represented in Africa. Many

Thymelaeaceae. 1 *Octolepis flamignii* (a) leafy shoot with flowers and flower buds ($\times\frac{2}{3}$); (b) flower ($\times 3$); (c) half flower ($\times 4$); (d) hypanthial cup with stamens, and style and stigma ($\times 4$); (e) gynoecium ($\times 5$); (f) stamen ($\times 5$); (g) dehiscing fruit ($\times 1\frac{1}{3}$). 2 *Pimelea buxifolia* (a) leafy shoot with terminal inflorescences ($\times\frac{2}{3}$); (b) flower ($\times\frac{2}{3}$); (c) flower opened out ($\times 3$); (d) vertical section of ovary ($\times 4$). 3 *Daphne mezereum* (a) flowering shoot ($\times\frac{2}{3}$); (b) leafy shoot with fruits ($\times\frac{2}{3}$); (c) flower opened ($\times 2$); (d) fruit ($\times 2$). 4 *Gonystylus augescens* flower with two sepals removed ($\times 4$).

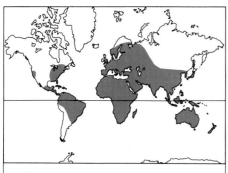

Number of genera: about 45
Number of species: about 500
Distribution: cosmopolitan, especially well represented in Africa.
Economic uses: some ornamentals and the bark is used locally to make paper.

genera are found in the Pacific Islands.
Diagnostic features. The leaves are alternate (occasionally opposite), entire and without stipules. The flowers are regular, usually bisexual, with parts normally in fours or fives and are grouped in racemes, capitula or fascicles. The flowers are basically cup-shaped, the hollowed-out receptacle forming a deep tube with the floral parts mostly

arranged at the rim. The sepals are petaloid, appearing like a continuation of the tube, and the stamens, usually half to twice as many as the sepals, are inserted in the tube; the corolla is inconspicuous or absent. The ovary is superior, situated at the base of the receptacular cup, and comprises one or two (rarely three to eight) fused carpels, containing as many locules, each with one axial or parietal, pendulous ovule. The style is simple. The fruit is variable, an achene, berry, drupe or occasionally a capsule; the seed has little or no endosperm and the embryo is straight.

Classification. Although relatively homogeneous this family is usually divided into four subfamilies (which have even been given family status), drawing attention to a few genera which differ from the main bulk of members. Most genera belong to the subfamily THYMELAEOIDEAE, including the largest genus, *Gnidia*, with 100 species extending from Africa to Madagascar and through India to Ceylon. The other large genera of this group are *Pimelea* with 80 species in Australasia, *Wikstroemia* with 70 species in Australasia reaching South China, *Daphne* with 70 species in Australasia extending across Asia to Europe and North Africa, and

Lasiosiphon with 50 species covering about the same area as *Gnidia*. While Thymelaeoideae have a single pendulous ovule, the next largest subfamily, the AQUILARIOIDEAE, have two (rarely more). This group contains seven small genera from the Pacific area and Africa; *Octolepis*, from West Africa, has four to five locules in the ovary, the fruit being a capsule. The GONYSTYLOIDEAE, with three small genera from Southeast Asia and Borneo, includes *Gonystylus* which has numerous stamens. The fourth subfamily, GILGIODAPHNOIDEAE, contains one genus (*Gilgiodaphne*) from tropical West Africa, with four stamens and four staminodes united in a tube, the four fertile filaments arising as if axially from near the base, and the staminodes remaining united for most of their length.

The affinities of the Thymelaeaceae are not obvious. It has usually been placed, as here, in the Myrtales, although some authorities consider that it should be associated with the Flacourtiaceae.

Economic uses. Species of *Daphne* are cultivated as ornamental shrubs, usually fragrant-flowered. Some are evergreen. The bark of several genera, particularly *Wikstroemia*, yields fibers which are used locally

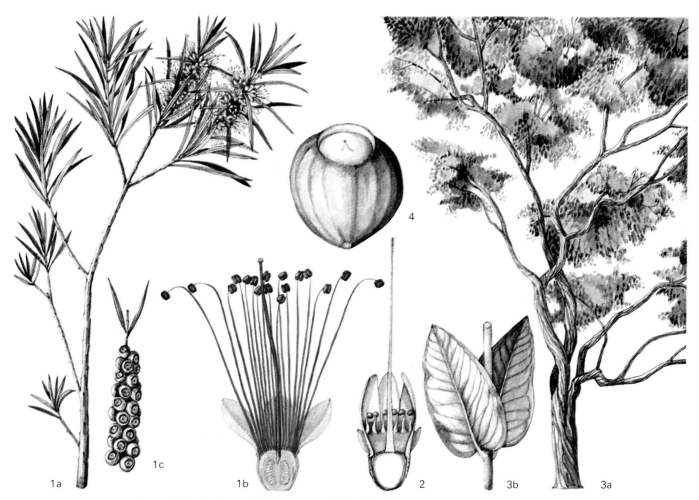

Myrtaceae. 1 *Callistemon subulatus* (a) leafy shoot and inflorescences ($\times\frac{2}{3}$); (b) half flower showing numerous stamens and inferior ovary crowned by a single style and containing ovules on parietal placentas ($\times 3$); (c) fruits ($\times\frac{2}{3}$). 2 *Darwinia citriodora* half flower with epipetalous stamens and a long style crowned by a hairy stigma ($\times 3$). 3 *Eucalyptus melanophloia* (a) habit; (b) adult leaves ($\times\frac{2}{3}$). 4 *Eugenia gustavioides* fruit—a berry with remains of the style ($\times 1$).

to manufacture paper. In some Mediterranean countries the bark of *Daphne* species is used to stupefy fish, and in the West Indies *Lagetto lintearia* yields the ornamental lace bark.   I.B.K.R.

MYRTACEAE

Myrtles, Eucalyptus and Cloves

The Myrtaceae is a large family whose habit ranges from straggling and small shrubs to the lofty *Eucalyptus* trees which dominate the forests of Australia. (See also p. 878.)

Distribution. The family is mostly tropical and subtropical, concentrated in America and eastern and southwestern Australia.

Diagnostic features. They are woody plants, mostly shrubs to large trees. The leaves are usually opposite (less often alternate), leathery, evergreen and typically entire, without stipules, and characteristically pellucid-dotted with subepidermal glands (also found on the young stem, floral organs and fruit) containing ethereal oils. The flowers are regular and bisexual, most frequently in cymose, less often in racemose, inflorescences, rarely solitary (*Myrtus communis*); they are generally epigynous, but varying degrees of perigyny are found. There are commonly four or five sepals, usually free (sometimes more or less united, then sometimes forming a cap which drops off as the flower opens), sometimes much reduced to virtually absent. There are four or five petals which are typically free, small and round (in *Eucalyptus* more or less united, falling as one piece). The stamens are numerous (rarely few), sometimes in tufts opposite the petals (*Melaleuca*), typically free and with versatile anthers, the connective often gland-tipped. The ovary is commonly inferior with one to many (often two to five) locules, each with usually two to many ovules on axile (rarely parietal) placentas. The style is long and simple with a simple capitate stigma. The fruit is usually a fleshy berry (rarely a drupe) or dry (then a capsule or nut). There is little or no endosperm.

Classification. The family is divided into two subfamilies.

MYRTOIDEAE: Flowers epigynous, leaves always opposite; fruit fleshy, typically a berry, rarely a drupe.

LEPTOSPERMOIDEAE: Perigyny occurs but epigyny is the rule; leaves opposite or alternate; fruit dry, a capsule or nut-like.

The affinities of the Myrtaceae are with the Lythraceae and Melastomataceae.

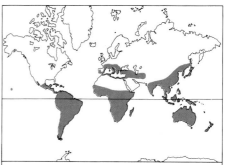

Number of genera: about 100
Number of species: about 3,000
Distribution: tropical and subtropical, chiefly America and Australia
Economic uses: timber, spices (cloves, allspice), essential oils, edible fruits and ornamentals

Economic uses. Economically the most important genus is *Eucalyptus*, chiefly for its timber. The family also yields some of the most valued spices – cloves (and clove oil) from *Syzygium aromaticum* (*Eugenia caryophyllata*); and allspice or pimento from *Pimenta dioica* (*P. officinalis*); *P. racemosa* provides oil of bay rum, and *Melaleuca leucadendron* cajeput oil. Eucalyptus oil, well known as a flavoring, expectorant and antiseptic, derives from several *Eucalyptus* species. Among the edible fruits are the tropical American and West Indian guava (*Psidium guajava*) and jaboticaba (*Myrciaria cauliflora*), and tropical American species of *Eugenia*, *Syzygium* and *Feijoa*. Ornamentals include the lillypilly (*Acmena smithii*), the bottlebrushes (*Callistemon* and *Melaleuca*), *Eucalyptus* (gumtrees, ironbarks, bloodwoods), the manuka or tea tree (*Leptospermum scoparium*), and the common myrtle (*Myrtus communis*, possibly the only European member of the family.   F.B.H.

PUNICACEAE
Pomegranate

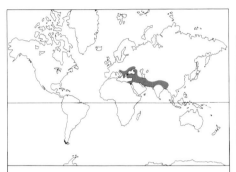

Number of genera: 1
Number of species: 2
Distribution: SE Europe to the Himalayas and Socotra.
Economic uses: fruit (pomegranate) eaten and used in grenadine drink, bark and fruit-skin used locally.

The Punicaceae contains a single genus with two species of shrubs and small trees.
Distribution. The family occurs from southeastern Europe to the Himalayas, and in Socotra.
Diagnostic features. The plants are deciduous, sometimes spiny, woody shrubs or small trees, with tapering cylindrical branches and simple opposite or subopposite entire leaves, without stipules. Four wings of epidermal and cortical parenchyma develop on young twigs but these are early deciduous. The flowers are solitary or in groups. They are bisexual, regular, with five to eight sepals, five to eight petals, numerous stamens and an inferior ovary of numerous fused carpels. Two whorls of carpels are laid down and then owing to peripheral growth are tilted from a vertical to horizontal position, so that the numerous locules are formed in two layers; numerous anatropous ovules are borne on parietal placentas in the upper locules and on axile placentas in the lower. This peculiar arrangement is also seen in the fruit, commonly called the pomegranate. The round fruit of up to 3.5in (9cm) diameter has a leathery brownish-red-yellow rind and characteristically a hard persistent calyx tube. The internal pulp contains numerous seeds, which lack endosperm.
Classification. The sole genus, *Punica*, is represented by two species, *Punica pro-*

topunica, native to Socotra, and *P. granatum*, which grows from the Balkans to the Himalayas and is also cultivated, mostly in southern Europe. The Punicaceae is taxonomically close to the families Lythraceae and Sonneratiaceae.
Economic uses. The chief economic use lies in production of pomegranates. The fruit ferments easily and is used in the production of the drink, grenadine. The fruit and bark have been used in Egyptian tanning processes and in medicinal preparations. Dwarf and double-flowered varieties of the red-flowered *P. granatum* are known in cultivation.   S.A.H.

ONAGRACEAE
Clarkias, Fuchsias and Evening Primroses

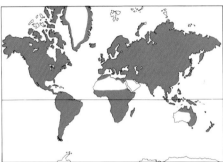

Number of genera: 18
Number of species: about 640
Distribution: cosmopolitan, centered in SW N America.
Economic uses: chiefly cultivated ornamentals (*Fuchsia*, *Oenothera*).

This widespread and botanically well-defined family of herbs and some shrubs contains a number of aquatics and popular ornamentals.
Distribution. Although virtually cosmopolitan, the family is most diverse in the western United States of America and Mexico, where all known genera occur. Most members occur in open habitats, either dry or moist, but *Ludwigia* is largely aquatic, while *Fuchsia* can inhabit wet woods.
Diagnostic features. The plants are herbs or rarely shrubs, often aquatic. The leaves are simple, opposite or alternate, usually without stipules. The flowers are solitary in axils or borne in racemes, and are bisexual or unisexual, then borne on separate plants (*Fuchsia*). Some are irregular, usually with a colored perigynous tube (hypanthium). The sepals are two, four or five in number, free and valvate. There are two, four or five free petals, rarely none. The stamens are usually eight in two whorls, but may be one, two, four, five or 10 in number. The anthers have two locules, dehiscing lengthwise. The ovary is inferior or rarely half-inferior, of four fused carpels, sometimes with one but usually with two, four or five locules, each containing one to many anatropous ovules on axile placentas. The single style is entire or has four lobes. The fruit is usually a

loculicidal capsule, sometimes a berry or indehiscent; seeds are numerous or solitary, without endosperm, with a plume of hairs at the chalaza in *Epilobium* and *Zauschneria*; the embryo is straight or almost so.

There has been a trend in flower structure from an original regular flower with parts in fours to more specialized, often irregular flowers with reduced numbers of petals. This can be associated with a change from cross-pollination to strict self-pollination, as in *Camissonia*, *Gaura* and *Ludwigia*. The earliest Onagraceae were presumably insect-pollinated, but the least specialized species of, for example, *Lopezia*, as well as many fuchsias, are bird-pollinated, insect-pollination being a derived condition. Many Onagraceae are pollinated by moths. Fly-pollination in *Lopezia coronata* results in a curious mechanism whereby the single stamen and mature stigmas are held under tension by the staminodes so as to snap apart when touched, flinging the pollen against the underside of the pollinating flies.
Classification. Developing from the intensive genetical work on the evening primroses (*Oenothera*) which started over 60 years ago, the Onagraceae has been the subject of considerable cytogenetical study. The most recent studies show it to comprise 18 genera, which are grouped into one large tribe, the ONAGREAE (*Calylophus*, *Camissonia*, *Clarkia* (including *Godetia*), *Gaura*, *Gayophytum*, *Gongylocarpus*, *Hauya*, *Heterogaura*, *Oenothera*, *Stenosiphon*, *Xylonagra*), and five smaller tribes: FUCHSIEAE (*Fuchsia*), LOPEZIEAE (*Lopezia*), CIRCAEEAE (*Circaea*), JUSSIAEEAE (*Ludwigia*) and EPILOBIEAE (*Boisduvalia*, *Epilobium*, *Zauschneria*).

The interrelationships are still a matter for debate, but Lopezieae and Jussiaeeae seem to have particularly close affinities, while the Onagreae stands apart as a distinctive group of genera, including all those in the family in which major chromosomal repatterning has been an important evolutionary mechanism.

Although the oldest fossils in the family belong to *Ludwigia*, it is *Fuchsia*, with fleshy fruits and unspecialized placentation, which appears to be the modern genus closest to the ancestors of all Onagraceae. The floral tube, once considered a derived condition, is present in the Lythraceae, Melastomataceae and Myrtaceae, which are presumed to have a common ancestry with the Onagraceae.
Economic uses. Many species are cultivated for ornament, as hardy or half-hardy annuals (eg *Clarkia*, *Oenothera* (evening primrose)) or as hardy or greenhouse shrubs (*Fuchsia*). Some *Ludwigia* species are grown as aquatics in greenhouses.   D.M.M.

OLINIACEAE
The Oliniaceae is a family of only one genus (*Olinia*) with 10 species of trees and shrubs native to eastern and southern Africa.

The leaves are simple, without stipules and opposite on four-angled branches. The

Onagraceae. 1 *Fuchsia regia* var *alpestris* (a) flowering shoot ($\times\frac{2}{3}$); (b) half flower showing free sepals that are longer than the purple petals ($\times1\frac{1}{2}$); (c) cross section of fruit ($\times3$). 2 *Circaea cordata* (a) dehisced capsule ($\times6$); (b) cross section of fruit ($\times6$). 3 *Epilobium hirsutum* (a) flowering shoot ($\times\frac{2}{3}$); (b) fruit (a capsule) with part of wall cut away ($\times2$); (c) ripe fruit dehiscing to release plumed seeds ($\times2$). 4 *Lopezia coronata* flower with upper petals marked with blotches that resemble nectar, one erect fertile stamen and petaloid spoon-shaped staminodes—all adaptations to a specialized form of insect pollination ($\times3$). 5 *Oenothera biennis* (a) flowering shoot ($\times\frac{2}{3}$); (b) partly opened flower with petals removed ($\times2$).

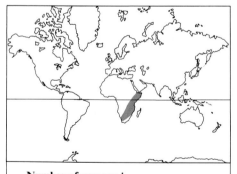

Number of genera: 1
Number of species: 10
Distribution: eastern and southern Africa.
Economic uses: none.

flowers are bisexual, regular and borne in cymes in the leaf axils or at the ends of stems. The four or five sepals are joined in a tube which is fused to the ovary and may have a limb of four or five teeth. The four or five petals are inserted on the margin of the calyx tube and alternate with as many incurved, colored, scales. The stamens are equal in number to the petals, and are also inserted on the margin of the calyx tube, immediately below the scales on very short filaments, expanding into a thickened connective. The ovary is inferior, of four or five fused carpels, with three to five locules, surmounted by a simple style ending in a club-shaped stigma. There are two or three pendulous ovules on axile placentas in each locule. The fruit is a false drupe, containing a single seed in each locule. The seed, without endosperm, contains a spiral or convoluted embryo.

Although relationships for this family have been suggested with the Cunoniaceae, the affinities are rather remote. It may be that the Thymelaeaceae are more closely related. There are no known economic uses for the family.   S.R.C.

MELASTOMATACEAE
Dissotis and Medinilla

A relatively large family, the Melastomataceae is composed mainly of shrubs and small trees, but also of a few vines, herbs, marsh plants and, rarely, epiphytes. A number of species are cultivated for their showy flowers.

Distribution. The family is mainly tropical, rather uncommon in temperate zones. It is one of the largest families of South American plants and forms a particularly characteristic feature of the Brazilian flora.

Diagnostic features. The most useful diagnostic features are found in the leaf venation and stamen shape. The leaves are opposite and decussate (each pair at right angles to the next) but sometimes with one of each pair smaller than the other, or rarely alternate by abortion. Stipules are absent. The main veins (three to nine pairs) are usually palmate and parallel. The stem is often four-angled. The flowers are bisexual, regular and usually have four or five each of sepals and free petals. The stamens are usually twice as many as the petals. The stamen filaments are geniculate (elbow-shaped) with sterile appendages of various shapes: awl-shaped, spiny, club-like, curved or pronged. The anther lobes usually dehisce by a single, terminal pore. The ovary is superior or more commonly inferior by fusion with the receptacle. There are one to 14 carpels with four or five locules containing two to numerous ovules on axile, basal or parietal placentas. The style is simple. The fruit is a berry or loculicidal capsule. The seeds are small, numerous and lack endosperm.

Classification. The family is subdivided into

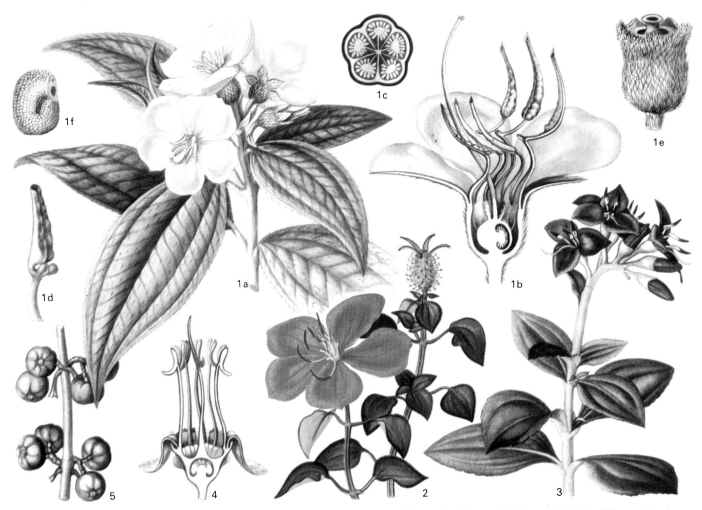

Melastomataceae. 1 *Melastoma malabathricum* (a) flowering shoot showing leaves with characteristic parallel veins ($\times\frac{2}{3}$); (b) half flower showing stamens with elbow-shaped filaments and anthers dehiscing by a single pore ($\times1\frac{1}{3}$); (c) cross section of ovary ($\times2\frac{2}{3}$); (d) stamen showing lobed appendages at base of the connective ($\times3\frac{1}{3}$); (e) fruit—a capsule ($\times2\frac{2}{3}$); (f) seed ($\times8$). 2 *Medinilla speciosa* flowering and fruiting shoot showing four-angled stem ($\times\frac{2}{3}$). 3 *Sonerila grandiflora* leafy shoot and cymose inflorescence ($\times\frac{2}{3}$). 4 *Memecylon laurinum* half flower showing inferior ovary with sub-basal placentas ($\times3\frac{1}{3}$). 5 *M. intermedium* fruits—berries ($\times\frac{2}{3}$).

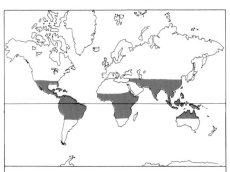

Number of genera: about 240
Number of species: about 3,000
Distribution: temperate but mainly tropical and subtropical, with center in S America.
Economic uses: local use of the hardwood and edible fruits of some species and some ornamentals.

three subfamilies and about 13 tribes. The largest subfamily, MELASTOMATOIDEAE, has an ovary of two to many carpels, either free from and superior to the receptacle, or more or less fused to the receptacle and inferior to the perianth parts; the numerous seeds have axile placentation; the fruit is a capsule or berry; principal genera *Tibouchina, Melastoma, Oxyspora, Sonerila* and *Miconia*. In the ASTRONIOIDEAE the ovary also comprises two to many carpels; the many seeds have subbasal or parietal placentation; the fruit is a capsule or berry; principal genera: *Astronia* and *Kibessia*. MEMECYLOIDEAE has ovaries of two to six carpels, sometimes reduced to one, with many seeds on subbasal or axile placentas; the fruit is a capsule or berry; principal genera: *Memecylon* and *Mouriri*. The Memecyloideae is considered a separate family, Memecylaceae, by some authorities.

The relationships of this family are indistinct and slender. One possibility is that some members of the Memecyloideae are related to some members of the Myrtaceae, since both have four to many carpels and axile placentation of the two to many ovules in each locule. Another possible resemblance is with the Combretaceae, which like the Melastomataceae has twice as many stamens as petals and usually an inferior ovary.

Economic uses. None of the family is economically important, except in horticulture. The hardwood of some *Astronia* and *Memecylon* species is used locally in furniture and construction. The fruit and leaves of *Medinilla hasseltii* are eaten in Sumatra and the fruit of some species of *Melastoma* and *Mouriri* are eaten in tropical America. A few species yield dyes (yellow from *Memecylon edule*, Indian Ocean, Sumatra).

A number of shrub species are cultivated in gardens and greenhouses for their attractive flowers, which are often red, blue and purple, less commonly pink, white or yellow. Among them are *Dissotis grandiflora, Medinilla curtisii, M. magnifica, Tibouchina urvilleana* (*T. semidecandra*), *Melastoma malabathricum* and *Monochaetum alpestre*.

H.P.W.

COMBRETACEAE
Terminalia, Combretum and Quisqualis

The Combretaceae is a family of tropical trees, shrubs and lianas which includes a number of plants of economic and ornamental interest.

Distribution. The family is found throughout the tropics, scarcely ever extending beyond.

Diagnostic features. They are forest trees, 165ft (50m) or more high, to dwarf shrubs with subterranean rhizomes and short aerial

Combretaceae. 1 *Combretum grandiflorum* (a) leafy shoot with flowers in elongated heads ($\times\frac{2}{3}$); (b) flower with five-lobed, green calyx, five, red petals, ten stamens and a filamentous style ($\times 1$); (c) half flower showing inferior ovary with one locule and a pendulous ovule ($\times 1$); (d) winged fruit ($\times\frac{2}{3}$). 2 *Quisqualis indica* leafy shoot bearing flowers with a long perianth tube ($\times\frac{2}{3}$). 3 *Terminalia chebula* (a) leafy shoot and inflorescence ($\times\frac{2}{3}$); (b) flower with toothed calyx and numerous stamens ($\times 7$); (c) flower with half of calyx and stamens removed to show hairs on top of ovary ($\times 8$); (d) woody fruits ($\times\frac{2}{3}$).

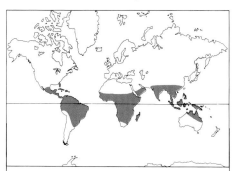

Number of genera: 20
Number of species: about 475
Distribution: mainly tropical, with a few species subtropical.
Economic uses: commercial wood, tropical and glasshouse ornamentals, tanning (fruits of *Terminalia* spp).

shoots which frequently become grazed or burnt off and may be more or less annual in appearance. In forests the large trees and lianas predominate, while in grassland the shrubby species are commoner. The leaves are entire, alternate or opposite and without stipules. The flowers are small, regular and bisexual (rarely unisexual), often clustered in globular or elongated heads, and nectar may be produced in abundance. There are usually five (sometimes four) valvate sepals, five (sometimes four) imbricate or valvate petals or the latter may be totally absent. The stamens are in one or two whorls of four or five (rarely they are numerous). The ovary is inferior, with one locule containing two to five pendulous ovules. The style is simple.

There is a tendency in many genera for the development of wind-dispersed winged fruits, dispersed aerially in the case of the lighter fruits but bowled along on the ground in the case of the heavier fruits, the rigid wings acting like spokes. In forests, however, where such methods are not practicable, most of the species have wingless fruits which are either fleshy and animal-dispersed or have spongy tissue and are water-dispersed. The mangrove genera have viviparous fruits which germinate on the parent plant. The seed has no endosperm, and the cotyledons are very variable in form.

Classification. Apart from one unusual African representative, the genera form three groups. One of these contains three genera, of which two are mangroves (*Lumnitzera* in East Africa, Asia and Australia; *Laguncularia* in West Africa and America).

The other two groups are centered on the large genera *Combretum* (200 species), mostly with petals, opposite leaves with glandular hairs and barely woody fruits, and *Terminalia* (150 species), mostly with no petals, spiral leaves without glandular hairs and strongly woody fruits. Both these genera are found virtually throughout the tropics (*Combretum* is absent from Australia), but the others related to them are much less widespread and most are restricted to one continent. *Conocarpus*, in the group related to *Terminalia*, is the third combretaceous mangrove genus.

The Combretaceae is probably most closely related to the Myrtaceae. All members of the family possess peculiar unicellular hairs which elsewhere in the angiosperms are known only in a few genera of the Myrtaceae.

Economic uses. Some of the trees of the genus *Terminalia* are important sources of timber for export; for example, idigbo is obtained from *Terminalia ivorensis* and afara from *T. superba*, both from West Africa. Many others are valued on a more local scale, eg assegai wood (*T. sericea*), and some of the larger trees are planted for shade.

Several of the climbers with attractive flowers are grown as ornamentals, either outdoors in the tropics or in glasshouses in temperate regions. The best-known are *Quisqualis indica* from Asia and various species of *Combretum*, notably *Combretum grandiflorum* from tropical West Africa.

Many of the Combretaceae are used locally as medicines and foods in a wide variety of situations. The Indian almond is the edible kernel of *Terminalia catappa*, from tropical Asia, which is now grown in many parts of tropical Africa and America as well. Myrobalans (species of *Terminalia*) yield fruit used in tanning.   C.A.S.

CORNALES

NYSSACEAE
Handkerchief and Tupelo Trees

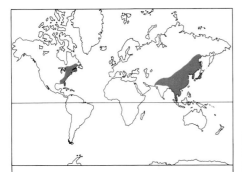

Number of genera: 3
Number of species: 8
Distribution: E N America, China and Tibet.
Economic uses: fruits, timber and valued ornamentals.

The Nyssaceae is a small family of trees and shrubs, including the ornamental handkerchief and tupelo trees.

Distribution. The family is represented by three genera, *Nyssa, Camptotheca* and *Davidia*. There are six species of *Nyssa*, four in eastern North America and two in east Asia. *Camptotheca* is represented by one species, *Camptotheca acuminata*, which grows only in China and Tibet. The single species of *Davidia* is native to China.

Diagnostic features. The leaves are alternate, entire or denticulate, and without stipules. The flowers are regular, unisexual and bisexual, the plants being polygamodioecious, with the males occurring in heads, racemes or umbels and the female and bisexual flowers occurring solitarily or in heads with two up to 12 flowers. The calyx is very small of five minute teeth or is totally absent. The petals usually number five, sometimes four or up to eight. There are usually ten stamens, sometimes eight to 16, each with a long narrow filament and small anthers. The ovary is inferior, consisting of one or two fused carpels, with a single locule (rarely more) containing a single apical,

pendulous ovule. The style may be simple or bifid, erect or spirally coiled. The fruit is drupe-like or samara-like. The single seed has thin endosperm and a fairly large embryo.

Classification. The three genera may be distinguished by a number of features. In *Davidia* the ovary has six to ten locules, the male flowers lack a perianth, the female and bisexual flowers have numerous perianth segments, the style is lobed and the fruit is a drupe. *Nyssa* and *Camptotheca* have a unilocular ovary, all flowers have sepals and petals, and the style is awl-shaped. In *Nyssa* the style is not divided and the fruit is a drupe, while in *Camptotheca* the style is forked and the fruit is a samara.

The family is related to the Cornaceae. *Davidia* is often considered to represent a separate family, the Davidiaceae.

Economic uses. Edible fruits and some timber are obtained from *Nyssa* (tupelo, black gum), but the greatest commercial value lies in the cultivation of the genus for its attractive autumn foliage. *Davidia involucrata* is the ornamental handkerchief tree. *Camptotheca acuminata* is also cultivated as an ornamental.   S.A.H.

GARRYACEAE

Number of genera: 1
Number of species: about 18
Distribution: SW N America, N Central America, W Indies.
Economic uses: winter-flowering ornamental shrubs.

The Garryaceae comprises a single genus (*Garrya*) of evergreen shrubs.

Distribution. The family is confined to western and southwestern North America, Mexico, Guatemala and the West Indies.

Diagnostic features. The leaves are opposite, oval to lanceolate, the margin being entire or slightly wavy. The flowers are unisexual, with sexes on separate plants in terminal or axillary catkin-like pendulous racemes. The male flowers have four introrse anthers with short filaments, surrounded by four valvate perianth segments. The female flowers are naked or with two to four small decussate bracts often united to form a cup and sometimes interpreted as sepals (or perianth segments). The ovary is inferior, of two to three united carpels, with one locule and two

pendulous ovules on parietal placentas. There are two slender styles. The fruit is a dryish, round, one- or two-seeded berry, with small seeds and abundant endosperm.

Classification. The catkin-like racemes and apetalous, unisexual flowers led 19th-century taxonomists to place the Garryaceae with other catkin-bearing plants, such as the Salicaceae and Myricaceae. There is now general consensus that the family is related to the Cornaceae, particularly through the genera *Griselinia* and *Aucuba*.

Economic uses. Several *Garrya* species are cultivated as winter-flowering ornamental shrubs.   F.B.H.

ALANGIACEAE

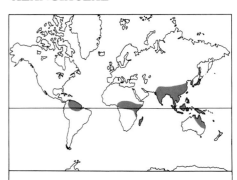

Number of genera: 2
Number of species: about 23
Distribution: Old World tropics and NW S America.
Economic uses: some ornamentals.

The Alangiaceae is a small, woody family of obscure affinities.

Distribution. Mainly tropical, the family comprises a single Old World genus, *Alangium*, with about 20 species from Africa to Japan and eastern Australia, and a single New World genus, *Matteniusa*, with three species in northern South America.

Diagnostic features. Both genera are trees or shrubs, sometimes spiny, with alternate, usually simple leaves without stipules. The flowers are bisexual and borne on bracteolate, jointed pedicels in axillary cymes. They are regular, with equal numbers (4–10) of sepals and petals, the sepals eventually bending backwards and downwards, often more or less twisted. The petals are sometimes united at the base, and are more or less hairy on the inner surface. The number of stamens varies from four to 40, and they are free or united with the petals, with often hairy filaments and usually basifixed, introrse anthers. A nectary disk is generally present at the base of the single style which surmounts the usually unilocular, inferior or superior ovary. The stigma is club-shaped, sometimes two- or three-lobed. One pendulous, anatropous ovule develops in the locule, and the drupaceous fruit is single-seeded with a hard endocarp, and usually crowned with the persistent calyx. The seed has a fleshy endosperm.

Alangiaceae. 1 *Alangium salviifolium* (a) leafy shoot and axillary flowers ($\times\frac{2}{3}$); (b) flower with short calyx tube, long, recurved petals, numerous stamens and single style with a lobed stigma ($\times 2$); (c) half section of gynoecium showing ovary with pendulous ovule ($\times 6$); (d) stamen with hairy filament and basifixed anther ($\times 3$); (e) fruiting shoot ($\times 1$); (f) cross section of fruit ($\times 2$).

Classification. The relationships of the family are obscure, although it is usually placed near the Cornaceae and related families.

Economic uses. Several species of *Alangium* are cultivated as half-hardy shrubs.

I.B.K.R.

CORNACEAE
Dogwoods

The Cornaceae is a small family of trees and shrubs, rarely herbs, known mainly for the dogwoods (various species of *Cornus*) and the several varieties of *Aucuba*, sometimes erroneously called laurels.

Distribution. The family is found growing mainly in north temperate regions, with a few species in the tropics and subtropics of Central and South America, Africa, Madagascar, Indomalaysia and New Zealand.

Diagnostic features. Members of the family are woody plants with opposite or occasionally alternate, simple leaves, sometimes evergreen (eg *Aucuba, Mastixia*). The inflorescences are usually corymbs or umbels, sometimes surrounded by large, showy bracts; flowers are small, bisexual or unisexual (the sexes are then on separate plants, eg *Aucuba, Griselinia*). The flowers are regular, with a four- or five-lobed calyx

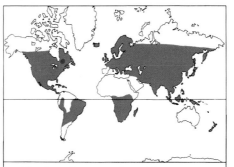

Number of genera: about 13
Number of species: over 100
Distribution: mainly N temperate; some species in tropics and subtropics.
Economic uses: popular ornamental shrubs (dogwoods), beverage and preserves from the fruit of *Cornus mas* and some useful timber.

tube (rarely absent). There are normally four or five free petals (rarely absent), and an equal number of stamens alternate with the petals. The short, bilocular anthers open lengthwise. The ovary is inferior, of two (rarely one, three or four) fused carpels, with one to four locules and axile placentation (parietal in *Aucuba*) with one anatropous, pendulous ovule in each locule. The style is simple and the stigma lobed. The fruit is a

drupe or berry with one to four locules and one or two stones.

Classification. *Cornus*, in the narrow sense (about four species), has a wide distribution in central and southern Europe as far as the Caucasus, eastern Asia and also California. *Cornus* in the wide sense includes species often separated into other genera such as *Afrocrania, Chamaepericlymenum, Benthamidia, Dendrobenthamia* and *Swida. Chamaepericlymenum*, the only herbaceous genus of this family, grows on mountains of North America, Europe, Asia and Japan. *Benthamidia* (three species) grows in east and west North America, Japan and the Himalayas. Thirty-six species of *Swida* grow in north temperate regions, three species in Mexico and one in the northern Andes. *Aucuba* is a genus of three species of hardy, evergreen, dioecious shrubs which is distributed from the Himalayas to Japan. *Toricellia* (three species), *Helwingia* (five species) and *Dendrobenthamia* (12 species) also range from the Himalayas to Japan. Two members of this family grow in tropical southern and East Africa, *Curtisia* and *Afrocrania*, a mountain tree. *Melanophylla* comprises eight species native to Madagascar. In the Indomalaysian region, there are some 25 species of *Mastixia*, which are medium to tall

Cornaceae. 1 *Curtisia faginea* (a) leafy shoot with terminal inflorescence (×⅔); (b) flower (×6); (c) fruit (×3); (d) half-section of fruit (×3); (e) seed (×3). 2 *Chamaepericlymenum canadense* (a) leafy shoot with inflorescence of small flowers surrounded by large bracts (×⅔); (b) fruits (×⅔). 3 *Corokia buddleoides* (a) flowering shoot (×⅔); (b) flower-bud (×3); (c) perianth opened out (×3); (d) vertical section of gynoecium (×3); (e) fruit, entire (left) and in vertical section (right) (×3); (f) fruits (×⅔). 4 *Aucuba japonica* (a) leafy shoot and female flowers (×⅔); (b) male flower (×2); (c) female flower (×2); (d) fruits (×⅔); (e) cross section of fruit (×⅔).

evergreen trees. *Griselinia* contains six species of trees or shrubs, sometimes epiphytic, which have a most disjunct distribution, with four species in Brazil and two in New Zealand.

The family is divided into two subfamilies and several tribes. The subfamilies are:
CURTISIOIDEAE. Ovules with ventral raphe; flowers bisexual; fruit a drupe with uni- or quadrilocular endocarp. *Curtisia, Mastixia.*
CORNOIDEAE. Ovules with dorsal raphe; flowers bisexual or unisexual; ovary of one to four parts, always unilocular. *Toricellia, Helwingia, Cornus, Aucuba, Griselinia, Melanophylla.*

Some taxonomists put *Curtisia, Mastixia, Toricellia, Helwingia, Aucuba, Griselinia* and *Melanophylla* each into separate families.

The Cornaceae is related to the Alangiaceae and Nyssaceae, but these families have stamens more numerous than the petals (except some Alangiaceae), and leaves strictly alternate. The secretory ducts and extrorse micropyle of *Mastixia* are thought to link the Cornaceae with the Araliaceae.

Economic uses. *Cornus, Aucuba* and *Griselinia* species are widely grown as ornamental shrubs. Fruits of *Cornus mas* can be used for

preserves and, in France, the alcoholic beverage vin de cornouille. The wood of several species of *Cornus* and of *Curtisia* (assegai wood) is used for furniture, agricultural implements and bobbins and shuttles for weaving.   H.P.W.

PROTEALES

ELAEAGNACEAE
Oleaster and Sea Buckthorn

The Elaeagnaceae is a small family of much-branched shrubs, covered with silvery or golden scales. It contains several ornamentals, such as oleaster (*Elaeagnus angustifolia*) and the sea buckthorn (*Hippophaë*).

Distribution. The family is mainly distributed in North America, Europe and southern Asia and Australia, frequently in coastal regions or steppes.

Diagnostic features. A considerable number of species (eg those of *Hippophaë*) are thorny. The stems and leaves are covered with silvery, brown, or golden hairs which are either peltate or scaly. The leaves are alternate, opposite, or in whorls, and are leathery in texture, simple, entire and without stipules.

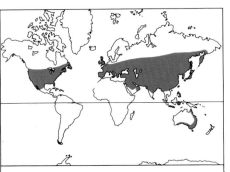

Number of genera: 3
Number of species: about 50
Distribution: N America, Europe, S Asia, Australia, mainly coasts and steppes.
Economic uses: ornamentals and limited uses of fruits and wood.

The flowers are regular and either solitary or borne in clusters or racemes. They are bisexual or unisexual, the male and female usually being borne on different plants (dioecious) in *Shepherdia* and *Hippophaë*. There are no petals, the perianth comprising a single whorl of two to eight fused sepals. In the male flower the receptacle is often flat,

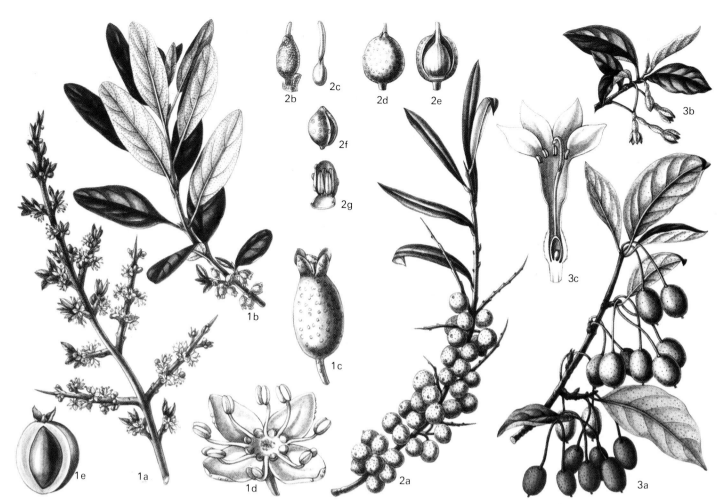

Elaeagnaceae. 1 *Shepherdia argentea* (a) flowering branch showing thorns and male flowers ($\times \frac{2}{3}$); (b) leafy shoot with female flowers ($\times \frac{2}{3}$); (c) female flower ($\times 6$); (d) male flower ($\times 6$); (e) fruit—a drupe-like structure cut away here to reveal the single seed ($\times 3$). 2 *Hippophäe rhamnoides* (a) thorny, leafy, shoot bearing fruits ($\times \frac{2}{3}$); (b) female flower with bilobed calyx-tube ($\times 3$); (c) gynoecium ($\times 3$); (d) fruit ($\times 2$); (e) fruit with part of fleshy calyx cut away ($\times 2$); (f) male flower ($\times 3$); (g) male flower opened out ($\times 2$). 3 *Elaeagnus multiflora* (a) shoot bearing fleshy fruits ($\times \frac{2}{3}$); (b) shoot bearing bisexual flowers ($\times \frac{2}{3}$); (c) flower opened out with vertical section of unilocular ovary ($\times 2$).

while in the bisexual and female flowers it is tubular. There are four to eight stamens, with free filaments and bilocular anthers. The ovary is superior, with one carpel containing a single, erect, anatropous ovule. The style is long and bears a simple stigma. The fruit is an achene or drupe-like structure enclosed by the thickened lower part of the persistent calyx. It contains a single seed with little or no endosperm and a straight embryo with thick, fleshy cotyledons.

Classification. The three genera, *Elaeagnus* (45 species), *Hippophaë* (two or three species) and *Shepherdia* (three species) may be distinguished by the following characters:

Shepherdia (North America): leaves opposite, plants dioecious, with four sepals and eight stamens in the male flower.

Hippophaë (Europe and Asia): leaves alternate, plants usually dioecious, female flower with elongated receptacle and short two-lobed calyx tube, male flower with two large sepals and four stamens.

Elaeagnus (Europe, Asia, North America, Australia): leaves alternate, flowers bisexual or unisexual, male and female on the same plant; four-lobed calyx tube is elongated beyond the ovary; four stamens present.

This family is considered to be related to the Thymelaeaceae or possibly to the Rhamnaceae but is distinguished by the golden or silvery hairy indumentum, by the nature of the fruits and by the presence of a basally inserted ovule in the ovary. It is here allied with the Proteaceae, sharing with it such features as perigynous flowers, reduced or absent petals and a single carpel.

Economic uses. A number of species are grown as ornamental shrubs, notably *Elaeagnus angustifolia* (oleaster), *E. pungens, E. umbellata* and *E. macrophylla*, which are mainly grown as deciduous or evergreen shrubs for their attractive foliage, and *Hippophaë rhamnoides* (sea buckthorn) whose female plants produce bright, orange berries in autumn and winter.

The fruits of a number of species are edible, for example those of *Shepherdia argentea* (silver buffalo berry). Its fruits are used as jelly and are also eaten dried with sugar in various parts of the United States of America and Canada. The berries of *S. canadensis* (russet buffalo berry) when dried or smoked are used as food by Eskimos. The berries of *H. rhamnoides* are made into a sauce in France, and into jelly elsewhere. The

wood of this species is fine-grained and is used for turnery. The fruits of the Japanese shrub *Elaeagnus multiflora* (cherry elaeagnus) are used as preserves and are used in an alcoholic beverage.   S.R.C.

PROTEACEAE
Proteas, Banksias and Grevilleas

The Proteaceae is one of the most prominent families of the Southern Hemisphere. It provides numerous examples of links between the floras of South America, South Africa and Australasia. One such example is the genus *Gevuina*, of whose three species one is native to Chile and the other two to Queensland and New Guinea. Many of the species can live in near-drought conditions but a few ancestral species are rain forest dwellers.

Distribution. The family is found in southern Africa, Asia, Australasia and Central and South America, especially in areas with long dry seasons.

Diagnostic features. Almost all of the species are trees or shrubs with alternate, entire or divided leaves which are without stipules, leathery and often hairy to some extent. The flowers are borne in sometimes showy

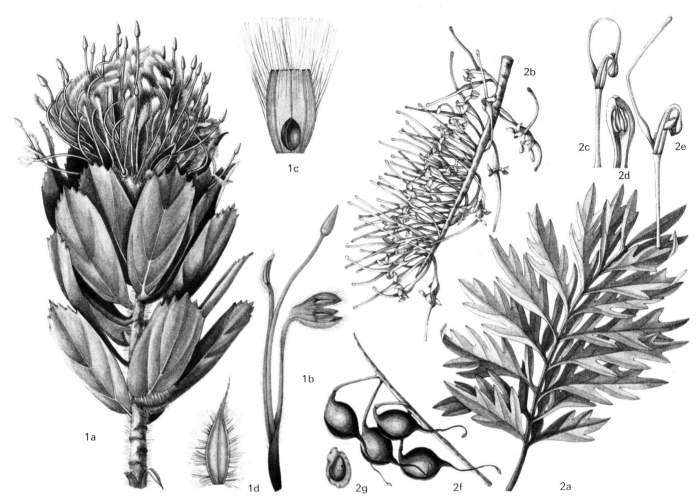

Proteaceae. 1 *Leucospermum conocarpodendron* (a) leafy shoot with terminal cone-like inflorescence, each flower with a conspicuous arrow-shaped stigma ($\times\frac{2}{3}$); (b) flower with stamens fused to perianth segments and long style with arrow-shaped stigma ($\times 1\frac{1}{2}$); (c) fruit opened out to show seed ($\times 10$); (d) hairy bract ($\times 4$). 2 *Grevillea robusta* (a) deeply-divided leaf ($\times\frac{2}{3}$); (b) inflorescence each flower with a projecting stigma ($\times\frac{2}{3}$); (c) young flower with stigma retained in bud ($\times 2$); (d) petal with anthers directly attached ($\times 5\frac{1}{2}$); (e) mature flower with extended style and stigma ($\times 2$); (f) fruits ($\times\frac{2}{3}$); (g) winged seed ($\times\frac{2}{3}$).

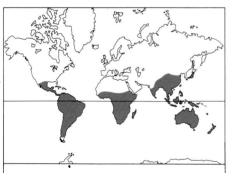

Number of genera: 62
Number of species: over 1,000
Distribution: Asia, southern Africa, Australasia, and C and S America, particularly dry regions.
Economic uses: ornamentals, edible seeds, honey and timber.

racemes, spikes or heads with a ring of bracts, in *Banksia* with up to 1,000 flowers. The flowers are normally bisexual but sometimes unisexual, with male and female on separate plants. They are irregular and have four perianth lobes (which some botanists regard as sepals) with reflexed tips. Two to four scales (which some regard as petals) alternate with the perianth lobes. There are four stamens inserted on the perianth lobes with often only the anther free and conspicuous, the fused filament not at all evident. The ovary may be stalked and is superior, with one carpel, and one to many ovules in the single locule. The style is long and terminal, often bent inwards and sometimes fleshy or wiry. The fruit is a follicle, drupe or nut; the seeds are often winged and have no endosperm.

The flowers tend to be protandrous, the male parts becoming functional before the female, with pollen exposed to the air on non-receptive stylar surfaces for transfer to pollinators such as birds or insects, a feature not found in groups from wetter climates.

Classification. There are two subfamilies: GREVILLEOIDEAE and PROTEOIDEAE. The former, generally considered the more primitive, has flowers in pairs and the latter has single flowers. The inflorescences of *Protea* and *Leucadendron* resemble genera of the Compositae and pine families respectively. The Proteaceae is generally regarded as taxonomically isolated and of uncertain affinities. It is probably most closely related to the Elaeagnaceae, sharing such common features as strongly perigynous flowers, with the petals reduced or lost, and the presence of only one carpel.

Economic uses. Primarily ornamental, this family has many genera (eg *Banksia*, *Embothrium*, *Grevillea* and *Telopea*) which have been successfully cultivated in tropical, subtropical and temperate climates. Examples are *Grevillea robusta* (silk oak or golden pine), *Protea cynaroides* (giant protea), *P. neriifolia*, the rare *P. stokoei*, *P. grandiceps*, *P. barbigera*, *Embothrium coccineum* (the Chilean fire bush) and *Hakea laurina* (pincushion flower). *Gevuina avellana* and the macadamia nut (*Macadamia integrifolia*) both yield edible seeds, the latter being farmed in Australia and Hawaii. Species of *Grevillea* (among others) provide timber.

B.M.

SANTALALES

SANTALACEAE
Sandalwood

The Santalaceae is a family of tropical and temperate herbs, shrubs and trees. Most, if not all, are semiparasites; they are able to manufacture their own complex food

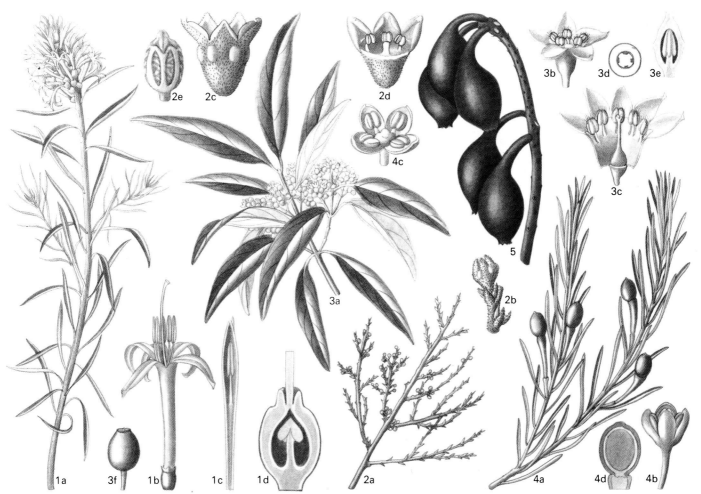

Santalaceae. 1 *Quinchamalium majus* (a) leafy shoot and terminal inflorescence (×⅔); (b) flower (×3); (c) stamen attached to perianth-segment (×4); (d) vertical section of ovary (×12). 2 *Thesium lacinulatum* (a) flowering shoot (×⅔); (b) shoot tip showing scale-like leaves (×3); (c) flower (×6); (d) flower with two perianth segments removed (×6); (e) fruit (×6). 3 *Santalum yasi* (a) flowering shoot (×⅔); (b) flower (×6); (c) flower opened out (×8); (d) cross section of ovary (×18); (e) vertical section of ovary (×18); (f) fruit (×⅔). 4 *Anthobolus foveolatus* (a) leafy shoot and fruits (×⅔); (b) partly open flower (×4); (c) flower (×4); (d) vertical section of fruit (×1⅓). 5 *Scleropyrum wallichianum* fruits (×⅔).

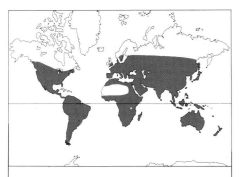

Number of genera: about 35
Number of species: about 400
Distribution: widespread in the tropics and temperate regions.
Economic uses: timber (sandalwood), oil and edible fruits.

substances by photosynthesis but require the presence of a host plant from which they absorb water and minerals through haustorial connections. They are mostly root-parasites but a few are epiphytic branch-parasites.

Distribution. The family is widespread throughout the tropics and in temperate regions, being concentrated in relatively dry areas.

Diagnostic features. The leaves are usually simple, entire, without stipules and spirally arranged, although a few genera, eg *Santalum*, have opposite leaves. However, members of several genera, including *Anthobolus*, *Exocarpos* and *Phacellaria*, have scale-like leaves and the plants then superficially resemble a *Cytisus* or *Cupressus*. *Exocarpos phyllanthoides* and other species have flattened branches (cladodes) which imitate true leaves. The flowers, borne in spikes, racemes or heads, are generally small and inconspicuous. The perianth comprises a single united whorl of three to six segments (tepals) which may be greenish or colored. The stamens are adnate to the perianth, one opposite each lobe. The ovary is inferior or semi-inferior, with a single locule containing one to five naked ovules (ie lacking an integument) suspended from a central placental column. The style is more or less simple. Only one ovule develops, and the fruit is a nut or drupe containing a single seed which has no testa and copious endosperm.

Classification. The Santalaceae has been divided into three tribes:

SANTALEAE. Ovary inferior; receptacle shallowly saucer- or cup-shaped, lined with a nectar-secreting disk. Twenty-seven genera including *Acanthosyris*, *Okoubaka*, *Osyris*, *Phacellaria* and *Santalum*.

THESIEAE. Ovary inferior; receptacle deeply cup-shaped, without a disk. Five genera including *Arjona*, *Quinchamalium*, *Thesium*.

ANTHOBOLEAE. Ovary superior to inferior. Ovules not fully differentiated from the placenta. Pedicel becoming swollen and fleshy as the fruit develops. Three genera including *Anthobolus* and *Exocarpos*.

The Santalaceae is related to the Loranthaceae which differs in the presence of a calyx (though very reduced) and in having viscid fruits adapted to dispersal by birds.

Economic uses. The best-known and most useful member of the Santalaceae is *Santalum album*, the sandalwood tree. The sapwood of this medium-sized tree yields a fragrant white timber suitable for fine carvings and carpentry, while sandal oil, used in eastern countries for anointing the body and in the manufacture of soap and perfumes, is distilled from the yellow heartwood and roots. Sandalwood is also used as a form of incense in Hindu, Buddhist and

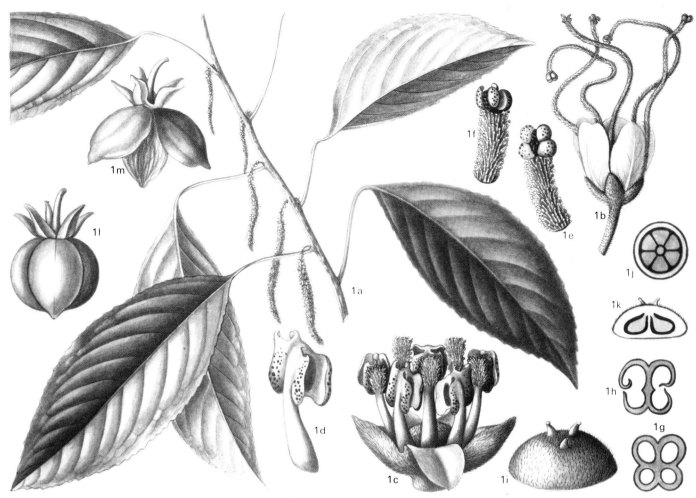

Medusandraceae. 1 *Medusandra richardsiana* (a) leafy shoot bearing axillary, pendulous racemes of flowers ($\times\frac{2}{3}$); (b) flower showing the five long, hairy staminodes ($\times 6$); (c) flower with petals removed to show the five short, fertile stamens and bases of the staminodes ($\times 18$); (d) stamen with dehisced anthers ($\times 26$); (e) tip of staminode ($\times 26$); (f) tip of staminode with vestigial anthers split open ($\times 26$); (g) cross section of anther ($\times 26$); (h) cross section of dehisced anther ($\times 26$); (i) gynoecium showing three short styles ($\times 26$); (j) cross section of ovary ($\times 10$); (k) vertical section of ovary showing pendulous ovules ($\times 14$); (l) fruit—a capsule ($\times 1$); (m) dehisced fruit showing the three valves ($\times 1$).

Muslim ceremonies, and used as joss sticks.

Exocarpos cupressiformis, known as the Australian cherry, is one of the few species with edible fruits. The fruit of *Acanthosyris falcata* is also edible.   F.K.K.

MEDUSANDRACEAE

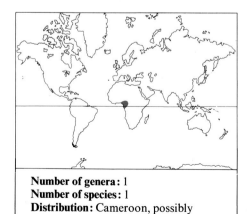

Number of genera: 1
Number of species: 1
Distribution: Cameroon, possibly Nigeria.
Economic uses: none.

The Medusandraceae is a curious family of trees from equatorial West Africa. It is generally accepted that the family is repre-sented by only one genus, *Medusandra*, containing a single species (*M. richardsiana*).

Distribution. *Medusandra richardsiana* grows in the rain forest of Cameroon and possibly Nigeria.

Diagnostic features. *M. richardsiana* is a smooth-barked understory tree of the rain forest, attaining a height of about 60ft (18m). The wood is pinkish and close-grained, with a white sapwood. The leaves are alternate, elliptic-ovate, leathery, slightly toothed 4in–12in (10cm–30cm) long, with eight lateral nerves on each side of the midrib. The young leaves are pinkish-green. The long petioles have a swelling at either end. The flowers are small, bisexual and are borne in dense pendulous racemes 1in–6in (3cm–15cm) long, which are solitary or paired in leaf axils. There are five small sepals and petals. Five short, fertile stamens with large four-locular anthers are borne opposite the petals, while five densely hairy staminodes are borne opposite the sepals; they are long and white and make the otherwise insignificant flowers conspicuous. The ovary is superior, with three fused carpels forming one locule, with six pendulous ovules attached to the roof. There are three short styles. The fruit is a three-valved, pale yellow or green capsule, with a silky-haired interior, subtended by five persistent sepals and containing a single seed. The fruits become brown and brittle on ripening, and are readily eaten by parrots and baboons, although few appear to be produced. The seeds have copious endosperm and a small straight embryo.

Classification. Two morphological features seem to distinguish the Medusandraceae from other families, the staminode and ovary structure. The staminodes appear short in the bud, but are in fact folded, and unfold to become much longer than the petals. The ovary is peculiar in having a central column. *Medusandra richardsiana* is not known to have any very close relatives. The leaves have curious bent hairs on their lower surfaces and a very complex vascular structure in the petiole, and also secretory cells. The Dipterocarpaceae exhibits similar secretory cells and petiolate vascular structures, and the Lacistemataceae possesses similar hairs, but neither family is considered closely related to the Medusandraceae. Affinities with the Olacaceae, Icacinaceae and Euphorbiaceae have been suggested.

Economic uses. None are known.   S.A.H.

Olacaceae. 1 *Heisteria parvifolia* (a) leafy shoot with small flowers ($\times\frac{2}{3}$); (b) half flower ($\times7$); (c) cross section of ovary ($\times7$); (d) fruit ($\times\frac{2}{3}$). 2 *Ximenia caffra* (a) fruits ($\times\frac{2}{3}$); (b) vertical section of fruit ($\times1$). 3 *Olax obtusifolia* (a) flowering shoot ($\times\frac{2}{3}$); (b) flower with calyx represented by a small rim below the recurved petals ($\times3$); (c) part of flower showing gynoecium and stamens ($\times3$). 4 *Schoepfia vacciniflora* (a) flowering shoot ($\times\frac{2}{3}$); (b) flower ($\times2$); (c) flower opened out showing disk around the ovary with below it the reduced calyx ($\times2$); (d) vertical section of ovary which is partly sunk in the disk ($\times4$); (e) cross section of ovary ($\times4$); (f) fruits ($\times\frac{2}{3}$).

OLACACEAE
American Hog Plum and African Walnut

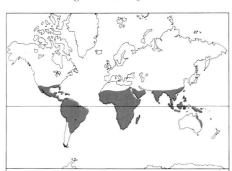

Number of genera: about 25
Number of species: about 250
Distribution: mainly tropical Africa, Asia and America.
Economic uses: timber, fruits eaten locally and a few ornamentals.

The Olacaceae is a family of shrubs, trees, climbers and lianas, most of which are native to the Old World tropics. Some have useful timber or edible fruits.

Distribution. The family is pantropical, but principally African and Asian, with a secondary concentration in America and some species in Australia and the Pacific Islands.

Diagnostic features. The leaves are alternate and entire, without stipules, and have a characteristically rough and parchment-like texture. The flowers are regular, green or white, each with a much-reduced calyx of four to six shallow lobes or teeth. The petals are valvate, equal in number to the calyx segments. The stamens are up to twice as many as the petals and opposite to them, with anthers opening often by pores. Excluding *Strombosia*, the ovary is never truly inferior, but usually partially sunk in a disk with one to three locules, each containing one ovule. There is a single style and a two- to five-lobed stigma. The fruit is a single-seeded nut or drupe. In *Harmandia* the drupe is on a conspicuous thick fleshy disk formed from the flattened calyx. The seed has a small, straight embryo and copious endosperm.

Classification. With their small, reduced flowers the Olacaceae are included in the order Santalales, many of whose members are adapted to a semiparasitic way of life. There are also affinities between the Olacaceae and members of the order Celastrales. Closely related and sometimes placed within the Olacaceae are *Opilia* and seven other genera which are more often separated into the family Opiliaceae.

Economic uses. Several genera are well known in the parts of the world where they grow and are worthy of note. *Olax* is an Old World genus represented by several climbers. Some species have leaves and fruits smelling of garlic, eg *Olax subscorpioidea, O. gambecola.* Seeds of the latter are used as condiments in parts of West Africa. In India *O. nana* is well known as one of the first species to emerge after forest fires, the shoots growing directly from buried roots. *Scorodocarpus* (literally "garlic-fruit") is another genus which smells strongly of garlic. Despite the odor, the timber is utilized in heavy construction work because of its great strength.

Ximenia americana is known as tallow wood or the hog plum. The wood is hard, yellow-pink in color and is used as a substitute for sandalwood in South America. The fruits of *Ximenia* are extremely bitter owing to the presence of prussic acid in the flesh.

Heisteria is predominantly American. Its timber is hard and is used in construction work. *Harmandia coccinea* is occasionally grown as an ornamental hothouse plant. *Coula edulis*, the African walnut, is so named because of its walnut-like nuts. They are eaten fresh, boiled or roasted. The timber also is useful; the wood is very strong and is used in house-building.   S.W.J.

LORANTHACEAE
Mistletoes

The Loranthaceae is a family of parasites with green leaves, most of which are anchored to a host plant by means of suckers usually regarded as modified adventitious roots. Many species do not require a particular host species, often even tolerating plants from different families. However, some are host-specific. A few root into the earth, and the Western Australian *Nuytsia* is a small tree.

Distribution. The family is widely distributed in wooded areas of the tropics and extends into temperate regions; some of the groups tend to have a restricted distribution, often being either Old or New World.

Diagnostic features. The stem of these usually shrubby parasites is sympodial, often dichasial. There is often a large outgrowth

Number of genera: at least 35
Number of species: about 1,300
Distribution: mainly tropical, extending into temperate areas.
Economic uses: none, except for the decorative and symbolic value attached to mistletoe.

where the parasite's root enters the host tissue, and the root often branches considerably within the host. The leaves are usually evergreen, leathery, opposite, and without stipules. The flowers are regular, in cymes which are often reduced to three (rarely two) flowers. More rarely the inflorescence is a spike, in which case flowers

will then also occur on the internodes. The cup-shaped receptacle bears perianth segments at its rim; the segments may be green or petaloid. The flowers can be bisexual or unisexual, with sexes on the same or separate plants. The stamens are equal in number to the perianth segments, and are fused to them; the pollen is often arranged in an unusual manner, in numerous cells within the anthers. The ovary has a single locule and is sunk into the receptacle. The ovules are usually numerous and more or less immersed in the placenta. The style is simple or absent. The fruit is usually a berry or drupe, and there is a characteristic layer of sticky viscin surrounding the seeds, which adheres to the beak of birds feeding on the fruits.

Classification. The family is readily divisible into two main subfamilies, Loranthoideae and Viscoideae – sometimes regarded as two separate families, Loranthaceae and Viscaceae. The LORANTHOIDEAE, with the exception of the aberrant *Nuytsia*, have a characteristic rim or fringe (calyculus) below the perianth on the receptacle. The pollen is usually three-lobed, and the fruit has its viscous layer outside the vascular strands leading to the perianth segments. *Nuytsia* is

Loranthaceae. 1 *Nuytsia floribunda* (a) shoot with flowers in threes (×⅔); (b) flower (×4); (c) dry three-winged fruit (×1). 2 *Dendrophthora cupressoides* (a) flowering branch (×⅔); (b) male inflorescence (×4); (c) male flower from above (×8); (d) part of female inflorescence (×4); (e) female flower with sessile stigma (×8). 3 *Viscum album* (mistletoe) (a) shoot with berries (×⅔); (b) leaf base (×2); (c) male flowers (×6); (d) stamen adnate to perianth segment (×8); (e) female flowers (×6); (f) ovary (×10); (g) fleshy fruit (×2). 4 *Loranthus kimmenzae* (a) terminal inflorescence (×⅔); (b) flower with rim (calyculus) at base (×2); (c) half of flower base with detail of calyculus (×5); (d) epipetalous stamen (×4).

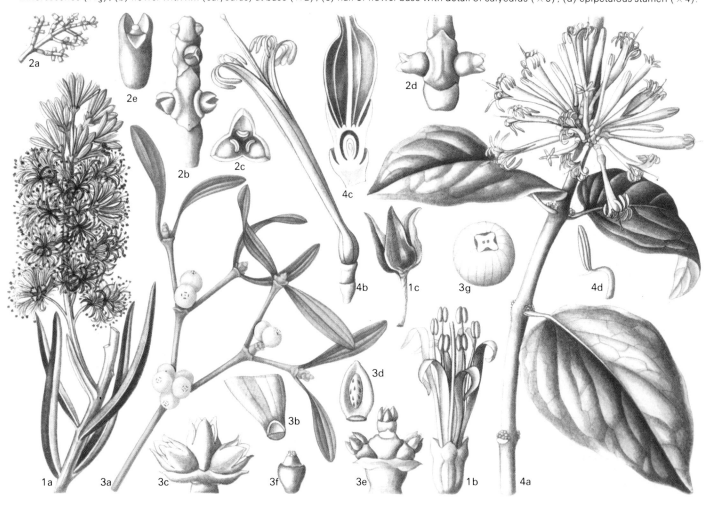

placed in a tribe on its own, the NUYTSIEAE; it has a dry, three-winged fruit. The other species belong to the tribe LORANTHEAE, and number about 850 in some 24 genera, the largest being *Loranthus* with 600 species. In the VISCOIDEAE, there is no calyculus, the pollen is spherical and the viscous layer is between the vascular strands leading to the perianth and the inner strands leading to the ovary. The ovules are reduced to sporogenous cells embedded in the tissue of the placenta. About 450 species are divided among some 11 genera, and four tribes are recognized (EREMOLEPIDEAE, PHORADENDREAE, ARCEUTHOBIEAE and VISCEAE).

The affinities of the family are rather obscure but there is a strong superficial resemblance in foliage and inflorescence to the Myrtaceae; probably the Santalaceae and Misodendraceae are the nearest-related families.

Economic uses. Of little economic value, the family provides the popular Christmas mistletoes (*Viscum album* in Europe, *Phoradendron flavescens* in North America). There is increasing evidence that some species can considerably threaten the establishment of indigenous hardwood trees in parts of the tropics, notably in eastern India; native conifers of North America, and *Citrus* plantations of Central America are now also recognized to be significantly affected.

I.B.K.R.

MISODENDRACEAE

The Misodendraceae is a family of semiparasitic shrubs comprising a single genus, *Misodendrum*, of mistletoe-like plants up to about 2ft (60cm) in diameter. All grow from the trunks and branches of the southern beeches (*Nothofagus*).

Distribution. The family is confined to the *Nothofagus* forests of the Andes south of about 38°S and southern Tierra del Fuego.

Diagnostic features. The primary root is transformed into a haustorium. The stems are woody, apparently dichotomously or trichotomously branched, and often articulated at the nodes, with numerous whitish lenticels. The leaves are alternate, deciduous, green or small, brown and scale-like. Stipules are absent. The flowers are unisexual with the sexes on separate plants. The parts of the flowers are arranged in threes (rarely twos) and the flowers themselves are minute, sessile or with short pedicels, and without bracts or bracteoles. They are borne in spikelets or clusters which are sometimes in pairs or solitary, and the whole inflorescence is racemose. The male flowers have two or three stamens and the anthers have one locule; the ovary is totally absent. The female flowers have three staminodes partly included in grooves at the corners of the ovary, which later extend into very long barbed bristles. The ovary is superior, formed of three fused carpels, with three locules at first, later only one. The placenta is

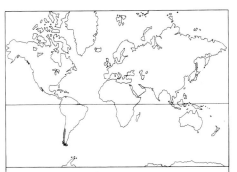

Number of genera: 1
Number of species: about 11
Distribution: southern S America.
Economic uses: none.

free and central, and three naked ovules hang from the apex of the placenta. The styles are very short (sometimes almost absent), with three stigmas, each bearing short hairs. The fruit is an achene with three barbed awns. There is a single albuminous seed with a short, erect embryo, bearing a minute sticky disk at the radical end.

Classification. The genus is normally divided into two subgenera: *Misodendrum*, which has leafy inflorescences and flowers with three stamens, and *Gymnophyton*, which has bracteate inflorescences and flowers with two stamens. The family is related to the Loranthaceae and Santalaceae.

Economic uses. The plants do not have any economic importance.

D.M.M.

CYNOMORIACEAE

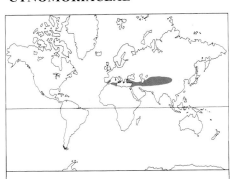

Number of genera: 1
Number of species: 1 or 2
Distribution: temperate Eurasia and the Mediterranean region.
Economic uses: occasional use as a condiment.

The Cynomoriaceae is a small family of obligate parasites of temperate Eurasia and the Mediterranean region.

Distribution. The family comprises the single genus *Cynomorium*, which has one or two species found very locally in dry coastal habitats from the Canary Islands and the Mediterranean basin to the steppes of Central Asia and Mongolia.

Diagnostic features. The whole plant is reddish-brown to purplish-black, the bulk

underground and comprising a thick rhizome bearing many haustoria and thick, simple, flowering stems, with many scales and club-shaped inflorescences of numerous epigynous flowers. The plants are polygamous (male, female and bisexual flowers on the same plant). The males have one to five or rarely up to eight linear petals and one stamen with a four-locular anther, while the females have one to five petals and one inferior carpel with a single ovule, which has a thick integument. The style is terminal. The fruit is nut-like, with a single seed which has abundant endosperm and a very small embryo.

Cynomorium coccineum of the Mediterranean is known to parasitize many salt-marsh plants, eg *Obione* and *Salsola* (Chenopodiaceae), *Inula* (Compositae), *Tamarix* (Tamaricaceae), *Melilotus* (Leguminosae) and *Limonium* (Plumbaginaceae). It is so unlike flowering plants in its appearance that in medieval times it was known as *Fungus melitensis*, or Maltese mushroom.

Classification. The family is often included in the Balanophoraceae, *Cynomorium* being linked to that family by the African *Mystropetalon*, which is the only balanophoraceous genus with an inferior ovary. Nevertheless, *Cynomorium* differs from the rest of that family in having a sculptured pollen wall (exine) and a well-developed ovule integument.

Economic uses. The roots of *Cynomorium coccineum* are used as a condiment by some African peoples, but only locally.

D.J.M.

BALANOPHORACEAE

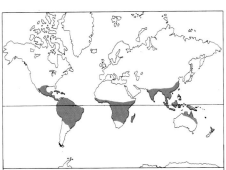

Number of genera: 18
Number of species: 120
Distribution: pantropical, particularly moist upland forests.
Economic uses: waxes burnt for lighting in Java.

The Balanophoraceae is a family of obligate parasites notable for their reduced structure, curious development and obscure affinities.

Distribution. The Balanophoraceae (excluding Cynomoriaceae) is a pantropical family, usually found in moist upland forest. The hosts, of which only roots are attacked, are varied and no specificity has yet been demonstrated. The hosts are normally trees.

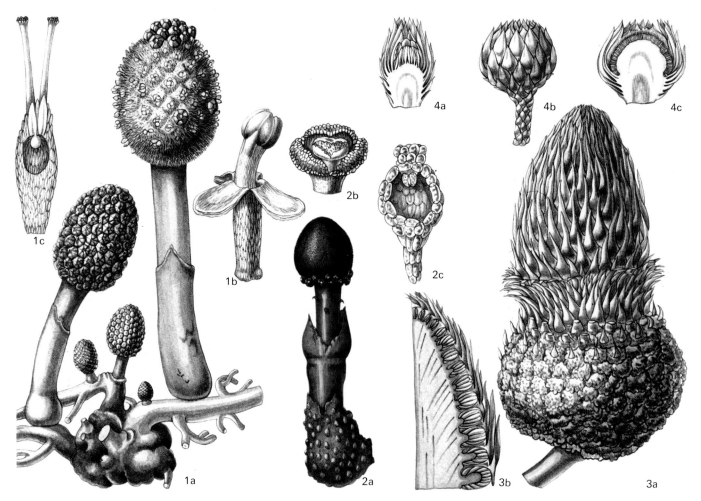

Balanophoraceae. 1 *Helosis mexicana* (a) habit showing irregular, underground tuber, spreading rhizomes and aerial, club-shaped inflorescences (× 2) ; (b) male flower with stamens fused into a tube (× 1,000) ; (c) female flower with part of wall removed to show pendulous ovule (× 1,000). 2 *Balanophora involucrata* (a) tuber and inflorescence (×⅔) ; (b) male flower (× 1,000) ; (c) vertical section of ovary (× 1,000). 3 *Lophophytum weddellii* (a) habit (×⅔) ; (b) vertical section of male inflorescence (×⅔). 4 *Thonningia sanguinea* (a) male inflorescence (×⅔) ; (c) vertical section of female inflorescence (×⅔).

Diagnostic features. The overground parts are usually fleshy, club-shaped inflorescences or "capitula" which have a very fungus-like appearance and are pale yellow to brown, pink or purplish, bearing many flowers which are amongst the smallest known. The underground parts, to which the host is attached, appear tuberous, and may reach the size of a baby's head; only in *Lophophytum* do they bear scale leaves.

The tuber may be entirely composed of parasite tissue as in *Dactylanthus* (New Zealand), *Helosis, Lophophytum* and *Scybalium* (all American). In others, the tuber is a "corpus intermedium," ie part parasite, part host, as noted by the Dutch botanist, Karl Blume, as early as 1827, when it was generally thought that these plants were fungi. The tuber is a chimerical system unknown elsewhere in higher plants.

The inflorescences develop inside the tuber, rupturing the tuber tissue which remains as a "volva" at the base; in *Chlamydophytum*, they mature completely before rupturing the tuber. The inflorescence may have spirally arranged branches as in *Sarcophyta*, or the capitula may be unbranched and flattened or club-shaped. The

flowers are unisexual with the sexes either on separate plants or the same plant; in the latter case there may be separate male and female inflorescences or mixed ones with the males towards the base. In *Helosis* the inflorescence is covered with startlingly geometrical hexagonal scales, each of which is surrounded by two concentric rings of female flowers, while the males occupy corners under the scales. In the male flowers the perianth is either lacking or may be valvate and three- to eight-lobed. The stamens are one or two in male flowers without petals and equal in number to the segments in those with a perianth. The anthers have two, four or many locules. In *Hachettea*, the filament is contracted and the single stamen has one locule. In *Helosis* and *Scybalium* the lower parts of the stamens are united into a tube with discrete anthers, and in other genera there is merely a tube tipped with pollen sacs. The pollen is much reduced as in many parasitic plants, and the outer wall (exine) is not sculptured. The female flowers lack a perianth and are so reduced that ovules, placentas and carpels are not easily recognizable. The ovary is normally superior, but in *Mystropetalon* it is inferior. There

are one to three locules, each with a single, usually pendulous ovule. The ovules are represented by embryo sacs without integuments. There are one or two styles with a terminal stigma; occasionally the stigma is sessile. The fruits are nut- or drupe-like, containing seeds with abundant endosperm and a small embryo.

Small flies are thought to visit those with a sickly sweet odor, though *Juelia*, which is largely subterranean, may be apomictic. The "pedicels" of some female flowers become elaiosomes, attractive to ants, which are known to disperse the seeds of *Mystropetalon*.

Classification. At different times the Balanophoraceae has been split into six discrete families, now treated as tribes. Five of these have a storage substance resembling starch, while species of the sixth (Balanophoroideae) accumulate a waxy substance called balanophorin. The pollen of *Mystropetalon* is unique in flowering plants in being triangular, square or pentagonal when viewed end on, but almost always square when viewed from the side. This is so characteristic as to suggest that *Mystropetalon* may be only distantly related to the rest of the genera.

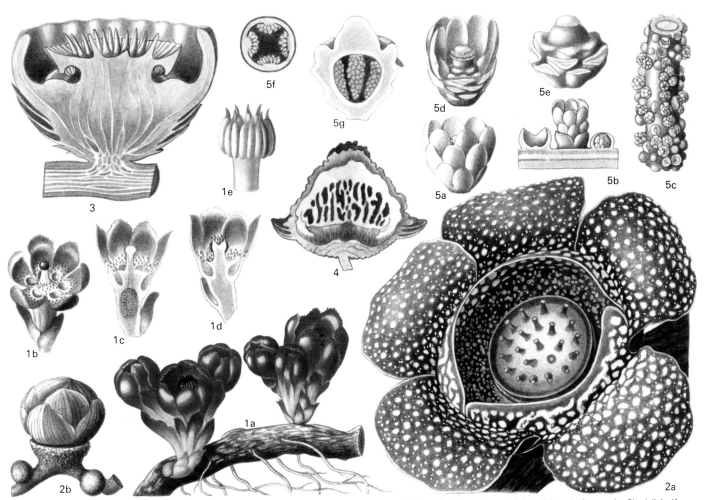

Rafflesiaceae. 1 *Cytinus sanguineus* (a) inflorescences on surface of host stem ($\times\frac{2}{3}$); (b) female flower ($\times\frac{2}{3}$); (c) half female flower ($\times\frac{2}{3}$); (d) half male flower ($\times\frac{2}{3}$); (e) staminal column ($\times2$). 2 *Rafflesia manillana* (a) male flower ($\times\frac{1}{3}$); (b) flower buds ($\times\frac{1}{4}$). 3 *R. patma* half male flower bud showing "mycelia" ramifying through the host tissue ($\times\frac{1}{4}$). 4 *R. rochussenii* vertical section of fruit ($\times\frac{1}{3}$). 5 *Apodanthus welwitschii* (a) male flower ($\times4$); (b) section of host branch showing flowers and flower buds ($\times2$); (c) host branch bearing flowers ($\times\frac{2}{3}$); (d) male flower with part of calyx removed ($\times4$); (e) female flower with perianth removed ($\times3$); (f) cross section of ovary ($\times3$); (g) vertical section of ovary ($\times4\frac{1}{2}$).

The Balanophoraceae is closely related to the Cynomoriaceae, which is often placed in it. As these plants are clearly reduced and simplified in structure, it is difficult to decide whether they represent a "natural" assemblage or are end products of convergent evolution; specialists tend to agree on the former idea. They are probably unrelated to other parasitic groups though they are often said to be related to Hydnoraceae and Rafflesiaceae. They also have affinities with other families of the Santalales, such as Santalaceae, Olacaceae and Opiliaceae. In the opinion of recent workers, the true relationship, albeit a distant one, may be with *Gunnera* (Haloragaceae).

Economic uses. These plants are sometimes considered to have aphrodisiac properties. The only place where real use is made of them is Java, where waxes are extracted and burnt for lighting. D.J.M.

RAFFLESIALES

RAFFLESIACEAE

The Rafflesiaceae are total parasites, invading the stems or roots of other flowering

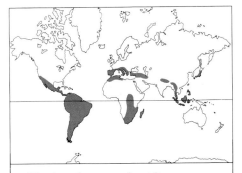

Number of genera: about 9
Number of species: about 500
Distribution: tropics and subtropics.
Economic uses: none.

plants. The flowers of *Rafflesia* are the largest known, some being up to 3ft (1m) across.

Distribution. The family is found mainly in the tropics and subtropics.

Diagnostic features. Only the reproductive parts of the Rafflesiaceae are recognizably angiospermous. Apart from a few scaly bracts below each flower, the vegetative tissues are represented by a kind of "mycelium" which ramifies through the host

cambium. The flower buds begin their development inside the host and then push through to the surface. In some species the "mycelium" penetrates into the growing points of the host's aerial or subterranean parts, and the parasite may then develop synchronously with the host. Thus in the Iranian *Pilostyles haussknechtii*, which infects *Astragalus* stems, the parasite's flowers are borne very regular in pairs at the base of leaves (belonging to its host) which were produced at the beginning of that growing season. Again, a Japanese species of *Mitrastemon*, which parasitizes the roots of *Quercus*, produces its flowers in annual "fairy rings" corresponding to a zone a few centimeters within the perimeter of the host's root system. In cases such as these the parasite eventually becomes fragmented into many parts occupying the terminal twigs or roots.

The flowers have no petals but a fleshy petaloid calyx with four to six lobes. They are usually unisexual (then borne on the same or separate plants) and rarely bisexual. In the center of the flower is a stout column with a grooved margin; in male flowers the numerous stamens occur on the column, under the margin, while in females the corresponding area is stigmatic. The ovary is inferior (rarely superior) of four to numerous fused carpels and either comprises one locule with four to 14 parietal placentas bearing very many ovules, or (in *Rafflesia*) consists of a honeycomb of irregular chambers lined with ovules. The fruit is fleshy, and contains numerous tiny hard seeds.

Classification. The Rafflesiaceae has been divided into four tribes:

MITRASTEMONEAE. Flowers bisexual and solitary, ovary superior. *Mitrastemon*, Southeast Asia, Central America.

APODANTHEAE. Flowers unisexual and solitary, small; stamens in two to four rings on the central column; ovary inferior with four placentas or one continuous placenta. *Apodanthes, Pilostyles, Berlinianche*, tropical America, tropical Africa and Iran.

RAFFLESIEAE. Flowers unisexual and solitary, large; stamens in one ring; ovary inferior with many irregular chambers. *Rafflesia, Sapria, Rhizanthes*, Southeast Asia from India to Indonesia.

CYTINEAE. Flowers unisexual and in racemes; stamens in one ring; ovary inferior with 8–14 placentas. *Cytinus, Bdallophyton*, Mediterranean region, South Africa, Madagascar, Mexico.

The closest relatives of the Rafflesiaceae are undoubtedly the Hydnoraceae, which differ in having root-like structures, no bracts below the flowers, bisexual flowers and stamens not borne on a column. Some botanists prefer to isolate *Mitrastemon* as a separate family placed between the Rafflesiaceae and Hydnoraceae. The affinities of this group are very uncertain. Most authorities link the Rafflesiaceae with the Aristolochiaceae because they have a similar perianth, but the evidence for this association is not conclusive.

Economic uses. None are known.   F.K.K.

HYDNORACEAE

Members of the Hydnoraceae are parasites which feed from the roots of the host plant. They are found in Madagascar and tropical Africa (the 12 species of *Hydnora*) and in South America (the six species of *Prosopanche*).

The plant is leafless and rootless; the large, solitary, bisexual flowers (the only aerial parts) are borne on the thick, creeping underground "stem." There are no petals, but three to five sepals (or perianth segments) are fused into a tube at the base, and open as valves above. Many anthers are united in a ring-like or undulating mass on the calyx tube with many parallel longitudinal or transverse locules, there being no stamen filaments. The ovary is inferior (usually well below soil level) and consists of three to five fused carpels with a single locule containing very many reduced ovules on placentas which are leaf-like or parietal or pendulous from the apex of the ovary. The

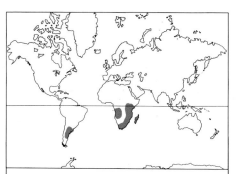

Number of genera: 2
Number of species: 18
Distribution: Madagascar, tropical Africa, S America.
Economic uses: none.

stigma is button-like and crowns the ovary, which matures into a large, thick-walled fleshy berry containing many minute seeds with copious endosperm. The plants are thought to attract pollinating beetles by generating a smell of carrion.

The Hydnoraceae is most closely related to its fellow parasite family, the Rafflesiaceae, from which it differs chiefly in having bisexual flowers. No economic uses are known.   B.M.

CELASTRALES

GEISSOLOMATACEAE

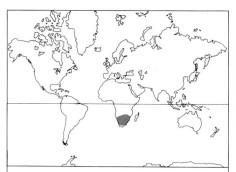

Number of genera: 1
Number of species: 1
Distribution: S Africa.
Economic uses: none.

The Geissolomataceae is a monotypic family with a single species (*Geissoloma marginatum*), native to South Africa.

Geissoloma is a small xerophytic shrub with entire sessile leaves, without stipules, arranged in opposite pairs in four rows down the stem. The flowers are bisexual, regular and arranged in a much reduced axillary racemose type of inflorescence. The flower is subtended by six persistent bracts. There are four petaloid sepals which are fused together at the base to form a short tubular structure. There are no petals and the eight free stamens with slender filaments are attached to the base of the calyx. The stamens are in two whorls of four, lying opposite and alternate with the sepals. The ovary is

superior, formed of four fused carpels, and has four locules, with two pendulous ovules inserted at the apex of each of the locules. The ovary is surmounted by four tapering styles which are separate at the base but coherent at their apexes. The fruit is a four-locular capsule with normally only a single seed in each locule. The seed contains a straight embryo and a little endosperm.

The relationships of Geissolomataceae are disputed. It has been related to the Thymelaeaceae and the Penaeaceae (order Myrtales), sharing with them such features as woody habit, apetalous flowers, a petaloid calyx, rather leafy bracts and a straight embryo in the seed. But it is barely perigynous and lacks internal phloem. Its pollen resembles that of the Celastraceae. No economic uses are known.   S.R.C.

CELASTRACEAE
Spindle Tree

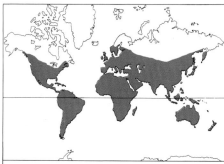

Number of genera: 55
Number of species: 850
Distribution: mainly tropical and subtropical regions.
Economic uses: source of Arabian tea (khat leaves), cultivated as ornamentals, timber used for carving and yields a seed oil and yellow dye.

The Celastraceae is a family of trees and shrubs, many of which are climbing (eg *Salacia*) or twining (eg *Hippocratea*) in habit.

Distribution. The family is widespread, but concentrated in sub- and tropical regions.

Diagnostic features. The leaves may be opposite or alternate even in a single genus as in *Cassine*. They are simple, often leathery, with or without small stipules. The flowers are small, greenish, regular, bisexual or unisexual and arranged usually in cymose inflorescences. The sepals and petals are inserted on or below the margin of a distinctive glandular fleshy disk. There are three to five sepals, free or united at the base, and three to five free petals (rarely none). The stamens alternate with and are equal in number to the petals and are inserted on the disk. The anthers have two locules and dehisce longitudinally (transverse dehiscence in *Hippocratea*). The ovary is superior and consists of two to five fused carpels with two to five locules, each usually with two (sometimes one, rarely many) erect ovules on axile placentas. There is a single, very short

Celastraceae. 1 *Euonymus myrianthus* (a) leafy shoot bearing fruits—loculicidal capsules ($\times\frac{2}{3}$); (b) flower with four distinct petals inserted on a fleshy disk ($\times 2$); (c) half flower showing stamens inserted on the disk and gynoecium with ovules on axile placentas ($\times 4$); (d) stamen ($\times 12$). 2 *E. vagans* cross section of ovary ($\times 14$). 3 *Hippocratea welwitschii* (a) shoot with dehiscing fruit ($\times\frac{2}{3}$); (b) seed with aril ($\times\frac{2}{3}$). 4 *Celastrus articulatus* (a) leafy shoot and cymose inflorescences ($\times\frac{2}{3}$); (b) flower ($\times 2$); (c) two stamens and gynoecium ($\times 2$); (d) fruit—a capsule ($\times 2$). 5 *Elaeodendron aethiopicum* (a) flower ($\times 6$); (b) half flower ($\times 8$).

style terminated by a capitate or two- to five-lobed stigma. The fruit is a loculicidal or indehiscent capsule, a samara, berry or drupe. The capsule of some species of *Euonymus* may possess spiny outgrowths. The seeds possess a large, straight embryo surrounded by fleshy endosperm and are often covered by a brightly colored aril which aids in dispersal by birds.

Classification. The chief genera are *Maytenus* (225 tropical species), *Salacia* (200 tropical species), *Euonymus* (176 species mostly from the Himalayas, China and Japan), *Hippocratea* (120 species, tropical South America, Mexico and southern United States of America), *Cassine* (40 species, South Africa, Madagascar, tropical Asia and the Pacific), *Celastrus* (30 subtropical and tropical species), *Elaeodendron* (16 subtropical and tropical species), *Pachystima* (five species, North America) and *Gyminda* (three species, Central America, Mexico and Florida).

The Celastraceae is probably related to the Aquifoliaceae but is distinguished from it by the presence of the glandular disk surrounding the ovary and by the brightly colored aril. The absence of aril and endosperm and

the unusual form of anther dehiscence in *Hippocratea* have been considered by some taxonomists to warrant separate family status (Hippocrateaceae).

Economic uses. The small khat tree, *Catha edulis*, is cultivated in the Middle East and Ethiopia for its leaves, used to make an infusion of tea (Arabian tea) or in the making of a honey wine (in Ethiopia). The seeds of *Kokoona zeylanica* (kokoon tree) are used as a source of oil in Sri Lanka. A number of species of *Euonymus* yield useful products, including the spindle tree (*Euonymus europaeus*) whose fine-grained wood is used for turnery and figure carving and as a source of charcoal. The seeds of this species yield an oil used in soap manufacture and a yellow dye for coloring butter. The heavy, durable, close-grained wood of the Japanese shrub, *E. hians*, is also used for turnery and for making printing blocks. Some species, such as *E. japonicus* and *E. sieboldiana* yield a rubberlike latex from the stems and roots. Extracts from *E. purpureus* and *E. americanus* are used in native medicines in North America. Species of other genera which yield medicinal extracts include *Elaeodendron glaucum*, *Maytenus boania*, *M. ilicifolia* and *M.*

senegalensis, and *Hippocratea acapulcensis*.

Species of *Celastrus*, *Euonymus*, *Elaeodendron*, *Pachystima* and *Maytenus* are cultivated as ornamentals. *Celastrus orbiculatus* and *C. scandens* are attractive, vigorous climbing shrubs. Although the flowers of *Euonymus* are inconspicuous, a number of deciduous species including *E. alatus*, *E. europaeus*, *E. latifolius* and *E. yedoensis* are grown for their attractive autumn tints and distinctive bright-colored fruits. The evergreen *E. japonicus* has an upright, bushy habit which makes it suitable for hedges.

S.R.C.

STACKHOUSIACEAE

The Stackhousiaceae is a small family of three genera of more or less xerophytic herbs with a branched rhizome system.

Distribution. The family occurs chiefly in Australasia, but also in Malesia.

Diagnostic features. The leaves are alternate, simple, with stipules, and are often leathery or succulent. The flowers are regular, bisexual and borne in racemes or spaced clusters, and consist of a five-lobed calyx tube on which the five petals and five alternating stamens (often three long and two

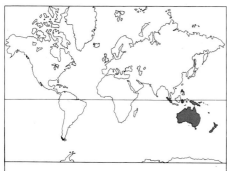

Number of genera: 3
Number of species: 27
Distribution: chiefly Australasia.
Economic uses: none.

short) are inserted. The petals may be linear or spoon-shaped, and free or partly fused together into a tube in the middle portion but not at the base. The ovary is superior, comprising two to five locules with one erect ovule at the base of each locule. The styles are the same number as locules and are partly fused. The fruit is a schizocarp which splits into two to five segments, each indehiscent and with one seed. The seeds have fleshy endosperm and a large, straight embryo.

Classification. *Macgregoria* differs from *Stackhousia* and *Tripterococcus* in having free petals, not partly fused, and stamens of equal length and is sometimes placed in a separate subfamily the MACGREGORIOIDEAE, the latter two being placed in the subfamily STACKHOUSIOIDEAE.

The only species of *Macgregoria*, *M. racemigera* (arid Australia), is a slender, glabrous annual with star-like, white, terminal racemes of flowers. *Stackhousia* comprises some 25 mostly Australian species. *Stackhousia intermedia* (Malesia) is a lank herb to 20in (50cm) in open grassy situations; *S. minima* (New Zealand) is a slender herb to 2in (5cm) tall with solitary flowers; *S. monogyna* (eastern Australia, including South Australia) has white to cream, densely flowered racemes. *Tripterococcus* contains a single species from southwestern Australia. The family is not clearly allied to any other but has been related to the Euphorbiaceae, Celastraceae and the order Sapindales.
Economic uses. None are known.   B.M.

SALVADORACEAE
The Salvadoraceae is a small family of trees and shrubs.
Distribution. The family is native to arid, often saline, areas in Africa, Madagascar, Arabia, India and Asia.
Diagnostic features. The leaves are opposite and simple, with minute stipules. Some species of *Azima* have axillary spines. The flowers are borne in dense axillary clusters or in branched racemes. They are regular, bisexual or unisexual (the male and female then being borne on separate plants). The calyx comprises two to four fused sepals. The

petals are free or partially fused, four or five, with teeth or glands on the inner side. There are four or five stamens which alternate with the petals. The filaments may be fused into a tube and are often inserted at the base of the petals. The anthers have two locules and open lengthwise. A disk in the form of separate glands may be present between the filaments. The ovary is superior and consists of one or two carpels with one or two erect ovules in each locule. The style is short and bears a forked stigma. The fruit is a berry or drupe and contains a single seed without endosperm and an embryo with thick cotyledons.

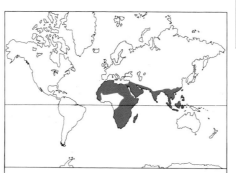

Number of genera: 3
Number of species: 11
Distribution: Africa and Madagascar to Arabia and Asia.
Economic uses: shoots and leaves used as salad, local medicinal uses, fat for candles, Kegr salt and perfume oil.

Classification. The three genera differ in habit and floral structure: *Azima* (four species), thorny shrubs whose flowers possess free petals and stamens and a bilocular ovary, *Dobera* (two species) and *Salvadora* (five species), spineless trees and shrubs. *Dobera* has free petals and the stamen filaments united at the base. The petals of *Salvadora* are united at the base and the stamens are epipetalous.

The relationships of this family are doubtful; it is here placed in the Celastrales.
Economic uses. The shoots and leaves of *Salvadora persica* (the toothbrush tree or salt bush) are used in salads or as food for camels. Kegr salt is obtained from the plant ash. The flowers of *Dobera roxburghii* provide an essential oil used by Sudanese women as perfume.   S.R.C.

CORYNOCARPACEAE
The Corynocarpaceae is a small family of Pacific trees and shrubs.
Distribution. The family is native to Polynesia, New Zealand and Australia and some other areas of the southwestern Pacific.
Diagnostic features. The leaves are alternate, simple, entire and without stipules. The flowers are bisexual, regular and borne on indeterminate branching racemes. The sepals are five in number, and are distinctly imbricate. The five petals are fused to the base of the sepals. The filaments of the five

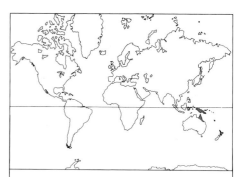

Number of genera: 1
Number of species: 5
Distribution: Australasia and Polynesia.
Economic uses: seeds eaten by Maoris and canoes made from trunks.

stamens are in turn attached to the base of the petals. The stamens are inserted opposite the petals (antipetalous) and not alternate with them as in most other families. In addition, there are five alternating, clawed, petaloid staminodes, opposite to each of which is a large disk-shaped gland. The ovary is superior, of one or two fused carpels containing one or two locules, surmounted by one or two free styles. When there are two locules, only one of them is fertile; each locule contains a single pendulous ovule. The fruit is a drupe, and the seed it contains is without endosperm, while the embryo has a tiny radicle.

Classification. There is only one genus, *Corynocarpus*, with five species. The affinities of the family are obscure, and it has been placed in a number of orders, including the Ranunculales and the Sapindales, but it is here referred to the Celastrales, having some features in common with the Celastraceae.

Economic uses. The fruits of *Corynocarpus laevigatus* are used as food by the Maoris and the seeds form a staple food. Some natives of the southwestern Pacific use the trunks of the trees for making canoes.   S.R.C.

ICACINACEAE
This family comprises trees, shrubs and lianas, almost all of which inhabit tropical rain forests.
Distribution. The family occurs mainly in Malaysia and tropical regions of India, Africa and Central America, decreasing rapidly toward the subtropics. Among the few species of tall trees are *Apodytes* (Malaysia, northeastern Australia and southern Africa), found in primary rain forest on steep slopes, ravine and stream edges, and the Malaysian *Stemonurus* found in peatlands (occasionally coastal mangroves), swamp forest, in lowlands or even dry hilly land. Among the tallest of southern African Icacinaceae are *Poraqueiba* and *Dendrobangia*. Smaller trees and shrubs such as *Gonocaryum* (Taiwan, Southeast Asia and Indomalaysia) and *Gomphandra* (Southeast

Icacinaceae. 1 *Pyrenacantha volubilis* (a) leafy shoot with axillary inflorescences ($\times \frac{2}{3}$); (b) female flower ($\times 6$); (c) male flower ($\times 6$); (d) vertical section of ovary ($\times 6$). 2 *Phytocrene bracteata* fruits ($\times \frac{2}{3}$). 3 *Citronella suaveolens* (a) leaf and fruits ($\times \frac{2}{3}$); (b) flower bud ($\times 3$); (c) inflorescence ($\times \frac{1}{3}$); (d) cross section of fruit ($\times 5$). 4 *Stemonurus vitensis* (a) flower ($\times 6$); (b) ovary ($\times 16$); (c) cross section of ovary ($\times 16$). 5 *Iodes usambarensis* (a) leafy shoot with tendril and inflorescence ($\times \frac{2}{3}$); (b) female flower ($\times 6$); (c) fruits ($\times 1$); (d) male flower ($\times 6$).

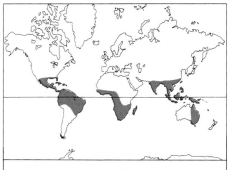

Number of genera: about 60
Number of species: about 400
Distribution: chiefly tropical rain forest.
Economic uses: timber, starches, oils and tea substitute.

Asia to Solomon Islands) grow in the forest understory in low montane zones. Some *Citronella* species (South America) have also been found on dry, barren soil as well as dense, moist forests. Most of the rain forest lianas are dioecious, such as *Miquelia* (Indochina and Indonesia) and *Phytocrene* (mainly Malaysia but also Asia),

Diagnostic features. The leaves are usually alternate, entire, and leathery, always with-out stipules. The inflorescence is usually a cyme or thyrse. The flowers are small, regular, not fragrant, bisexual or unisexual, the sexes then borne on separate plants. There are four or five each of sepals, petals and stamens (no sepals in *Pyrenacantha*). The stamens alternate with the petals and the anthers have two locules, rarely four lobes. The ovary is superior, initially of three (sometimes two or five) carpels; there is usually one locule, rarely two or more. There are two anatropous ovules, pendulous from the top of each locule. The style is simple and short, with three (rarely two or five) stigmas. The fruit is usually a one-seeded drupe, sometimes a samara; the endocarp is often laterally flattened and ornamented with depressions or pits and the seeds usually have endosperm and a small, straight embryo.

Classification. The Icacinaceae is subdivided into four tribes:

ICACINEAE. Trees or shrubs, rarely climbers; flowers bisexual; vessels in wood with ladder-like perforations; chief genera *Citronella*, *Gonocaryum*, *Gomphandra*, *Poraqueiba* and *Icacina*.

IODEAE. Climbers or twining shrubs; plants dioecious; vessels in wood with simple perforation plates; chief genus *Iodes*.

SARCOSTIGMATEAE. Climbing shrubs, inner surface of endocarp weakly wrinkled; chief genus *Sarcostigma*.

PHYTOCRENEAE. Climbing or twining shrubs; endocarp inner wall always warty; chief genera *Pyrenacantha* and *Phytocrene*.

The Icacinaceae shows connections with the Celastraceae, Aquifoliaceae and Olacaceae. The differences are in such characters as presence or absence of stipules, petals and floral disk, aestivation of perianth parts and number of locules in the fruit.

Economic uses. The hard, heavy, fragrant timber of *Cantleya corniculata* is exported from Sarawak and Brunei and is used for house- and shipbuilding, and as a sandal-wood substitute. The wood of *Apodytes* is used in Indochina for cabinet work. The tubers and seeds of *Humirianthera* have abundant starch. *Poraqueiba* fruits and seeds yield starch and oil. Leaves of *Citronella* species are used as a substitute for yerba maté tea. The seeds of *Sarcostigma kleinii* yield a useful oil in India used to treat rheumatism. The leaves and bark of *Cassinopsis madagascariensis* yield an antidysenteric. Cut stems of *Miquelia* and *Phytocrene* yield drinkable water.   H.P.W.

Aquifoliaceae. 1 *Ilex aquifolium* (a) leafy shoot and fruits ($\times\frac{2}{3}$); (b) female flower with four staminodes ($\times 4$); (c) male flower with four stamens alternating with the petals ($\times 4$); (d) corolla of male flower opened out showing stamens attached at the base ($\times 4$); (e) gynoecium with sessile stigma ($\times 4$). 2 *I. anomala* (a) flowering shoot ($\times\frac{2}{3}$); (b) bisexual flower ($\times 3$); (c) perianth opened out to show stamens fused to the base of the perianth tube and alternating with the lobes ($\times 3$); (d) fruit—a berry ($\times 4$). 3 *I. paraguaensis* (a) leafy shoot with fruits ($\times\frac{2}{3}$); (b) fruit with wall cut away to show four hard pyrenes each containing a single seed ($\times 4$).

AQUIFOLIACEAE
Hollies and Yerba Maté

This family of trees and shrubs comprises the large genus *Ilex* (holly) with about 400 species, *Nemopanthus* with two species and *Phelline* with ten.

Distribution. The family is widely distributed in both temperate and tropical regions, though relatively poorly represented in Africa and Australia. *Nemopanthus* is restricted to northeastern North America and *Phelline* to New Caledonia.

Diagnostic features. The leaves are leathery, sometimes evergreen and usually alternate; stipules are present (except in *Phelline*) but may fall soon after enlargement of the leaf. The inconspicuous, greenish-white flowers are bisexual or unisexual (in which case male and female are normally borne on different plants). They are regular and usually in bundles or cymes (spikes or panicles in *Phelline*), rarely solitary, with minute bracts. The sepals and petals, usually four of each (four to six in *Phelline*), are imbricate (petals valvate in *Phelline*); the petals are united at the base (free in *Nemopanthus* and *Phelline*), and the stamens, usually equal in number to and alternating with the petals, are freq-

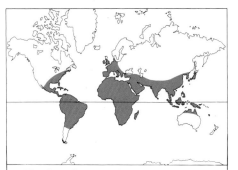

Number of genera: 3
Number of species: about 400
Distribution: widespread in tropical and temperate regions.
Economic uses: valued ornamental trees and shrubs, useful hardwood and tea (yerba maté).

uently fused to the petals; otherwise they are free, and are often represented as staminodes in female flowers. The anthers have two locules and open inward. The ovary is superior, of three or more united carpels, comprising three or more locules with a single terminal, sometimes minute, style; placentation is axile, with one or rarely two pendulous, usually anatropous, ovules in

each locule. The fruit is a berry with usually four hard pyrenes each with one seed with copious endosperm.

Classification. The genus *Phelline* is sometimes separated as the family Phellinaceae. Closely allied to the Celastraceae, the family is distinguished mainly by the absence of a distinct, annular nectary disk at the base of the stamens, and by the usually solitary ovule in each locule.

Economic uses. The family is important for the hard, white wood of *Ilex* species, used in carving, inlay and many other ways. Holly has long been used as decoration, for its attractive foliage and berries. There is a Christmas trade in holly in several countries and many species are grown as ornamentals. The leaves of *Ilex paraguensis* are used as a tea (yerba maté).   I.B.K.R.

DICHAPETALACEAE

This is a family of tropical shrubs and a few climbers and small trees, some of which are very poisonous. It is sometimes incorrectly known as the Chailletiaceae.

Distribution. There are about 200 species in four genera: *Dichapetalum* (150 or more tropical species, notably in Africa); *Stepha-*

Dichapetalaceae. 1 *Stephanopodium peruvianum* (a) leafy shoot and axillary inflorescences united to the leaf stalk ($\times\frac{2}{3}$); (b) half flower with sessile epipetalous anthers ($\times 8$); (c) vertical section of ovary showing pendulous ovules ($\times 14$); (d) fruit—a hairy drupe ($\times\frac{2}{3}$); (e) flower ($\times 8$). 2 *Dichapetalum mombongense* (a) flowering and fruiting shoot ($\times\frac{2}{3}$); (b) half flower ($\times 8$); (c) cross section of ovary ($\times 21$); (d) cross section of fruit ($\times 1\frac{1}{2}$). 3 *Dichapetalum toxicarum* (a) flower with gynoecium removed ($\times 14$); (b) gynoecium ($\times 14$). 4 *Tapura ciliata* (a) leafy shoot with small stipules and axillary inflorescences ($\times\frac{2}{3}$); (b) flower ($\times 4$); (c) corolla opened out ($\times 6$); (d) hypogynous gland ($\times 12$); (e) ovary ($\times 12$).

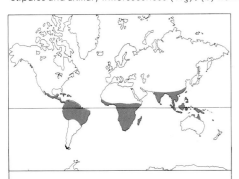

Number of genera: 4
Number of species: about 200
Distribution: throughout the tropics, with one S African species.
Economic uses: a few ornamentals and leaves and seeds used as a poison.

nopodium (seven species, tropical South America); *Tapura* (20 species, tropical South America and the West Indies, and four species in tropical Africa); and *Gonypetalum* (five species in tropical South America). The only extra-tropical species is a South African *Dichapetalum*.

Diagnostic features. The leaves are simple, alternate, with stipules, and often covered with fine gray hairs. The inflorescence is an axillary cyme or fascicle, its stalk often united to the leaf petiole below as in some species of *Dichapetalum* and *Tapura*. The flowers are regular or irregular, bisexual or unisexual (then with both types on the same plant). They have five imbricate sepals and four or five petals; the petals are forked or bilobed and often dry black. The five stamens are borne on the petals or are free. The ovary is superior with two or three united carpels, each with two pendulous ovules; it is surrounded by a cup-shaped or lobed disk and topped with two separate or united styles. The fruit is a lobed drupe, which is usually pubescent, containing one to three locules each with a single seed. The seeds often bear a caruncle, have no endosperm but a large, straight embryo.

Classification. Both *Dichapetalum* and *Stephanopodium* have five fertile stamens in each bisexual flower, those of the latter being sessile. *Tapura* and *Gonypetalum*, united by some authors, have only three fertile stamens. The Madagascan *Falya* is now placed in the same genus as the West African *Carpolobium* (Polygalaceae), but was at one time placed in the family Dichapetalaceae.

The affinities of the Dichapetalaceae are a matter for debate, and it has been referred to the Rosales, Celastrales or Euphorbiales.

Economic uses. A few species are grown as ornamentals in the tropics, and the fruits of some East African species are said to be edible. The leaves and seeds of all species of *Dichapetalum* tested are poisonous. The leaves of *Dichapetalum stuhlmannii* are used to poison wild pigs, monkeys and rats in East Africa, where an extract is said to have been used in arrow poisons. The seeds of *D. toxicarium* are similarly used in West Africa, particularly as an effective rat poison. *D. cymosum* of the high veldt of southern Africa begins growth before the veldt grasses, and is therefore eaten by cattle, giving rise to "gifblaar" poisoning with disastrous effects. The toxic principle is fluoracetic acid, which disrupts the tricarboxylic acid cycle of respiration.   D.J.M.

EUPHORBIALES

BUXACEAE
Box

The Buxaceae is a small family of six genera of evergreen shrubs (rarely trees or

Buxaceae. 1 *Buxus sempervirens* (a) leafy shoot with axillary clusters of flowers ($\times \frac{2}{3}$); (b) female flower surrounded by cluster of male flowers ($\times 6$); (c) male flower with four stamens having introrsely dehiscing anthers ($\times 8$); (d) female flower with three styles crowned by convolute stigmas ($\times 8$); (e) fruit—a capsule dehiscing by three valves ($\times 2$); (f) seed ($\times 4$). 2 *Pachysandra terminalis* (a) leafy shoot and inflorescence ($\times \frac{2}{3}$); (b) half male flower ($\times 3$); (c) female flower ($\times 6$); (d) vertical section of ovary ($\times 6$); (e) fruit ($\times 4$); (f) seed ($\times 4$).

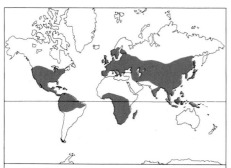

Numbers of genera: 4 or 6
Number of species: about 100
Distribution: temperate, subtropical, tropical.
Economic uses: ornamentals (box, *Sarcococca*) and high quality timber.

herbs) whose best-known member is the box tree.

Distribution. The family is scattered throughout temperate, subtropical and tropical regions.

Diagnostic features. The leaves are alternate or opposite, simple and without stipules, and have a rather leathery texture. The flowers are regular, unisexual, and borne on the same plant or separate plants in spikes, racemes or fascicles. They are bracteate and have no petals. There are usually four imbricate sepals fused together at the base, sometimes six or more. The male flowers usually possess four or six stamens (rarely seven to ten) but in two genera (*Simmondsia* and *Styloceras*) they are numerous. When there are four stamens they are opposite the sepals, and when there are six, two of the pairs are opposite the inner two sepals. The anthers are often large and are either sessile or on long filaments. They have two locules, dehiscing by valves or longitudinal slits. Sometimes a rudimentary ovary is present. The female flowers are fewer (sometimes solitary) and possess a superior ovary of three fused carpels with three locules (four to six in *Styloceras*). The placentation is axile with normally one or two ovules in each locule. The ovary is surmounted by three styles which may be separate or fused at the base. The fruit is a loculicidal capsule or a drupe, containing black, shiny seeds, sometimes with a caruncle. They possess fleshy endosperm surrounding a straight embryo with flat cotyledons.

Classification. Two of the genera, *Simmondsia* (native to California) and *Styloceras* (native to South America) are sufficiently distinct to be sometimes considered as separate families (Simmondsiaceae and Stylocerataceae). *Styloceras* (three species, South America) has alternate leaves, six to 30 stamens and male flowers lacking a perianth. *Simmondsia* (one species, California) has opposite leaves and numerous stamens. In both genera the rudimentary ovary is absent from the male flowers. All other genera have flowers with either four stamens, ie *Sarcococca* (16–20 species, China and Indomalaysia) which has alternate leaves and *Buxus* (70 species, temperate Northern Hemisphere, southern and tropical Africa, West Indies) which has opposite leaves; or six stamens, ie *Notobuxus* (seven species, southeast Africa) and *Pachysandra*. The four species of *Pachysandra* (eastern Asia and the United States of America) are distinguished by their herbaceous habit and their alternate, coarsely toothed leaves.

This family is thought to be related to the Euphorbiaceae and the Celastraceae but shows a number of clearly distinguishing features, eg absence of milky sap, apetalous flowers, the black, shiny, carunculate seeds and leaves always without stipules.

Economic uses. Economically the Buxaceae is important for its ornamentals. The best-known is *Buxus sempervirens* (common box), a slow-growing species with ovate, glossy, dark-green leaves, which is often used as hedges, border edgings etc. *Pachysandra procumbens* (eastern North America) and *P. terminalis* (Japan) are spreading subshrubs, grown as ground-cover plants. Species of *Sarcococca* have small but strongly fragrant flowers in winter. The wood of common box and of Cape box (*B. macowani*) is particularly valuable for carving, inlaying furniture and for making rulers and instruments and has been prized by wood engravers.

S.R.C.

PANDACEAE

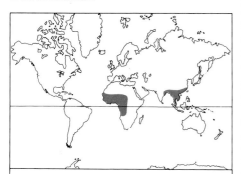

Number of genera: 3
Number of species: about 28
Distribution: W Africa, Asia, Indomalaysia.
Economic uses: seeds eaten locally.

The Pandaceae is a small family of tropical trees, comprising about 28 species in three genera.

Distribution. The genus *Panda* is restricted to tropical West Africa, *Microdesmis* to tropical West Africa and Asia and *Galearia* to Indomalaysia.

Diagnostic features. All members of the family have alternate, simple, often serrate leaves arranged in two rows on shoots which have buds in their axils. The leaves have no axillary buds, the terminal bud of the leafy shoot is reduced and non-functional, and the stipules which would normally subtend the shoot are reduced or absent. Thus the whole leafy shoot resembles a pinnate leaf. A similar arrangement is found in some members of the Euphorbiaceae.

The flowers are regular, unisexual with male and female on different trees in closely crowded inflorescences in the axils of shoots (*Microdesmis*) or directly on the stems of older wood (*Galearia* and *Panda*). They have five fused sepals and five petals. There are one, two or three series of five stamens and a rudimentary ovary in the male flowers, and a superior ovary of two to five locules each with one apical, pendulous ovule in the female flowers. The fruit is a drupe, the innermost layer of the ovary wall being stony. The seeds are flattened, and contain

copious oily endosperm. The embryo has cordate cotyledons.

Classification. Although the Pandaceae are close relatives of the Euphorbiaceae the similarities are not sufficient to merit their inclusion in that already large family. The stony fruit of the Pandaceae is a character not found anywhere in the Euphorbiaceae.

Economic uses. *Panda oleosa* yields edible, oily seeds which are used locally for cooking, but is of no economic importance.

S.W.J.

EUPHORBIACEAE
The Spurge Family

The Euphorbiaceae is a large family of flowering plants, including some 300 genera and over 5,000 species of dicotyledonous herbs, shrubs and trees. Some of the genera are very large, such as *Phyllanthus*, *Euphorbia*, *Croton* and *Acalypha*, but a great number are monotypic. Important products of the family include cassava, rubber (from *Hevea brasiliensis*) and tung oil.

Distribution. The family is predominantly tropical in its distribution, although there are strong local concentrations, particularly of the genus *Euphorbia*, in such extratropical regions as the southern United States of America, the Mediterranean basin, the Middle East and South Africa; the greatest number of the genera, however, are entirely tropical. In the tropics, the richest concentration of the family is perhaps in the Indomalaysian region, with the New World tropics coming a close second; the genus *Croton*, for example, is remarkably well developed in South America, with about 300 species in Brazil alone. Although it is a large family in Africa, it is not quite as rich and varied there as in the other two tropical realms. (See also pp. 768, 848.)

Diagnostic features. The leaves are alternate or rarely opposite, and have stipules. They are usually simple, and when they are compound they are always palmate and never pinnate.

The flowers are regular, unisexual, and may occur either on the same plant (monoecious), as in *Euphorbia*, or on different plants (dioecious), as in *Mercurialis*. The flowers usually have five perianth segments, but in some genera (eg *Jatropha*, *Aleurites* and *Caperonia*) petals are also present and in others the perianth is lacking altogether. There are one to very numerous stamens, and anthers with two (sometimes three or four) locules usually opening lengthwise, rarely by pores. A pistillode (non-functional ovary) is often present in male flowers. The ovary is superior and usually consists of three fused carpels having three locules with one or two ovules on axile placentas in each locule; the styles are free or variously united.

The fruit is usually a schizocarp, sometimes a drupe; the type of schizocarp commonly found in the family is known as a regma, where the mericarps themselves

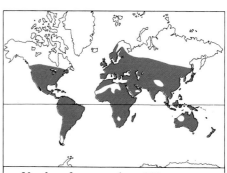

Number of genera: about 300
Number of species: over 5,000
Distribution: mostly tropical, but with some temperate species.
Economic uses: rubber, castor oil, cassava, tung oil, vegetable tallow, timber, purgatives, dyes, many ornamental species, including the poinsettia.

dehisce after having separated from each other. In a number of genera, the seeds are carunculate, eg *Euphorbia*, *Jatropha* and *Ricinus*; they usually have copious endosperm.

Latex is present in the tribe Euphorbieae, but is generally absent from the other tribes; it is usually poisonous, especially in *Hippomane mancinella*, the mancineel tree of the West Indies, and can cause temporary blindness.

Glands are a noteworthy feature of many Euphorbiaceae; they are generally associated with the flowers, where they either encircle or are situated among the stamens or encircle the base of the ovary, or else they are associated with the inflorescence, as in the tribe Euphorbieae, or with the vegetative organs, as in many other tribes; the leaf glands of *Macaranga aethiadenia* from Borneo are very large and shaped like volcanic cones.

Pseudanthial states are characteristic of the tribe Euphorbieae and the genus *Dalechampia*, where the close aggregation of the tiny simple flowers in the inflorescence, in conjunction with bracts, glands and appendages which may be petaloid in appearance, often produces an effect akin to that produced by a true flower. Thus *Dalechampia roezliana* has large bright pink bracts, *Euphorbia fulgens* has bright scarlet glands and *E. corollata* has white gland appendages, and all of these serve to heighten the likeness of the inflorescence to a flower, as do the florets in the capitulum of the Compositae.

The highly specialized inflorescence of *Euphorbia* is called a cyathium. This is usually a small cup-shaped structure consisting of a turbinate involucre which bears a number of glands (usually four or five) of varying shape around its rim. Within the involucre are numerous male flowers, each of very simple structure, surrounding a single central female flower. The inflorescences are commonly protogynous, and cross-pollination is effected chiefly by flies of the

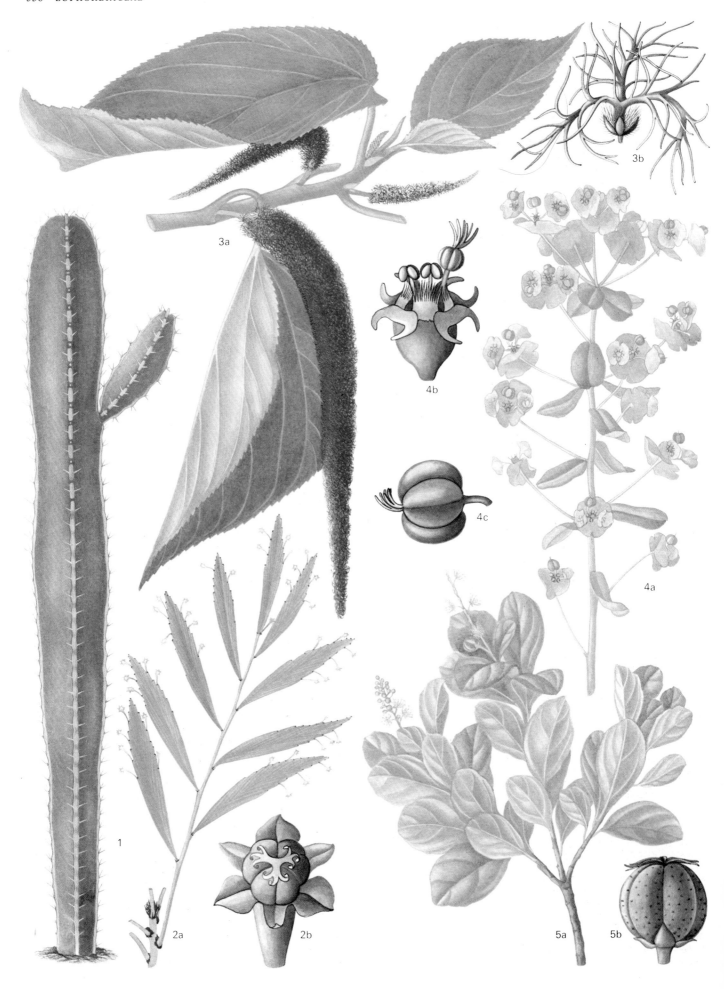

order Diptera, which are attracted to the cyathia by the flat gland-platforms which produce copious nectar. After fertilization, the female pedicel elongates, pushing the developing fruit up and out into the open above the gland-platform. It then commonly bends over at a point where there is a gap between the glands, the fruit then occupying a position beside or below the involucre. The fruit is almost invariably an explosively dehiscent three-lobed regma.

Classification. The family can be divided into the following major tribes:

PHYLLANTHEAE, eg *Phyllanthus, Breynia.*

BRIDELIEAE, eg *Bridelia.*

CROTONEAE, eg *Croton, Chrozophora, Caperonia, Mallotus, Macaranga, Mercurialis, Dalechampia.*

ACALYPHEAE, *Acalypha.*

RICINEAE, *Ricinus.*

JATROPHEAE, eg *Jatropha, Aleurites, Manihot, Codiaeum, Ricinodendron, Hevea.*

SUREGADEAE, *Suregada.*

EUPHORBIEAE, eg *Hippomane, Hura, Sapium, Sebastiania, Euphorbia.*

Some genera traditionally referred to the Euphorbiaceae, although rather anomalous with respect to the "main mass" of the family, have in recent years been segregated therefrom, usually into small families of their own specially erected to receive them. Notable in this respect are *Buxus* and its allies into the Buxaceae and *Panda, Microdesmis* and *Galearia* into the Pandaceae. Other genera often similarly treated include *Aextoxicon, Androstachys, Antidesma, Bischofia, Centroplacus, Daphniphyllum, Hymenocardia, Pera* and *Uapaca.*

The family has links with several other families, such as the Flacourtiaceae, Malvaceae and Urticaceae, but these are regarded by other authorities as being of secondary importance; here the family is placed in a separate order close to the Celastrales.

Although the family takes its name from the genus *Euphorbia,* the largest of the family, *Euphorbia* is not a typical member on account of the extreme simplicity of the

Euphorbiaceae. 1 *Euphorbia stapfii* a cactus-like species (×⅔). 2 *Phyllanthus* sp (a) shoot with flat green phylloclades (modified stems) that bear flowers on their margins (×⅔); (b) female flower with single perianth whorl and three-lobed stigma (×12). 3 *Acalypha* sp (a) leafy shoot and lateral inflorescence (×⅔); (b) female flower with large, branched styles (×6). 4 *Euphorbia amygdaloides* (a) flowering shoot showing inflorescences (cyathia) condensed to resemble a single flower (×⅔); (b) the cyathium consisting of an outer cup-shaped structure bearing horseshoe-shaped glands on the rim, within which is a ring of male flowers each consisting of a single stamen and in the center the female flower which consists of a stalked ovary and branched stigmas (×6); (c) three-lobed fruit (×4). 5 *Croton fothergillifolius* (a) flowering shoot (×⅔); (b) fruit (×4).

flowers. Apart from some other members of the tribe Euphorbieae, the flowers in the family, although simple, are not as reduced as in the type-genus.

Economic uses. A number of genera include species of considerable economic importance. *Hevea,* for example, has *Hevea brasiliensis,* the para rubber tree which is the source of most of the world's natural rubber. *Manihot* also includes rubber-producing species such as the ceara rubber, *Manihot glaziovii,* but this genus is best known on account of the manioc, cassava or tapioca plant, *M. esculenta,* source of a staple foodstuff of poorer people in many tropical countries. Castor oil comes from *Ricinus communis. Aleurites moluccana* is the source of candlenut oil, used in the manufacture of soap, paints and varnishes; candles shaped from the paste of the kernels were formerly used for illumination, hence the common name. *Vernicia* is a genus related to *Aleurites;* it comprises three species, from each of which is obtained an oil of commercial value known as tung oil, used mainly in varnishes and paints. The large genus *Sapium* includes the Chinese tallow tree, *Sapium sebiferum,* which has a greasy tallow surrounding the seeds, used in making soap and candles; the leaves yield a black dye.

The genus *Jatropha* includes the physic nut, or purging nut, *Jatropha curcas,* from the seeds of which a powerful purgative is obtained. The most drastic of all purgatives, however, comes from the seeds of *Croton tiglium;* it is now generally considered unsafe to use, and has been dropped from the British and certain other pharmacopoeias. A red dye is obtained from the regmata of *Mallotus philippinensis,* and *Chrozophora tinctoria* yields purple and blue dyes. The timber of *Ricinodendron* species is known in the trade as African oak. The unripe fruits of the sandbox tree, *Hura crepitans,* were formerly used as containers of sand for blotting ink, or, filled with lead, as paperweights. The seeds of the jumping bean plant, *Sebastiania pringlei,* contain larvae of the moth *Carpocapsa saltitans,* and they show characteristic jumping movements when warmed up. Some species of the genus *Colliguaja* are also jumping bean plants.

A number of genera include species of horticultural merit, eg *Euphorbia* (including the poinsettia, *Euphorbia pulcherrima*), *Breynia, Jatropha, Codiaeum, Acalypha, Ricinus* and *Dalechampia.*   A.R.-S.

RHAMNALES

RHAMNACEAE
Buckthorn and Jujube

The Rhamnaceae is a large family of temperate and tropical trees and shrubs with some climbers. The American genus *Ceanothus* provides the finest of the family's cultivated ornamental species, while its

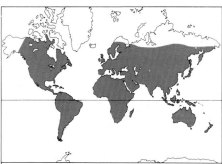

Number of genera: 58
Number of species: about 900
Distribution: cosmopolitan
Economic uses: medicinal (chiefly purgative), some fine ornamentals, dyes, charcoal and a soap-substitute.

better-known products include cascara and the jujube.

Distribution. The family is widely distributed throughout the world.

Diagnostic features. Most species are trees or shrubs, but several are adapted to climbing by the use of twining stems (*Berchemia*), tendrils (*Gouania*) or hooks (*Ventilago*). Some are armed with spines, eg *Rhamnus* and *Paliurus* (Christ's crown of thorns was reputedly made from *Paliurus spina-christi*) *Colletia* is odd, having not one but two buds in each leaf axil, the upper one developing into a thorn, the lower into a shoot. The leaves are alternate or opposite, simple and with stipules. Throughout the family the flowers are similar. They are small, inconspicuous, sometimes without petals, bisexual (rare unisexual), regular and usually borne in cymes. There are four or five valvate sepals and four or five small, incurved petals that are often closed over the four or five stamens. The ovary is superior and free or sometimes embedded in a prominent disk. There are three or two locules (or one by abortion), each with a single (rarely two) basal, anatropous ovule. The style is simple or divided.

The fruits vary in form according to their means of dispersal. Some are dry, dehiscent and wind-dispersed (eg *Paliurus*), but most are fleshy drupes or nuts, dispersed by the mammals and birds which eat them.

Classification. The chief genera include *Rhamnus, Hovenia, Zizyphus, Ceanothus, Ventilago, Phylica* and *Frangula.*

Various classification schemes have associated the Rhamnaceae with the families Vitaceae and Celastraceae. The Vitaceae are probably the closest relatives, differing only in their larger petals, in small features of the receptacle and fruit, and in their leaves which are never simple but lobed or compound. The Rhamnaceae shows some relationships with the Celastraceae, but differs in having stamens opposite the petals not opposite the sepals.

Economic uses. Some *Rhamnus* species are used in the manufacture of dyes. Sap-green is derived from the berries of *Rhamnus cathar-*

Rhamnaceae. 1 *Zizyphus jujuba* (a) shoot bearing inconspicuous flowers and leaves with thorny stipules ($\times \frac{2}{3}$); (b) fruits ($\times \frac{2}{3}$); (c) cross section of fruit ($\times \frac{2}{3}$). 2 *Gouania longipetala* (a) inflorescence, leaf and coiled tendril-like stipule ($\times \frac{2}{3}$); (b) half flower ($\times 6$); (c) section of ovary ($\times 12$); (d) winged fruit ($\times 4$). 3 *Phylica nitida* (a) flowering shoot ($\times \frac{2}{3}$); (b) flower ($\times 6$); (c) vertical section of gynoecium and receptacle ($\times 12$); (d) cross section of fruit ($\times 3$). 4 *Paliurus virgatus* winged fruits ($\times \frac{2}{3}$). 5 *Ceanothus veitchianus* (a) flowering shoot ($\times \frac{2}{3}$); (b) flower ($\times 8$). 6 *Colletia cruciata* (a) flowering shoot ($\times \frac{2}{3}$); (b) flower opened out ($\times 4$); (c) vertical section of flower base ($\times 4$); (d) cross section of flower base ($\times 6$).

tica, yellow from the berries of *R. infectoria* and Chinese green indigo from the bark of *R. chlorophora*. Other species are used in medicine, notably for their purgative properties. The best-known of these is *R. purshiana*, a North American species whose bark yields cascara sagrada (sacred bark), a well-known purgative. In the West Indies the bark of *Gouania domingensis* is chewed as a stimulant. *Hovenia dulcis* (Japan, China) has pink fleshy flower stalks which are dried and used locally in medicine. Leaf and bark extracts of African *Gouania* species are often applied to sores and wounds. *Ventilago oblongifolia* is similarly used in Malaya as a poultice to cure cholera. Chemical analysis has shown that many members of the Rhamnaceae contain substances related to quinine. This may account for their wide use in medicine.

In the Philippines the root extract of *Gouania tiliifolia* is used as a substitute for soap. The roots contain saponin, which froths readily when mixed with water. *Zizyphus jujuba* is the jujube or Chinese date. *Zizyphus lotus* is believed to be the lotus fruit of antiquity. The timber of members of this family is not particularly strong or useful, and few species are of any importance.

Several genera of the Rhamnaceae are well-known ornamentals. The best-known is *Ceanothus* which contains many beautiful flowering shrubs. Other genera which are occasionally cultivated include *Pomaderris*, *Phylica*, *Noltea*, *Rhamnus* and *Colletia*.

S.W.J.

VITACEAE
Grapevine and Virginia Creeper

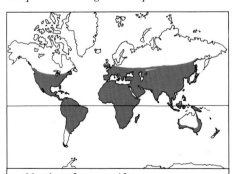

Number of genera: 12
Number of species: about 700
Distribution: tropics and subtropics.
Economic uses: wine, grapes, dried grapes (raisins, sultanas, currants), ornamentals.

The Vitaceae is a family of mainly climbers and some shrubs, celebrated on account of one species, *Vitis vinifera*, the grapevine, age-old provider of wine and fruit. Several genera are grown as ornamental creepers, eg *Cissus*, *Parthenocissus* and *Vitis* itself.

Distribution. The Vitaceae is mainly found in the tropics and subtropics. *Vitis vinifera* is widely cultivated in temperate climates and as far north as the lower Rhineland.

Diagnostic features. Most members of this family are climbing shrubs with tendrils, but there are also some small erect shrubs and trees, the nodes of which are often jointed or swollen. The tendrils are either modified shoots or inflorescences and may end in disk-like suckers. In the case of the grapevine (*Vitis*) the tendril is negatively phototropic and thus forces its way into crevices in the supporting structure. Here the tendrils expand into large balls of tissue, which become sticky and mucilaginous and help the tendril to adhere firmly to its support.

The leaves are alternate and simple or pinnately or palmately compound, often possessing stipules, and with pellucid dots on the blade. The flowers are very small, regular and bisexual or unisexual (usually

Vitaceae. 1 *Vitis thunbergii* (a) inflorescence ($\times\frac{2}{3}$); (b) flower bud ($\times 3$); (c) flower with petals removed showing cup-like calyx and five stamens ($\times 3$); (d) gynoecium ($\times 3$); (e) part of shoot with leaf and immature and mature fruits—berries ($\times\frac{2}{3}$). 2 *Tetrastigma obtectum* (a) leafy shoot with axillary inflorescences ($\times\frac{2}{3}$); (b) flower bud ($\times 4$); (c) flower viewed from above showing four petals and four stamens ($\times 3$); (d) stamens ($\times 6$). 3 *Cissus velutinus* (a) leafy shoot with axillary inflorescence and unbranched, coiled tendrils ($\times\frac{2}{3}$); (b) flower ($\times 4$); (c) vertical section of gynoecium showing erect ovules and short style with a discoid stigma ($\times 4$).

with male and female on the same plant). They are usually arranged in cymose or racemose inflorescences, arising opposite a leaf. There are four or five sepals, fused into a cup-like structure which is toothed or lobed, and four or five petals which may be free but are often united at the tips. In the latter condition they often fall off as a hood on the opening of the flower bud. The stamens are equal in number to the petals and opposite to them. They are inserted on a ring-like or lobed disk, the anthers being free or joined. The ovary is superior and consists usually of two fused carpels, with two to six locules each usually containing two erect ovules. The style is short, ending in a discoid or rarely four-lobed stigma (as in *Tetragyna*). The fruit is a berry; the seeds have a straight embryo surrounded by copious endosperm.

Classification. The largest genus is *Cissus* whose 350 species are almost entirely tropical in distribution. The flowers of nearly all the members of the genus are bisexual with four free petals and four stamens. Some of the species of *Cissus* are erect and others tendril-climbing as in *Vitis* (50 species in the subtropics and warm temperate regions), but the latter usually has flower-parts in fives and

united petals. Other important genera include *Ampelopsis* (about 25 species in Asia and North America) which also normally has a climbing habit but has flower-parts in fives and free petals, and *Parthenocissus* (about 15 species of tendril-bearing climbers in Asia and North America) whose flowers lack the ring-like or lobed disk found in most genera. The family also includes *Pterisanthes* (about 20 species in Burma and West Malaysia) and *Leea* (about 70 species throughout the tropics). The latter genus is sometimes separated as the family Leeaceae.

The Vitaceae is most closely related to the Rhamnaceae with which it shares the predominantly woody climbing habit, bisexual or unisexual flowers, a single whorl of stamens opposite the petals, and only one or two ovules per locule in the syncarpous ovary. Both families also contain many species whose flowers possess a ring-like or lobed disk.

Economic uses. Economically the Vitaceae is important because of the grapevine (*Vitis vinifera*) which originates from the Orient and northwest India. More than 25 million tonnes of wine are made annually from the fruit of this species, and viticulture is now a

scientific study. When dried, the fruits are termed raisins, or sultanas if the grape is of the seedless variety. Currants are the dried fruits of the Corinthian variety. Grapes of the Muscatel variety are used to make the wine of that name, as well as raisins. The fruits of some other species of *Vitis*, eg *V. aestivalis* and *V. labrusca*, are also used for wine-making. These are North American species which are resistant to the insect *Phylloxera*. On account of the devastation caused by this pest, most European vines are now grafted on to American root stocks. The stems of some species, eg *V. papillosa* (Java) and *V. sicyoides* (Mexico) are used locally as cordage.

Some other members of the family are prized as ornamentals, notably the 10 species of *Parthenocissus* (Virginia creeper). All are climbers, *Parthenocissus quinquefolia* or "true" Virginia creeper, possessing leaves with three or five coarsely serrated leaflets which turn crimson in autumn. This and other species of *Parthenocissus*, eg *P. inserta* and *P. himalayana*, are suitable for covering walls, fences and pergolas, as are some species of *Vitis* such as *V. amurensis* and *V. davidii*, and of *Cissus*.   S.R.C.

ILLUSTRATION CREDITS

Artwork panels: Victoria Goaman, Judith Dunkley, Christabel King.